QUALITATIVE ANALYSIS

QUALITATIVE ANALYSIS
Using Semimicro Methods

ESMARCH S. GILREATH
*Professor and Head of Chemistry
Department, Washington and Lee University*

McGRAW-HILL BOOK COMPANY, INC.

New York   Toronto   London

1954

QUALITATIVE ANALYSIS

Library of Congress Catalog Card Number 54-7356

IV

THE MAPLE PRESS COMPANY, YORK, PA.

PREFACE

The conventional course in qualitative analysis has lost favor as a subject of study in the curriculums of many colleges and universities during the past several years. Oftentimes, where this course has disappeared, there has appeared a simplified version of the qualitative scheme of analysis within the laboratory exercises of general chemistry. Perhaps there are many good reasons underlying these changes, but without any attempt to list or analyze them, it is evident that qualitative analysis as taught in the past does not meet the requirements of a present-day course of instruction in chemistry. In those schools where the subject of qualitative analysis is retained, there is a demand for a broader theoretical approach with less emphasis upon laboratory exercises. This textbook was written with this demand in mind, and with the hope of reversing the trend away from a subject which offers unparalleled opportunities for presenting and amplifying many of the fundamental principles of inorganic chemistry.

This book is designed as the basis for a one-semester course to follow general chemistry. Although the name "Qualitative Analysis" is retained, for want of a better title, the theoretical portion is not built, as were the older textbooks in this field, around the laboratory schemes of analyses for the separation and identification of a restricted number of ions. Instead, it presents an integrated discussion of the concepts, theories, and laws relating to solutions. Especial emphasis is laid upon the properties of solutions of electrolytes, and, wherever possible, there is an attempt to correlate the theoretical discussions with the laboratory procedures of qualitative analysis. With respect to ionic solutions, the theory of qualitative analysis partially bridges the gap between general chemistry and physical chemistry. Certainly, the experience obtained in qualitative analysis, in both theory and practice, with various applications of the principle of chemical equilibrium will serve as an excellent introduction to the more advanced study.

The experimental section offers systematic schemes of analyses for the cations and the anions, which are relatively simple but quite adequate for teaching purposes. The analytical procedures within the cation scheme are based upon the time-honored system of analysis devised by Fresenius.

The departures from this system, which occur in Cation Groups III and IV, are those which have been found by experience to increase the sensitivity and efficiency of the system of analysis. The scheme of analysis for the anions is an adaptation from the one developed by J. T. Dobbins and H. A. Ljung [*J. Chem. Educ.*, **12,** 586 (1935)]. This scheme differs from many others in that it is truly systematic. It is also quite flexible, permitting the omission of any ion or ions as the instructor may desire.

The author wishes to express his appreciation to the many students who have served as "guinea pigs" in the development of the laboratory procedures. He is particularly grateful to Dr. L. J. Desha for his helpful criticisms and kindly suggestions, and to his wife, Sally, for her encouragement, inspiration, and aid during the preparation of the manuscript.

E. S. GILREATH

CONTENTS

PREFACE v

PART I · THEORETICAL ASPECTS

Introduction 3
1. Forces between Atoms 6
2. Solutions 27
3. Chemical Equilibrium 48
4. Ionization of Weak Electrolytes. 60
5. The Solubility Product Principle 83
6. Hydrolysis 104
7. Complex Ions 118
8. Colloids. 141
9. Oxidation and Reduction Theory 152
10. Balancing of Oxidation-Reduction Equations (a Review from General Chemistry). 168

PART II · EXPERIMENTAL PROCEDURES

11. General Laboratory Directions—Introduction to Cation Analysis . . 179
12. Group I Cations 185
13. Group II Cations 190
14. Group III Cations 204
15. Group IV Cations. 215
16. Group V Cations 220
17. Introduction to Anion Analysis—Group I Anions 224
18. Group II Anions 231
19. Group III Anions. 233
20. Group IV Anions 236
21. Group V Anions 241
22. Complete Analysis 245

APPENDIX

Special Laboratory Directions 257
Notebook Record of Analytical Results 261
Assignment Schedule 262

List of Desk Apparatus 264
Reagents 264
Test Solutions 266
Distribution of Electrons in the Atoms of the Elements. 267
Ionization Constants of Weak Bases 269
Ionization Constants of Weak Acids 269
Acid Constants of Hydrated Ions and Hydroxides 270
Dissociation Constants of Complex Ions 270
Table of Solubility Product Constants 271

LOGARITHMS 273

INDEX 275

ATOMIC WEIGHT CHART . . . . *Inside front cover*

PERIODIC TABLE OF THE ELEMENTS . . . . *Inside back cover*

PART I

THEORETICAL ASPECTS

INTRODUCTION

Qualitative analysis was originally a laboratory course which dealt with methods for determining the composition of a limited number of substances. The laboratory procedures of this course were largely restricted to a scheme of analysis for the identification of the common metallic elements. As a consequence, the first attempts toward the development of the theory of qualitative analysis were in the form of explanatory notes for the analytical steps within these procedures. Unfortunately, the separation and identification of some 23 cations, as carried out in this scheme, were of such an unconnected chemical sequence as to discourage a logical development of the underlying theories of the particular steps.

A modified form of the original scheme of analysis is still retained in qualitative analysis, but the development of theory follows an orderly manner with little regard to its immediate application to laboratory procedures. This dilemma of utilizing a specialized scheme of analysis in conjunction with an elementary discussion of the behavior of electrolytes in solution has not been resolved quite satisfactorily, but certainly both approaches deserve to be a part of the study of qualitative analysis. The subject matter of qualitative analysis, therefore, consists of two general divisions, the theoretical and the experimental, each of which involves a different line of approach. The relation of the theoretical aspects to the experimental procedures may not be apparent at first, but as the course progresses, the degree of integration increases rapidly.

Theoretical Aspects of Qualitative Analysis. In many respects, the theory of qualitative analysis is a continued study of the fundamentals of general chemistry. But whereas general chemistry is a broad survey of the behavior of all types of substances under varying conditions, qualitative analysis is primarily concerned with solutions of electrolytes. The term *electrolyte* is used to identify a substance which is composed of ions, or which produces ions in aqueous solution. The theory of qualitative analysis is, therefore, a study of the behavior of ions in solution. Of necessity, this study is quite elementary and often incomplete, partly because students in the course have not had the mathematical background for a more comprehensive treatment, and partly because much of the theory is still in the speculative stage.

In the study of ionic solutions many aspects of fundamental chemistry, which were barely mentioned in general chemistry, will be reintroduced

3

and amplified. It might be said that qualitative analysis bridges the gap between general chemistry and the study of physical chemistry. Both of these latter fields of study are overcrowded with important topics that can neither be omitted completely nor covered adequately. Some of the theoretical items which are most opportunely presented in this study are velocity of reactions, theories of ionization, properties of solutions, the solubility product principle, complex-ion formation, the colloidal state, and oxidation and reduction theory.

In connection with the elementary discussion of the foregoing topics an attempt will be made to explain why certain substances are soluble and others are not. Such an explanation requires some description of the general physical and chemical properties of soluble and insoluble substances, and of the structure of water in its role as a solvent. To examine, even superficially, the structures of inorganic substances in relation to their solubilities necessitates a brief analysis of the forces, or bonds, which hold atoms, ions, and molecules together.

Certain laws have been discovered and special theories have been developed to explain the physical and chemical behavior of ions in solution. Most important are the laws and theories which pertain to the various types of equilibria which may exist in aqueous solution. Among these equilibria are those which apply to ionization, solubility, complex formation, and oxidation-reduction.

A weak acid in a water solution, such as acetic acid, exists largely in the form of molecules, yet there is sufficient interaction with water to produce a small concentration of hydronium ions and acetate ions. This reaction with water, called *solvation*, creates an equilibrium which may be indicated in the form of a mathematical expression to denote the quantity of ions and molecules that may exist together. A fairly insoluble electrolyte also sets up an equilibrium with its ions in water solution. Thus, silver chloride dissolves to a slight extent in water to release silver and chloride ions, and there is an equilibrium between the undissolved silver chloride and the two ions in solution. The mathematical equation which signifies this equilibrium in quantitative terms is known as the solubility product expression. Other ionic equilibria which can be expressed in quantitative terms are complex ions and their components, and the reactants and products of oxidation-reduction reactions.

Experimental Aspects of Qualitative Analysis. The laboratory procedures of qualitative analysis are designed for identifying and determining the approximate amounts of the constituents present in a substance. These procedures differ from those of quantitative analysis in that the latter is concerned with determining the exact amounts of the constituents present. The reactions of qualitative analysis are ionic, and in most cases the constituents of the substances undergoing analysis are identified as ions. If, for example, an ionic compound such as magnesium chloride were subjected to a qualitative analysis, the identifying tests would not indicate the compound, magnesium chloride, or the atoms, magnesium and chlorine, but would instead confirm the presence of the magnesium ion and the chloride ion.

The ions which are identified in qualitative analysis are divided into two types: those ions which carry a positive electrical charge, called *cations*, and those ions which carry a negative electrical charge, known as *anions*. As a result of these two types of ions, there are two general divisions in the laboratory procedures, one designed for the identification of various cations, and the other for determining the presence of certain anions. Neither of these two divisions pretends to be in any way inclusive. Only 23 of the most commonly occurring cations and 21 anions are included in these schemes of analyses. Through the use of these two schemes, the student is enabled to separate and identify the ionic constituents of almost any mixture of common inorganic chemicals which may be given to him for analysis.

Adeptness in the use of these two schemes of analysis is not a primary objective of experimental qualitative analysis. In terms of practical and industrial applications, there is no qualitative scheme of analysis that can be justified or defended. The classical procedures of analysis have long since been superseded, in industry, by instrumental methods and spot tests. The justification of the use of a scheme of analysis in laboratory procedures designed for second-year college chemistry is as a powerful tool to impart some knowledge of inorganic chemistry to the student. In addition to the assimilation of certain facts of inorganic chemistry through observations in analytical procedures, it is possible that the student may also develop some degree of confidence in his laboratory technique, and a certain amount of reliance upon his own judgment in making decisions involved in his individual analyses.

CHAPTER 1

FORCES BETWEEN ATOMS

Chemistry is concerned with the structure, properties, and reactions of substances. The building blocks which make up substances are the atoms of the several elements. These building blocks—atoms—may be assembled and held together in a variety of ways, resulting in the formation of hundreds of thousands of different compounds. Among these many compounds, definite types may be recognized. In beginning the study of qualitative analysis we are particularly interested in the distinction between two types, *electrovalent* and *covalent* compounds, and in an understanding of the forces which hold atoms together in compounds of these types.

Any attempt to explain how atoms assemble to form compounds, and to interpret the forces which operate between them when thus combined, must begin with a consideration of the internal structure of atoms. Such a discussion presupposes some knowledge of the theories of atomic structure as these are usually presented in a course in general chemistry. For the purpose of review and as an introduction to the subject of chemical binding, the fundamentals of these theories are summarized briefly here.

1·1 Atomic Structure. Almost all the *mass* of an atom is concentrated in its *nucleus*, the diameter of which is about 1/10,000 that of the atom as a whole. The nucleus contains subatomic particles, called *protons* and *neutrons*, each of which has a mass of substantially 1 on the scale $O = 16.0000$. The proton carries a unit positive charge while the neutron is electrically neutral. The *atomic number* of an atom is the total positive charge of its nucleus and is equal, therefore, to the number of protons which it contains. The *mass number* of an atom is the sum of the numbers of protons and neutrons in its nucleus. Most of the chemical elements occur in nature as mixtures of *isotopes*[1] having different

---

[1] The isotopes of any element all have the same atomic number but differ in the numbers of neutrons in the nucleus and, therefore, in their mass numbers. The relative masses of individual atoms are very close to—but not quite—whole numbers when expressed on the oxygen scale, *e.g.*, the values observed in the mass spectrograph for the two natural isotopes of chlorine are 34.97867 and 36.97750. The nearest integers, 35 and 37, are the respective mass numbers, corresponding to 17 protons + 18 neutrons and 17 protons + 20 neutrons, respectively. The fractional atomic weight of chlorine, 35.457, results from the fact that the element occurs in nature as a mixture of constant

mass numbers. The *atomic weight* is the average mass of these isotopic atoms, expressed on the oxygen scale. While it may be altered by bombardment with high-velocity projectiles—such as neutrons, in the atomic pile—the nucleus of an atom remains unchanged throughout all ordinary chemical reactions.

Surrounding the atomic nucleus is a system of rapidly moving *electrons*, which must be regarded as patrolling—rather than as filling—the extranuclear space belonging to an atom. The electron is a particle with a mass only 1/1,840 that of a proton, but with a *negative* charge exactly equal to the positive charge of the proton. When in the free or uncombined state, an atom possesses the same number of electrons as there are protons in its nucleus. Hence, *any uncombined atom is electrically neutral.* Experimental evidence indicates (as quantum mechanics predicts) that the orbits in which electrons move about the nucleus are distributed in a series of concentric energy levels, commonly called *shells.* Beginning with the one nearest the nucleus, successive energy levels are designated by the numbers 1, 2, 3, 4, 5, 6, respectively, indicating the values of the *principal quantum number n*, which is one of the four quantum numbers necessary to describe an electron. (The older shell notation employed the letters K, L, M, N, O, P, and Q.) The behavior of an element in all ordinary chemical reactions depends primarily upon the electron distribution in its atoms. *The formation of a chemical bond between atoms is due to some redistribution of their electrons to form a more stable arrangement.*

1·2 Electron Grouping in Atoms. The chemical properties of the elements depend upon the extent to which their electron shells are *completed.* By the completion of a shell, we mean agreement between the number of electrons it contains and the number in the corresponding shell of the noble gas of next higher or lower atomic number (Table 1·1). Upon the basis of complete and incomplete electron shells, four types of atoms are recognized:

Type I. Atoms in which *all* the electron shells are complete. These are the atoms of the noble or inert gases (Sec. 1·3), which have attained an electronic stability which cannot be increased either by electron transfer or electron sharing. In consequence, they are highly indifferent to chemical change.

Type II. Atoms in which only the *outermost* electron shell is incomplete. These elements tend to enter chemical combination through *los-*

---

composition, containing 75.4 per cent of the lighter and 24.6 per cent of the heavier isotope.

Since all isotopes of any element have the same atomic number, they also have the same number of extranuclear electrons and are, consequently, *identical in their chemical properties.* For this reason we shall not have need to give further consideration to isotopes in this book, except incidentally.

ing, gaining, or *sharing* electrons, in such wise as to attain the electronic configuration of a noble gas. Many of the elements most often encountered belong to this type (which are sometimes called the *representative* elements). The forces operating between their atoms are discussed in some detail below (Sec. 1·4*ff.*).

Type III. Atoms in which the *two* outermost shells are incomplete. These are the so-called *transition* elements. Because of their electronic structure, such elements exhibit variable valence. Their tendency to form *coordination compounds* is discussed in Chap. 7.

Type IV. Atoms in which the *three* outermost shells are incomplete. These are the elements of the *rare earth* or *lanthanide* series (atomic numbers 57 to 71, inclusive) and those of the *actinide* series (atomic numbers 89 to 98). We shall not have occasion to discuss these further in this book. It suffices to say that the elements within each one of these groups are very similar in their chemical properties because the differentiating electrons of their atoms are in the third from the outermost shell.

The arrangement in shells and subshells of the electrons of all the known elements is given in Table A·4 in the Appendix.

1·3 Electronic Structure of Noble Gases. Atoms containing a total of 2, 10, 18, 36, 54, or 86 extranuclear electrons are remarkably stable. The elements with atoms containing electrons of these totals are known as the *noble gases*, which are so inert that they form no chemical combinations. With the exception of helium, the atoms of these elements contain 8 electrons in their outermost shells. Apparently, electron totals of 2, 10, 18, 36, 54, and 86 attain electronic configurations that are more stable than any intermediate numbers. These electronic structures are shown in Table 1·1.

TABLE 1·1 ELECTRONIC STRUCTURES OF THE NOBLE GASES

Atomic number	Element	Number of electrons in shells					
		Main energy level or principal quantum number					
		1	2	3	4	5	6
2	He	2					
10	Ne	2	8				
18	A	2	8	8			
36	Kr	2	8	18	8		
54	Xe	2	8	18	18	8	
86	Rn	2	8	18	32	18	8

1·4 Electronic Structures of Type II Elements. The chemical properties of these elements can be explained in terms of the electrons of their incomplete, outermost shell—often called the *valence electrons*. The number of electrons in this shell may lie between one and seven. Chemical behavior may be described as a tendency to gain, or to lose, or to share these electrons in chemical reactions, in such fashion that the outer shell may contain eight, as in one of the noble gases. (A few of the lightest elements tend toward an outer shell of two, as in helium.) This apparent tendency of the Type II elements is sometimes called the *octet rule*, or rule of eight.

Type II atoms with one or two electrons in the outer shell appear to hold these electrons comparatively loosely and to *lose* them readily to form positive ions, *e.g.*,

$$Na\ (2,8,1) \rightarrow e + Na^+\ (2,8) \qquad \text{isoelectronic with Ne (2,8)}$$
$$Ca\ (2,8,8,2) \rightarrow 2e + Ca^{++}\ (2,8,8) \qquad \text{isoelectronic with A (2,8,8)}$$

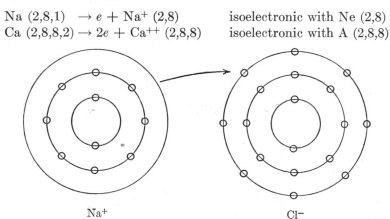

$$Na^+ \qquad\qquad\qquad Cl^-$$

Fig. 1·1   Diagram illustrating electron transfer to form an ionic compound.

At the other extreme, atoms with seven electrons in the outer shell show a strong tendency to *gain* one electron, and thus form negative ions which are isoelectronic with the next higher noble gas, *e.g.*,

$$Cl\ (2,8,7) + e \rightarrow Cl^-\ (2,8,8) \qquad \text{isoelectronic with A (2,8,8)}$$

The formation of an ionic compound such as sodium chloride (Fig. 1·1) is a typical example of an electron *transfer* taking place in accordance with the octet rule. Each sodium atom loses its one outer-shell electron, thus forming the Na^+ ion which is isoelectronic with neon; each chlorine atom gains one electron, forming a Cl^- ion with the electron configuration of argon.

Between the two extremes just mentioned lie the atoms of those elements which have more than two and fewer than seven valence electrons. These atoms seldom react by electron transfer. They are much more inclined to attain the noble gas structures by *sharing* electrons in the formation of *covalent* molecules. The sharing process presumably requires for the atoms of these particular elements a lower expenditure of energy than does electron transfer. A favorite illustration of the process of elec-

tron sharing (cf. Sec. 1·7) is the electron distribution found in the carbon
tetrachloride molecule, which is diagrammed in Fig. 1·2.   In this molecule, four chlorine atoms have attained the structure of argon by sharing
four electron pairs with the carbon atom.   At the same time, the sharing
of the four electron pairs permits the carbon atom to become isoelectronic
with the neon atom.

The octet rule is by no means universal.   It applies only to the Type
II elements and, even among these, there are well-known exceptions.
For example, the compounds $BeCl_2$ and BCl_3 have properties characteris-
tic of covalent compounds, yet neither the beryllium nor the boron atom

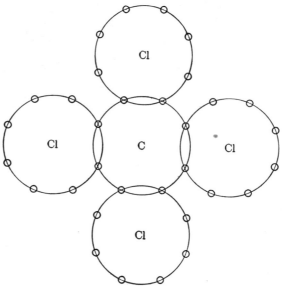

FIG. 1·2   Diagram of the carbon tetrachloride molecule.

has attained eight electrons in the valence shell by forming these compounds.   Other exceptions include PCl_5 and SF_6.   In short, the octet
rule—which has its uses in an elementary discussion of valency—over-
simplifies the factors involved in the formation of many chemical bonds.
A better basis for predictions in regard to bond formation is one that
utilizes the concept of *uncompleted orbitals* in one atom which may be
filled by electrons from another atom.

1·5 Atomic Orbitals and the Origin of the Chemical Bond.   The
interpretation of bond formation by the completion of orbitals involves
a more extensive description of the electronic configuration of atoms than
has been given in previous discussions.   As has been stated elsewhere,
electrons are arranged in principal shells (energy levels) which for purposes of identification are designated by the numbers 1, 2, 3, 4, 5, 6,

and 7. (Less frequently these shells are indicated by the letters K, L, M, N, O, P, and Q.) The actual distribution of electrons in an atom is determined by the number of electrons and follows an important rule of quantum mechanics known as *Pauli's exclusion principle*. This rule states that no two electrons in an atom can have the same four quantum numbers.[1] Of the four quantum numbers necessary to describe an electron, the first three numbers describe its orbit in terms of size, shape, and orientation in space, the latter in reference to an applied magnetic field. The fourth quantum number refers to the direction of spin of the electron about its axis. Thus it is possible for two electrons to have orbits of the same size, shape, and orientation, if the two electrons are of

---

[1] The principal quantum number n distinguishes the energy level in which a particular electron exists. For the first energy level, $n = 1$; for the second energy level, $n = 2$, etc. An energy level may be considered as equivalent to an electron shell, although the former is a more accurate descriptive term. Consequently, $n = 1$ for the K shell, $n = 2$ for the L shell, etc. The value n for circular orbits indicates roughly the binding force and distance between the nucleus and the electron. Hence, this quantum number represents the *size of the electron orbit*.

The second (or azimuthal) quantum number l designates the angular momentum of the electron in its motion around the nucleus. In other words, this value indicates the ellipticity (deviation from the form of a circle) of the orbit of an electron and, therefore, describes the *shape of the electron orbit*. The energies of elliptical orbits vary slightly for sublevels in the principal energy level. However, l may have only a limited number of values for a neutral atom. These values range from zero as a minimum to $n - 1$ for a maximum. Electrons with $l = 0$, 1, 2, and 3 are called s, p, d, and f electrons. (These letters designate old spectral terms, sharp, principal, diffuse, and fundamental.) Although larger l values are possible, these four energy sublevels are all that are necessary to describe the electrons of neutral atoms. For $l = 0$, the angular momentum is zero; these are the s orbitals with the most eccentric elliptical orbits. In other words, they deviate most from circular orbits, except the s electrons in the K shell. An electron with such an orbit approaches the nucleus more closely than an electron with a more circular movement. Therefore, electrons in the s orbitals have lower energy states (are held more tightly) than p, d, and f electrons. Consequently, it is to be expected that the orbits of the p, d, and f electrons are successively more circular, and in successively higher energy states.

The third or magnetic quantum number m defines the orbit of an electron in a magnetic field. Under the influence of a magnetic field superimposed upon the field of the nucleus, the plane of the electron orbit is so oriented as to form a definite angle with the direction of the applied field. The magnetic quantum number may have any integral value, including zero, from $-l$ to $+l$, giving a total of $2l + 1$ possible values.

In a magnetic field an electron behaves as if it were spinning rapidly about its own axis. Therefore, a fourth or spin quantum number s is necessary to define the angular momentum of this electron spin. Since the spin may be in one of two directions, s can have only two values, $+\frac{1}{2}$ and $-\frac{1}{2}$.

The four quantum numbers n, l, m, and s indicate the number of electrons which can be accomodated in each energy level. The possible arrangements of the quantum numbers also indicate the possible number of electrons which may exist in a given

opposed spins.   Two electrons of this description are referred to as *paired electrons.*

Each principal shell of an atom may contain up to four sublevels or orbits.   The possible subshells are indicated by the small letters *s*, *p*, *d*,

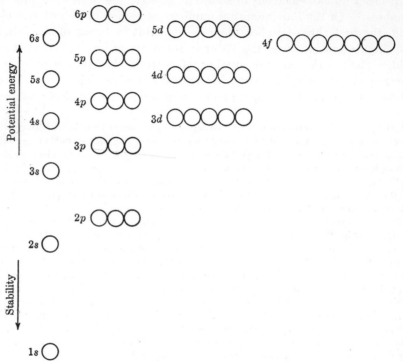

Fig. 1·3   The approximate stability sequence for atomic orbitals.   (*Linus Pauling,* "*The Nature of the Chemical Bond,*" *p. 26, Cornell University Press, Ithaca, New York,* 1940.)

and *f*.   Each of the subshells can contain electrons, up to a definite maximum, as single electrons or paired electrons.   These single or paired electrons are called *orbitals*.   In Fig. 1·3, each circle represents an orbital, which may contain either one or two electrons.   If two electrons are present, they must be of opposed spins, as will be explained later.

---

energy level.   This is another way of phrasing the Pauli exclusion principle.
  In the first energy level, $n = 1$, therefore l and m are both zero; s can have two values, $+\frac{1}{2}$ and $-\frac{1}{2}$; hence, only two electrons are possible in this level.
  If $n = 2$, then $l = 0$ or 1.   For $l = 0$, $m = 1$ and s can be $+\frac{1}{2}$ or $-\frac{1}{2}$, giving two possible electrons.   For $l = 1$, m has three possible values: 1, 0, and -1.   In each case the spin s may be $+\frac{1}{2}$ or $-\frac{1}{2}$, so that six electrons are possible.   Therefore, eight electrons are possible in the second energy shell.   Working in a similar manner, it may be shown that 18 electrons are possible in the third shell, and 32 in the fourth.

Again, from Fig. 1·3, it can be seen that sublevel s can contain only one orbital, sublevel p may contain three orbitals, sublevel d may contain a maximum of five orbitals, and sublevel f may contain up to seven orbitals.

In general, the electrons occupy the energy levels nearest the nucleus first. During the process of atom building, one electron goes into each possible orbital in a given sublevel until each of the orbitals in that sublevel contains one electron; then another electron is added to each orbital to form coupled electrons, or paired electrons, until each orbital contains two electrons. The opposed spins of the electrons result in an electromagnetic attraction which is more than sufficient to overcome the repulsion of the two negative charges of the same electrons.

For specific examples of the electronic configurations, consider the elements phosphorus and sulfur. In the following symbolic representation of these elements, the numbers designate the principal shells, the letters indicate the subshells, and the superscript numbers give the number of electrons in each orbital. The repetition of numbers and letters designates the number of orbitals in each subshell.

$$_{15}P \quad 1s^2 2s^2 2p^2 2p^2 2p^2 3s^2 3p^1 3p^1 3p^1$$
$$_{16}S \quad 1s^2 2s^2 2p^2 2p^2 2p^2 3s^2 3p^2 3p^1 3p^1$$

From the foregoing symbols it can be seen that phosphorus contains four orbitals in its valence shell, the s orbital of this shell contains a pair of electrons, and the other three orbitals contain single electrons. Sulfur contains four orbitals in its valence shell, two of which contain electron pairs, and the other two, single electrons. A simpler symbolic method of indicating the outer orbitals with paired or single electrons is

$$: \overset{\cdot}{\underset{\cdot}{P}} \cdot \qquad\qquad\qquad : \overset{\cdot}{S} :$$

In the explanation of chemical behavior of atoms by the octet rule, stress is placed upon the tendency of atoms to attain eight electrons in their outermost shell. A better explanation emphasizes the tendency of atoms to fill *uncomplete* (either unoccupied or incomplete) orbitals. Thus, incomplete orbitals containing only one electron tend to pair with an electron from another atom to complete the orbital, and unoccupied orbitals which may exist tend to be filled by electron pairs. Going back to the specific examples of phosphorus and sulfur, the atoms of these elements have incomplete and unoccupied orbitals in the M shell ($n = 3$ energy level). From Fig. 1·3, the atoms of these elements may enter into chemical combination to fill the incomplete and also unoccupied orbitals of this shell.   If the five unoccupied orbitals are designated as d^0 each, then the symbolic representations of these atoms are

$$_{15}P \quad 1s^2 2s^2 2p^2 2p^2 2p^2 3s^2 3p^1 3p^1 3p^1 3d^0 3d^0 3d^0 3d^0 3d^0$$
$$_{16}S \quad 1s^2 2s^2 2p^2 2p^2 2p^2 3s^2 3p^2 3p^1 3p^1 3d^0 3d^0 3d^0 3d^0 3d^0$$

Considering the outermost shells of the phosphorus and sulfur atoms, the above symbols indicate that phosphorus has a complete orbital in the $3s$ subshell, three incomplete orbitals in the $3p$ subshell, and five unoccupied orbitals in the $3d$ subshell; sulfur has a complete orbital in the $3s$ subshell, one complete and two incomplete orbitals in the $3p$ subshell, and five unoccupied orbitals in the $3d$ subshell.   Theoretically, a maximum of nine covalent bonds can be formed by the nine possible orbitals of the $n = 3$ energy level (M shell), but spatial limitations due to the volumes of the atoms concerned limit the number of atoms which can be bonded to the central atom.

Phosphorus and sulfur enter into chemical combinations to fill either the incomplete, or the incomplete and some of the unoccupied orbitals. The filling of only the incomplete orbitals accounts for compounds such as H_2S and PH_3.   The filling of incomplete and some unoccupied orbitals produces the bonding found in PCl_5 and SF_6.   In phosphorus pentachloride the phosphorus atom has formed five covalent bonds.   In forming these bonds the three incomplete $3p$ orbitals are completed, and the electron pair in the $3s$ orbital is uncoupled to form two additional bonds with chlorine atoms.   The uncoupling of the $3s$ electron pair to produce additional bonds causes an expansion of the atom to utilize one of the $3d$ orbitals.   The process of uncoupling an electron pair requires considerable energy, but the stability of PCl_5 indicates that the reaction produces more than sufficient energy for this purpose.   In sulfur hexafluoride the paired electrons in the $3s$ and $3p$ orbitals are uncoupled, in addition to the two $3p$ electrons, to make six electrons available for bond formation. Therefore, two of the $3d$ orbitals are utilized in forming the six covalent bonds formed by sulfur in this compound.

The foregoing explanation is sufficient for atoms containing few shells. In complex atoms containing many shells, there may be considerable overlapping of subshells.   Chemical bonding by such atoms is more complex, and its explanation is beyond the scope of this book.

CHEMICAL BONDS

Many factors determine the manner in which two atoms unite and the type of bond that is formed.   Among these are the nuclear charges, the distribution of electrons in the various shells, and the radii of the combining atoms.   Such factors differ for atoms of different elements; therefore, these variables multiplied by the number of chemically active elements indicate the different types of chemical bonds that are possible. In other words, the atoms of each element differ from all other elements, to some extent, in the fashion in which they combine with other atoms. Hence there is no simple, collective way of describing the manner in which atoms unite.

Pauling[1] divides chemical bonds roughly into three extreme types: electrostatic bonds, covalent bonds, and metallic bonds. This division is based largely upon the mechanism of formation and the properties of each type of bond. It is a loose classification since there are many intermediate types which represent a transition between the extremes. Metallic bonds are not relevant to solution chemistry, and our attention will be focused upon the other two general types of chemical bonds.

1·6 Ionic Bond. The electrovalent or ionic bond is that type which is produced when one or more electrons have been transferred from one atom to complete the orbitals of another atom. This bond is typical between atoms of those Type II elements (Sec. 1·2) whose outermost shells contain not more than three electrons, and the atoms of those elements which need not more than two electrons to fill incomplete or unoccupied orbitals. The transfer of electrons from one atom to another results, as we have seen, in the formation of ions (cf. Fig. 1·1). Ions carrying high charges are rare because of the extremely large amounts of energy involved in transferring electrons from one atom to another.

The electrovalent bond results from a coulombic attraction between the excess charges on the oppositely charged ions. The strength of the bond is roughly proportional to the product of the charges of the ions, and inversely proportional to the square of the distance between the effective centers of the ions. This is not a true bond in a strict sense of the word, in that it is neither rigid (in the sense of nonelastic) nor directed. The electrostatic fields of the ions extend in all directions; a crystal of sodium chloride is a cluster of ions in which six chloride ions are grouped spatially around each sodium ion, and six sodium ions are grouped around each chloride ion. The number of ions which may be grouped around a central ion is determined by the radii of the respective ions involved. The arrangement of ions in the crystal lattice of sodium chloride is indicated by Fig. 1·4.

1·7 Covalent Bond. The formation of a chemical bond, whether it be ionic or covalent, involves the filling of incomplete stable orbitals in one atom by electrons from another atom. Each orbital can contain only two electrons of opposed spins. The filling of an orbital by a loose electron (one which may be removed from another atom with a compara-

[1] Linus Pauling, "The Nature of the Chemical Bond," p. 3, Cornell University Press, Ithaca, N.Y., 1940.

tively small amount of energy) results in an electrovalent bond. The filling of an orbital by an electron which is not removed from its atom but is held mutually by the two atoms concerned, produces a covalent bond.

The formation of either an ionic or covalent bond is the result of a magnetic attraction between electrons of opposed spins. The magnetic attraction must be considerable to overcome the force of repulsion between the two like charges of the two electrons. In the case of the ionic bond, the electron is lost from one atom completely and becomes attached to the atom in which the orbital is completed. The magnetic attraction which causes the formation of the negative ion stabilizes the

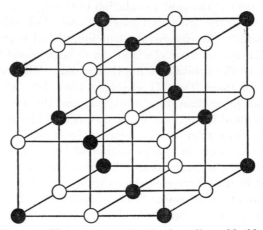

FIG. 1·4   Type of crystal lattice in sodium chloride.

internal structure of the ion, but the ionic bond itself is one of electro-static attraction, as explained above. In the formation of a covalent bond there is insufficient energy in the chemical reaction to remove the electron from one atom to fill the orbital of another atom. Such a bond is electromagnetic rather than electrostatic, since it involves the magnetic forces exerted between paired (coupled) electrons in an orbital.

The covalent bond is the only true bond in chemistry in the sense of distance and direction. The shells of two atoms held by an electron pair are separated by a definite distance, which if increased by as much as 10^{-8} cm causes a rupture of the bond. Multiple covalent bonds in the same molecule operate at definite angles, as is illustrated by the geometric symmetry of organic molecules.

Whether an atom will enter into chemical combination depends upon the amount of energy necessary to establish a bond between this atom and another atom. Likewise, the type of bond which may be formed is dependent upon the amount of energy necessary to remove an electron completely from the atom, and the amount of energy that is available when this electron is added to an orbital of another atom. The highly stable helium atom contains two electrons which are paired (of opposed spins, which produces an electromagnetic coupling) in the $1s$ orbital. The removal of an electron from the helium atom involves uncoupling the electron pair and lifting the electron against the attractive force of the nucleus. The total energy for the process of removing one of the electrons from the helium atom is 570 kcal/gram atom. This may be compared with the value of 312 kcal/gram atom to remove an electron from the hydrogen atom, and 117.9 kcal/gram atom to remove an electron from the sodium atom. Table 1·2 gives energy values for the removal of an electron from other atoms. Ordinary chemical reactions do not involve sufficient energy changes to remove electrons from helium atoms either completely or incompletely. Nor can the electron be removed from the hydrogen atom, by chemical action, to form an electrovalent bond between a positively charged hydrogen ion and another ion which is negatively charged, because of the large amount of energy necessary for this process. However, the electron is incompletely removed from the hydrogen atom to form a covalent bond between the hydrogen atom and another atom; e.g., H:Cl is a covalent compound produced by such a bonding. The amount of energy necessary to remove the unpaired electron from the sodium atom is available in many chemical reactions; consequently, sodium atoms react readily with many atoms and molecules to produce sodium ions.

Covalent bonds may be formed by atoms when less energy is available than is necessary to remove an electron completely from the valence shell. This statement does not imply that the bond energy is less for the covalent bond than for the electrovalent bond. It simply states that, when the available energy is not sufficient for the formation of an electrovalent bond, a covalent bond may be formed. Actually, the energies of the covalent and ionic bonds are difficult to compare because the factors involved in them are different. But the heat of dissociation of a covalent compound and the energy of formation of ionic crystals from gaseous atoms are comparable. The heat of dissociation of hydrogen molecules into atoms is 104 kcal/mole, and the energy of formation of solid sodium chloride from its gaseous atoms is 98.3 kcal/mole. Such values indicate that the bond energies of covalent and electrovalent compounds are of the same general magnitude.

1·8 Ionization Energy and Electron Affinity. The formation of a positive ion by the removal of one or more electrons from a neutral atom involves the expenditure of a considerable amount of energy, since the electron or electrons must be removed against the electrostatic attraction of the resulting positive ion. The energies of ionization in kilocalories per gram atom per electron (the amount of energy necessary to remove one electron per atom for a gram atomic weight) for some of the univalent elements are given in Table 1·2.

Neutral atoms, which tend to acquire electrons to fill incomplete orbitals, release energy in exhibiting the property of *electron affinity*. For example, the chlorine atom readily acquires one electron with the release of 92.5 kcal/gram atom. The electron affinities of some other atoms which tend to form univalent negative ions are also given in Table 1·2.

TABLE* 1·2   MEAN IONIZATION ENERGIES AND ELECTRON AFFINITIES

Element	Ionization energy, kcal/gram atom	Electron affinity, kcal/gram atom
F	429.0	98.5
Cl	298.9	92.5
Br	272.1	87.1
I	240.8	79.2
H	312.0	16.4
Li	123.8	Assumed zero
Na	117.9	Assumed zero
K	99.7	Assumed zero
Rb	95.9	Assumed zero
Cs	89.4	Assumed zero

* Linus Pauling, "The Nature of the Chemical Bond," p. 66, Cornell University Press, Ithaca, N.Y., 1940.

In the chemical union of two atoms the values for the ionization energy and electron affinity of the two atoms involved are rarely equal or even approximately the same. As a general rule the ionization energy is much greater than the electron affinity. However, the comparative values for the energies involved in these two processes suggest a possible prediction as to whether the resulting compound will be electrovalent or covalent. If the difference in energy is small, as in the formation of sodium chloride from neutral atoms of sodium and chlorine,

$$117.9 - 92.5 = 25.4 \text{ kcal}$$

the deficiency of energy necessary to transfer the electron completely is supplied by a release of energy in the process of setting up the electrostatic bond between the two ions as they are brought together. When the difference is great—so great that the difference cannot be supplied by energy released by building up the crystal lattice or by solvation— the compound produced will be either partly or almost completely covalent. Examples of such compounds are beryllium chloride, $BeCl_2$, and boron trichloride, BCl_3. The ionization energy necessary for the removal of two electrons from 1 gram atom of beryllium is 594.5 kcal. The energy supplied from 2 gram atoms of chlorine is 185 kcal. Subtracting

185 from 594.5 kcal leaves a difference of 409.5 kcal. This difference may be, in part, supplied by the lattice-building energy released or by the solvation energy produced by solution (the solvation energy of the beryllium ion is quite high), but beryllium chloride is partly covalent as is indicated by its solubility in benzene and the low conductivity of the molten compound. The compound boron trichloride is almost completely covalent. The ionization energy necessary to remove three electrons from a gram atom of boron is 1,648 kcal. The addition of 3 gram atoms of chlorine supplies only 277.5 kcal of energy. The difference between the two values is 1,370.5 kcal, which is a value too large to be supplied by any other process in connection with the reaction. Therefore, the atomic binding between the boron atom and the chlorine atoms is one in which the electrons are shared and not exchanged.

1·9 Lattice Energy and Energy of Solvation. Whether an ionic or covalent compound is formed in the chemical union of atoms is dependent not only upon the difference between the amount of energy released due to electron affinity and the amount of energy required for ionization, but also upon the lattice energy of the salt produced.[1] When ions from solution precipitate to form a solid, energy is released in the building of the crystal lattice. The setting up of electrostatic forces between ions in a crystal is an exothermic process, as evidenced by the energy necessary to convert a crystal to a molten condition by heat. This lattice energy is available to supply the difference between ionization energy and electron affinity as explained in the preceding section. This explanation accounts for the fact that a compound such as silver chloride is largely electrovalent and also fairly insoluble. The ionization energy of the neutral silver atom is 174 kcal/gram atom, and the difference between this value and the electron affinity of the chlorine atom is 81.5 kcal. The difference is supplied by the lattice energy of silver chloride, or that energy released by the setting up of electrostatic forces between the silver and chloride ions in the crystal. The very strong attractive forces between these ions account for the relative insolubility of silver chloride, since such forces must be broken before the ions can reenter solution.

There are chemical compounds in which the large differences between the ionization energies and electron affinities of the constituent atoms produce covalent compounds, but which act as electrolytes in water solution because the energy of solvation is sufficient to complete the transfer of the electrons shared in the covalent bond. Hydrogen chloride is typical of such compounds. The bond between the hydrogen and chlorine atoms in HCl is covalent because the ionization energy of hydrogen is

---

[1] This is somewhat of an oversimplification of the true facts. In most cases it is impossible to measure lattice energies directly, and they must be calculated from other thermochemical quantities. However, for the purposes of this discussion the above statement is relatively true.

312.0 kcal/gram atom and the electron affinity of the chlorine atom is only 92.5 kcal/gram atom, leaving a difference of 219.5 kcal. When placed in water solution, hydrogen chloride reacts with water to produce hydronium ions and chloride ions, indicating that the energy of solvation is sufficient to convert the covalent bond into an electrovalent bond.

From the foregoing discussion it may be concluded that atoms of elements with high ionization energies will form covalent bonds in chemical union, unless the energies of solvation or lattice building are sufficient to supply the difference in energy necessary to complete the transfer of the electron in the chemical bond. Emeleus and Anderson[1] point out that this criterion is reflected in the properties of the metallic chlorides. "The remarkably sharp demarcation between true salts and covalent chlorides is shown by a comparison of the fusibility, volatility and equivalent conductivity of the molten compounds. According to the magnitude of the difference between ionization energy and electron affinity the chlorides fall unambiguously into one class or the other."

TABLE 1·3 TRUE SALTS AND COVALENT CHLORIDES*

	HCl			
Melting point	-114			
Boiling point	-85			
Equivalent conductance†	10^{-6}			
	LiCl	BeCl$_2$	BCl$_3$	CCl$_4$
Melting point	606	404	-107	-23
Boiling point	1,337	500	12.6	77
Equivalent conductance	166	0.086	0	0
	NaCl	MgCl$_2$	AlCl$_3$	SiCl$_4$
Melting point	800	718	. . .	-70
Boiling point	1,442	1,000	183	58
Equivalent conductance	134	29	1.5×10^{-5}	0
	KCl	CaCl$_2$	GaCl$_3$	GeCl$_4$
Melting point	768	774	75.5	-50
Boiling point	1,415	1,100	205	87
Equivalent conductance	104	52	10^{-7}	0
	RbCl	SrCl$_2$	InCl$_3$	SnCl$_4$
Melting point	717	870	586	-30
Boiling point	1,388	1,250	. . .	114
Equivalent conductance	78	56	15	0
	CsCl	BaCl$_2$	TlCl$_3$	PbCl$_4$
Melting point	645	960	25	-15
Boiling point	1,289	1,350	100	105 d.
Equivalent conductance	67	65	10^{-3}	2×10^{-5}

* The heavy line marks the division between electrovalent and covalent chlorides as reflected in each of the properties cited.

† Equivalent conductance is for the molten compound at its melting point.

[1] H. J. Emeleus and J. S. Anderson, "Modern Aspects of Inorganic Chemistry," p. 47, D. Van Nostrand Company, Inc., New York, 1952.

1·10 Other Types of Bonds. Before leaving the topic of chemical bonding, there are two other special types of bonds which are of interest in solution chemistry. The *coordinate* bond is a type of covalency in which the shared electron pair is furnished by one atom. This differs from the covalent bond in which each of the atoms, joined by the bond, contributes one electron to the shared pair. But once the coordinate bond is formed, it cannot be distinguished from any other covalent bond. For example, the nitrogen atom has the following electronic configuration:

$$_7N \quad 1s^2 2s^2 2p^1 2p^1 2p^1$$

In the valence shell there are four orbitals, of which the $2s$ orbital contains an electron pair, and the three $2p$ orbitals contain single electrons. Nitrogen combines with three hydrogen atoms in a normal covalent way to form a molecule of NH_3 in which the $3p$ orbitals of the nitrogen atom are completed. However, the resulting molecule is electrically unsymmetrical (Sec. 1·11) and as a result tends to share its $2s^2$ electrons with atoms which have *uncomplete* orbitals. In the case of the ammonium ion, the $2s^2$ electrons of nitrogen are shared with a proton to complete the $1s^2$ orbital of hydrogen.

$$
\begin{array}{ccc}
\text{H} & & \text{H} \\
\text{\tiny ..} & & \text{\tiny ..} \\
\text{H : N :} + \text{H}^+ \rightarrow & \left[\text{H : N : H} \right]^+ \\
\text{\tiny ..} & & \text{\tiny ..} \\
\text{H} & & \text{H}
\end{array}
$$

The coordinate bond is discussed in more detail in the chapter on Complex Ions (Sec. 7·4 *ff.*).

The other special type of bond pertinent to solution chemistry is the *hydrogen bond.* Although the hydrogen atom possesses only one electron and is therefore univalent, it can form a bridge between two other atoms if these two atoms are of elements that are strongly electronegative in character, *e.g.*, fluorine, oxygen, and nitrogen. The salt KHF_2 in water solution produces K^+ and HF_2^- ions. In the latter ion the hydrogen acts as a bridge between the two fluorine ions $(F\text{—}H\text{—}F)^-$. Since the hydrogen atom has only one stable orbital $(1s^1)$, it can form only one covalent bond. Therefore, the hydrogen bond must be partly ionic, and because of this partly electrostatic nature, it is formed only between strongly electronegative atoms.

The formation of hydrogen bonds is responsible for the association of molecules in water, in which the hydrogen atom forms a bridge between oxygen atoms with unshared electron pairs, such as

$$
\begin{array}{ccc}
\text{\tiny ..} & \text{\tiny ..} & \text{\tiny ..} \\
\text{H : O :} \rightarrow & \text{H : O :} \rightarrow & \text{H : O :} \\
\text{\tiny ..} & \text{\tiny ..} & \text{\tiny ..} \\
\text{H} & \text{H} & \text{H}
\end{array}
$$

In ice, four molecules of H_2O are coordinated about a central H_2O molecule to form a tetrahedral structure. With a rise in temperature some of these bonds are broken, yet sufficient hydrogen bridges remain between aggregates of two or more molecules to account for the abnormally high boiling point of water. Hydrogen bonds also account for the unusually high dielectric constant of water, which in turn is responsible for that liquid's remarkable solvent power for electrolytes.

1·11   Electronic Explanation of Molecular Polarity.   In the formation of sodium chloride there is a complete transfer of an electron from the sodium atom to the chlorine atom to produce two electrically charged particles—ions. In the formation of the chlorine molecule, Cl_2, the single $3p$ electron of each chlorine atom is coupled to form an electron pair. This electron pair is shared mutually by each atom and serves to fill the

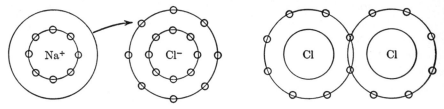

Sodium chloride   Chlorine molecule

FIG. 1·5   The electronic structures of sodium chloride and the chlorine molecule.

incomplete $3p$ orbital in each chlorine atom. Sodium chloride is an example of an electrovalent compound (electron transfer), and the chlorine molecule is a covalent compound (electron sharing). The electronic structures of these compounds may be represented by the diagrams in Fig. 1·5. Intermediate between these two extreme types of compounds there is an important group of molecules in which the electrons are incompletely transferred and unequally shared. For example, when two atoms combine to form a simple molecule, unless the atoms are identical, the electron pair which makes up the bond will be drawn more closely to one atom than to the other. In a molecule containing two dissimilar atoms there is a displacement of electric charge so that the center of the positive charge does not coincide with the center of the negative charge. The bond so produced is partly covalent and partly electrostatic. Molecules containing displaced electron pairs are described as *polar*, and the forces which hold them together may be called *polar bonds*. Examples of such molecules are H_2O, HCl, and NH_3.

An atom may be regarded as a positive center with an atmosphere of negative charges about it. In the case of the chlorine molecule, two atoms of the same radii and with positive nuclear charges equal to each other have combined to fill incomplete orbitals. In the resulting molecule the electron densities of the chlorine atoms are the same and, therefore, the bond is completely covalent in character. When two atoms of different radii, with positive centers of different magnitudes, combine to share an electron pair, the most probable position of the latter will not be equidistant from the two positive centers. An excellent illustration of the electronic structure of such a molecule is furnished by iodine monochloride, ICl. The chlorine atom is smaller than the iodine atom, and in the ICl molecule the attractive force of the positively charged nucleus of the chlorine atom for the electron pair is greater than that of the iodine atom. For this reason, the two electrons making up the bond are drawn nearer to the chlorine atom than to the iodine atom, giving the chlorine atom a slightly negative charge and the iodine atom a slightly positive charge, as indicated in Fig. 1·6. Such a molecule never actually

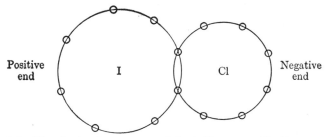

FIG. 1·6   The electronic structure of the iodine monochloride molecule.

ionizes into negative chloride ions and positive iodide ions, but the molecule is electrically unsymmetrical. This accounts for the fact that polar molecules orient themselves in an electrostatic field similarly to small magnets, with separate positive and negative centers.

The separation of charges in a molecule, called its *dipole moment*, cannot be predicted quantitatively with any degree of exactness, but it can be determined by a number of experimental methods. In the case of diatomic molecules, the attractive forces exerted by the two positive nuclei for the electron pair are related to the magnitude of the nuclear charges and the radii of the two atoms. The hydrogen chloride molecule illustrates the combination of two atoms with widely different radii and nuclear charges. Despite the smaller size of the hydrogen atom, the greater nuclear charge of the chlorine atom causes the electron pair to be shifted toward the chlorine atom. Consequently, the separation of charges in the HCl molecule, as shown in Fig. 1·7, is such that the chlorine atom is negatively charged with respect to the hydrogen atom.

The attraction of a neutral atom in a stable molecule for electrons is a property that Pauling designates as *electronegativity*. For a univalent atom, the average of the ionization energy and the electron affinity is a measure of its electronegativity. From heats of formation of the most common elements in some of their compounds, Pauling has set up an arbitrary electronegativity scale for atoms of these elements (Table 1·4). From the relative positions of the elements on this scale a prediction can be made as to the type of bond which may be formed between two atoms. According to Pauling, if the separation on the scale is 1.7, the bond is 50 per cent ionic in character. When the separation is greater than 1.7 the bond is correspondingly more ionic.

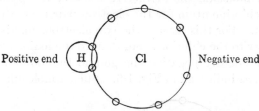

Positive end   H   Cl   Negative end

FIG. 1·7   The electronic structure of the hydrogen chloride molecule.

In the case of polyatomic molecules, an explanation of polarity becomes more complex. In addition to the factors already mentioned, the shape of a polyatomic molecule may affect the extent to which there is an effective separation of charges within the molecule. Thus the water molecule, which has an angular structure in which the two hydrogen atoms are on the same side of the oxygen atom, has a permanent dipole

TABLE 1·4   RELATIVE ELECTRONEGATIVITY OF THE ELEMENTS*

Element	Relative electro-negativity	Element	Relative electro-negativity
Cesium	0.7	Antimony	1.8
Rubidium	0.8	Silicon	1.8
Potassium	0.8	Boron	2.0
Sodium	0.9	Arsenic	2.0
Barium	0.9	Hydrogen	2.1
Strontium	1.0	Tellurium	2.1
Lithium	1.0	Phosphorus	2.1
Calcium	1.0	Selenium	2.4
Magnesium	1.2	Iodine	2.4
Yttrium	1.3	Carbon	2.5
Scandium	1.3	Sulfur	2.5
Beryllium	1.5	Bromine	2.8
Aluminum	1.5	Chlorine	3.0
Zirconium	1.6	Nitrogen	3.0
Titanium	1.6	Oxygen	3.5
Tin	1.7	Fluorine	4.0
Germanium	1.7		

* Linus Pauling, "The Nature of the Chemical Bond," p. 64, Cornell University Press, Ithaca, N.Y., 1940.

moment. As indicated in Fig. 1·8, the oxygen side of the molecule is negatively charged and the hydrogen side is positively charged. If the structure of the HOH molecule were linear, the separation of charges in the two OH bonds would cancel each other, giving the molecule a zero dipole moment.

The polarity of molecules becomes significant in a broad interpretation of the problem of solubility. As a general rule, polar substances dissolve

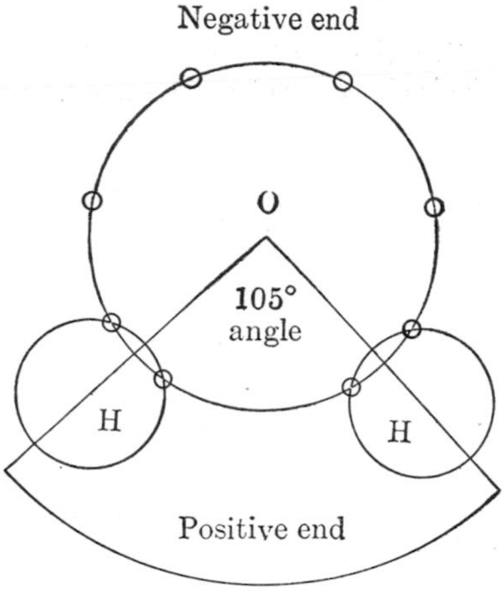

FIG. 1·8 The electronic structure of the water molecule showing the angle formed by the two OH bonds.

in polar solvents but are insoluble in nonpolar solvents. The problem of solubility is discussed more completely in the next chapter.

Exercises

1. Describe the differences in physical properties between covalent and electrovalent compounds.

2. Describe the differences in chemical properties between covalent and electrovalent compounds.

3. How does the size of an atom affect the number of chemical bonds it may form?

4. The boiling point of H_2S is $-59°C$ and the boiling point of water is $100°C$. Explain the wide difference in the boiling points of hydrogen compounds of these closely related chemical elements.

5. What orbitals of the O shell of iodine are utilized in the bonding of iodine heptafluoride, IF_7?

6. Strong hydrogen bonds exist between fluoride ions in a water solution of hydrogen fluoride. Why is the same not true between chloride ions in a water solution of hydrogen chloride?

7. Explain why mercuric chloride is more soluble in benzene (a nonpolar solvent) than is barium chloride.

8. Why is a solution of hydrogen chloride in benzene a nonconductor of electricity, whereas a solution of hydrogen chloride in water is a good conductor?

9. The fluoride atom has a small radius. How does this fact affect the degree of ionization of hydrofluoric acid?

10. An atom of a certain element has ten electrons in a certain shell. Assuming that the s and p sublevels are filled, how many electrons are in the d sublevel?

11. The mean ionization energy per electron removed from Pb^{++} is 257 kcal/gram atom. $PbCl_2$ is a fairly insoluble compound. Predict, with explanation, whether $PbCl_2$ should be a covalent chloride or a true salt.

12. Antimony trichloride has a melting point of 73.4°C and a boiling point of 220°C. Explain why $SbCl_3$ should be a partly covalent compound.

13. The ammonia molecule has a pyramidal structure with the three NH bonds forming angles of 109°. Predict, with explanation, the expected solubility of true salts in liquid ammonia.

14. From Pauling's relative values of electronegativity, as given in Table 1·4, determine the percentage ionic character of the HI bond.

CHAPTER 2

SOLUTIONS

The majority of the chemical reactions encountered in analytical chemistry take place in aqueous solution. It is also true that most of the theories of qualitative analysis pertain to the physical and chemical properties of solutions. As an introduction to these reactions and theories, which are sometimes collectively called *solution chemistry*, it seems worthwhile to examine, in an elementary fashion, the general concepts and properties of solutions.

2·1 Definitions. A solution is a homogeneous mixture of two or more substances, these substances being of molecular dimensions, whose composition may be varied within certain limits. In other words, a solution may be regarded as a molecular dispersion of substances within each other. In aqueous solutions the water is usually considered as the solvent or medium in which the solute is dissolved. There are, however, conditions where the two components of a simple solution, the solvent and solute, cannot be distinguished from each other, as illustrated by a mixture of water and ethyl alcohol. In a mixture of 75 per cent alcohol and 25 per cent water, the alcohol might well be regarded as the solvent and water as the solute. Another point of view is to regard the solute as the most active component chemically, and the solvent as the least active. However, the differentiation between solvent and solute is fairly well defined in the solutions of qualitative analysis. In these solutions, the substances dissolved in water are usually of sufficiently low concentrations that water can always be considered as the solvent.

As a general rule, the solutions encountered in qualitative analysis are composed of solids dissolved in water. There are, however, other mixtures recognized as solutions. For example, gases such as ammonia and carbon dioxide, or liquids such as alcohol and glycerin, can be dissolved in water to form solutions. Various other types of solutions are possible, *e.g.*, a gas dissolved in a gas, or a solid within a solid, but these types are not relevant to this discussion.

2·2 Concentration Units. In an aqueous solution, the weight of the solute in a given quantity (weight or volume) of water is known as the *concentration* of the solution. The concentration of an aqueous solution is expressed by two general methods, namely, the weight of the solute in a given volume of solution, and the weight of the solute in a given weight of solvent or solution.   An outline explanation of these methods follows:

I. Weight of Solute in a Given Volume of Solvent

    A. **Molarity.**   A *molar* solution contains 1 mole (1 gram-molecular weight) of the solute dissolved in sufficient water to make a liter of solution.   The molecular weight is the sum of the atomic weights of the elements indicated in the formula of the substance, and this weight, expressed in grams, is the gram-molecular weight.

       However, the term *molecular weight* is somewhat of a misnomer for ionic substances, since ions are not molecules in either the crystal lattice or aqueous solution.   It is also true that certain substances, usually considered as existing as the "simplest formula" molecules, may associate so that two or more simple molecules may form larger aggregates.   For example, association due to hydrogen bonding causes carboxylic acids, such as acetic acid, formic acid, benzoic acid, etc., to form double molecules in the following manner:

$$CH_3-C \overset{O-H \leftarrow O}{\underset{O \rightarrow H-O}{\Big\langle\ \ \ \ \ \ \Big\rangle}} C-CH_3 \qquad \text{(acetic acid)}$$

       Therefore, the designation of concentration as molarity may be misleading for either ionic substances or substances existing as associated molecules.   A more unambiguous method of expressing concentration is that of formality.

       To illustrate specifically the use of molarity as a concentration unit, if 36.46 g (1 + 35.46) of HCl is dissolved in sufficient water to produce a liter of solution, the resulting solution is 1 M in respect to HCl.   Therefore, the term *molarity* designates moles per liter of solution.

    B. **Formality.**   A *formal* solution contains 1 gram-formula weight of the solute dissolved in sufficient water to produce a liter of solution.   The formula weight is the sum of the atomic weights of those elements in the assumed formula of the solute.   Usually, but not always, the assumed formula is the simplest formula for an inorganic substance.   This method of expressing concentration applies equally well to either ionic substances or substances that exist as molecules.   By definition, *formality* is equal to the number of gram-formula weights per liter of solution.   To illustrate this concentration unit, a formal solution of NaCl contains

58.46 g (23 + 35.46) of sodium choride in a liter of solution. Formality and molarity become equivalent terms when the formula weight is known to be the same as the molecular weight.

C. **Normality.** A *normal* solution contains 1 gram-equivalent weight of the solute in a liter of solution. A gram-equivalent weight of an acid or a base is that weight (in grams) of the solute which will furnish or react with 1 gfw of hydronium ions. A normal solution of HCl contains 36.46 g (1 + 35.46) of hydrogen chloride in a liter of solution, in that a solution of this concentration will furnish 1 g of hydronium ions. A normal solution of sulfuric acid contains $\dfrac{(2 + 32 + 64)}{2}$ or 49 g of H_2SO_4 in a liter of solution, since only $\frac{1}{2}$ gfw is required to supply 1 g of hydronium ions.

In redox (reduction-oxidation) reactions the equivalent weight is defined in terms of electrons lost or gained in the reaction. The equivalent weight is equal to the molecular weight divided by the number of electrons lost or gained as determined from the redox reaction. For example, in an acid solution the MnO_4^- ion may be reduced to the Mn^{++} ion, indicating a gain of five electrons, since the oxidation number of the manganese atom is changed from +7 to +2. Therefore, the equivalent weight of $KMnO_4$ is the molecular weight divided by five (158.03/5 = 31.61). Hence, a normal solution of $KMnO_4$, when used as an oxidizing agent in an acid solution, contains 31.61 g of the solute in a liter of solution.

II. Weight of Solute in a Given Weight of Solvent or Solution

A. **Molality.** A *molal* solution contains 1 gram-molecular weight (1 mole) of the solute dissolved in 1,000 g of water. It differs from a molar solution in being a ratio of solute to solvent by weight.

B. **Percentage Composition.** The percentage of a solution is the weight in grams (or any other weight unit) of the solute contained in 100 g (or corresponding weight unit) of solution. Thus, 10 g of sodium chloride in 100 g of solution is a 10 per cent solution of NaCl.

This outline gives the most common units for expressing concentrations of solutions. Other units such as mole ratios, mole fractions, and mole percentages are employed for special purposes, but these units are not used in qualitative analysis.

In this text and the accompanying laboratory procedures, concentrations of solutions are expressed in terms of *formality*, since this method of designating concentrations is unambiguous under all possible applications.

2·3   Solubility.   Alcohol and water are completely miscible.   In other words, no limit exists as to the extent of the solubility of either compound within the other.   Totally miscible combinations of this type are not common.   Usually there is a limit to the solubility of a substance in water, and when this limit is reached, the undissolved solute exists in equilibrium with the dissolved solute, as a saturated solution.   Accordingly, the solubility of a substance may be expressed in terms of its concentration within a saturated solution.   Since the concentration of solids in a saturated solution varies with temperature, it is necessary to specify temperature with solubility data.   The extent of solubility for a given temperature may be expressed in any of the concentration units of the preceding discussion.

The range of solubility of solids in liquids is quite wide.   Potassium nitrate dissolves to the extent of 31.6 g in 100 ml of water at 20°C, whereas silver chloride is soluble only to the extent of 0.0001 g/100 ml of water at 10°C.   Why one substance is very soluble and another only slightly soluble may be explained in terms of the attractive forces between the solute ions and the solvent molecules.   A completely satisfactory analysis of these attractive forces is yet to be made, but sufficient basic facts about solubility are known to enable us to visualize a partial picture of what takes place when a solute dissolves in a solvent.

2·4   Some Factors Affecting Solubility.   Two factors are known which affect the solubility of solids in liquids.   They are (1) temperature, and (2) the physical and chemical structure of the solvent and solute particles.

Temperature.   A rising temperature produces a wide range of effects upon the solubilities of solids in water.   Usually, the solubilities of substances are increased with an increase in temperature, but there are exceptions to this general rule.   Among these exceptions are anhydrous sodium sulfate whose solubility decreases with rising temperature, and sodium chloride whose solubility is little affected by temperature change.   The solubility-temperature curves in Fig. 2·1 illustrate the different effects of temperature upon three different salts.

The solution of a solid is analogous to a melting process.   Pure solids are usually crystalline in structure, and the atoms or ions in the crystal lattice are geometrically interspaced so that each ion or atom has the same pattern with respect to neighboring ions or atoms.   The forces which hold these ions or atoms in their relative positions are large. When a crystal is heated the kinetic energy of the particles within the crystal is increased.   This increased kinetic energy is manifested, at first, by an increased vibration of the particles composing the lattice structure.   When the amplitude of vibration becomes sufficiently large, the forces holding the particles together are overcome, and the ions or atoms break away from their relatively fixed positions.   In this manner a crystal melts and the particles of which it was originally composed are free to move throughout the molten substance. When a solid enters into solution, the solvent particles exert sufficient attraction to overcome the attractive forces holding the solute particles in the crystal lattice. As a general rule, a rise in temperature favors an increase in solubility. The electrostatic forces holding ions or molecules within a crystal are weakened by an increase in the kinetic energy of these particles, thereby enabling the attractive forces of the solvent molecules to be more effective in breaking down the crystal lattice. It is also true that substances

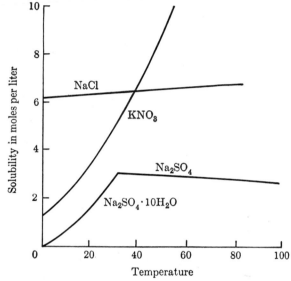

FIG. 2·1 Effect of temperature on the solubility of certain soluble salts.

with high melting points are more insoluble than those with low melting points. A high melting point indicates a greater intermolecular or interionic attraction. However, so many factors enter into the complicated picture of the solution process that the foregoing explanation is far from complete.

Physical and Chemical Structure of Solvent and Solute Particles. When two atoms combine chemically to form a covalent linkage, the electrons which are held between the atoms may be shared equally or unequally (Sec. 1·11). If the bond is produced by an unequal sharing, the electrons which form the bond are believed to be nearer one atom than the other. Since the atoms, before chemical union, were electrically neutral, the molecule which is produced will contain separate positive and negative centers, resulting from the unequal sharing of electrons. A molecule containing separate negative and positive charges is known as a *polar* molecule, and a molecule with little or no separation of charges is a *non-*

polar molecule. The degree of polarity depends upon the distance between charges within the molecule. Ordinarily, the degree of polarity is designated as the *dipole moment* of the molecule, and the dipole moment is calculated by multiplying the charge on one of the atoms by the distance between the centers of the two charges. Thus

$$\mu = de$$

where mu denotes the dipole moment. Figure 2·2 indicates polar molecules with different polarities resulting from differences in the extent of the separation of the intramolecular charges. The dipole moment is always of the order of 10^{-18} electrostatic units. This magnitude is to be

FIG. 2·2   Schematic representation of molecules of increasing degree of polarity.

anticipated since the unit electronic charge is 4.8×10^{-10} esu and the diameter of most molecules is of the order of 10^{-8} cm. Table 2·1 lists a number of liquid compounds according to their decreasing dipole moments.

TABLE 2·1   DIPOLE MOMENTS OF A NUMBER OF LIQUIDS

Liquid compound		Dipole moment, esu
$C_6H_5NO_2$	(nitrobenzene)	4.18×10^{-18}
H_2O	(water)	1.84×10^{-18}
C_2H_5OH	(ethyl alcohol)	1.70×10^{-18}
C_6H_5OH	(phenol)	1.70×10^{-18}
NH_3	(liquid ammonia)	1.46×10^{-18}
$CHCl_3$	(chloroform)	1.15×10^{-18}
HBr	(liquid hydrogen bromide)	0.79×10^{-18}
C_6H_6	(benzene)	0
CCl_4	(carbon tetrachloride)	0

"Like dissolves like" is a familiar rule in organic chemistry and is also applicable to inorganic chemistry. Polar molecules of a solvent attract polar molecules or ions of a solute to produce solutions. On the other hand, polar molecules of a solvent do not attract nonpolar molecules. In fact, the strong attractive forces between the polar molecules prevent the entrance of nonpolar molecules into the intermolecular spaces of the solvent. Thus, water dissolves ammonia, both substances being strongly polar, but water will not dissolve benzene which is nonpolar. Conversely, nonpolar solvents dissolve nonpolar solutes but will not dissolve polar substances. To illustrate, heptane, a nonpolar liquid, will dissolve in benzene but will not dissolve in water.

Nonpolar molecules are not attracted to each other by dipole charges; consequently, nonpolar solvent molecules do not offer any resistance to the entrance of nonpolar solute molecules into the intermolecular spaces of the solvent.

The rule of "like dissolves like" refers not only to similarity in relation to dipole moment but also to chemical composition. Therefore, it is generally true that a substance tends to dissolve in a solvent which is chemically related in composition to the substance. For example, gasoline readily dissolves paraffin, or water is a good solvent of cane sugar. Gasoline and paraffin are both hydrocarbons—compounds containing only carbon and hydrogen. Cane sugar is a carbohydrate and, as the name "carbohydrate" implies, is a composition of carbon, hydrogen, and oxygen in which the ratio of hydrogen to oxygen is the same as in water.

The explanation of the process of solution becomes more complex when the solvent is a liquid whose molecules are associated as a result of hydrogen bonding. Among solvents of this type are water, liquid ammonia, and liquid hydrogen fluoride. The hydrogen bond serves as a bridge between strongly electronegative atoms; therefore, molecules containing hydrogen and the more electronegative atoms tend to group into clusters which are held together by hydrogen bridges. The tetrahedral arrangement of water molecules in ice is a result of hydrogen bonding, and this tetrahedral structure persists, to some extent, after ice is converted into a liquid. Consequently, the composition of water is not that of simple H_2O molecules, but that of multiple molecules held together somewhat loosely by hydrogen bonds. Water, liquid ammonia, liquid hydrogen fluoride, and solvents of this type, because of their associated structures, will not necessarily dissolve polar molecules, unless the solute molecules can form hydrogen bonds with the solvent molecules. For example, nitrobenzene, $C_6H_5NO_2$, has a dipole moment of 4.2×10^{-18} esu, which is large as compared with the dipole moment of water, but nitrobenzene molecules are practically insoluble in water because they cannot form hydrogen linkages with water molecules. On the other hand, phenol, C_6H_5OH, is forty times as soluble in water as nitrobenzene. Phenol, which is similar to nitrobenzene in that it is a monosubstituted benzene product, has a dipole moment of 1.7×10^{-18} esu, and should be less soluble than nitrobenzene if relative solubility were entirely dependent upon the magnitude of the dipole moment. This unexpected solubility must be due to the formation of hydrogen bonds between the hydroxyl groups of the phenol molecules and the oxygen atoms in the water molecules.

Another complex form of solubility is presented by organic molecules whose structures are such that they are partly polar and partly nonpolar. A molecule of this type is exemplified by heptyl alcohol, $CH_3CH_2CH_2$-$CH_2CH_2CH_2CH_2OH$, which is composed of a hydrocarbon chain with a hydroxyl group attached to one end. The hydroxyl end of this molecule is soluble, because it penetrates the structure of water to form hydrogen bonds. The hydrocarbon end of the molecule is nonpolar and cannot form hydrogen bonds and is, therefore, insoluble. Molecules of heptyl alcohol, when placed in water, are pushed to the surface where they orient themselves so that the soluble ends are in the water and the nonpolar ends protrude above the surface. Figure 2·3 illustrates this arrangement. It is of interest that hydrocarbon molecules with soluble, polar end groups such as —CH_2OH or —COOH may form unimolecular (a depth of one molecule) films upon the surface of water. Films of this type also occur at any interface of water and its container, and as a result the surface tension of water and its "wetting" properties may undergo decided changes. Wetting agents of this general type have wide commercial applications.

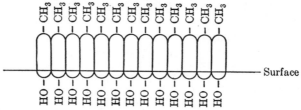

FIG. 2·3 Diagrammatic representation of the unimolecular film formed on an interface of water by long-chain organic molecules with polar end groups.

From the foregoing discussion, it is apparent that the difference between a physical solution and a chemical solution offers no sharp line of demarcation. A physical solution is one in which the solute and solvent are both nonpolar with no associating tendencies or solvating propensities. A solution of paraffin in benzene is a typical example of a physical solution. On the other hand, the solubility of calcium oxalate in dilute hydrochloric acid is the result of a chemical reaction, and such a solution is clearly a chemical solution. Between the two extremes of physical and chemical solubilities are solutions formed by attractive forces which are intermediate between physical and chemical. The solubility of sugars in water can be attributed to the formation of hydrogen bonds. The solubility of most ionic compounds in water results from the solvation of ions to form hydrated ions. Yet, neither the solubility of sugars nor the solubility of ionic compounds is caused by either physical or chemical forces alone. It is more likely that such intermediate types of solubility are a result of a combination of chemical and physical forces.

PROPERTIES OF SOLUTIONS

Aside from their chemical behavior, solutions as a whole have many special properties or qualities, which may be classified into general types.

Included in these types are specific properties, electrical properties, and colligative properties. The specific properties are those physical properties of a solution which depend upon the nature of the solute particles, *e.g.*, the viscosity, the density, or the surface tension. The electrical properties are dependent upon the number and nature of the charged particles within the solution, which move between electrodes under the influence of an electric current. The colligative properties depend only upon the number of solute particles which are present. The latter two properties are quite pertinent to the study of qualitative analysis and will be examined in more detail.

2·5 Conductance of Electricity by Solutions. The electrical properties of a solution are closely associated with its chemical behavior, since both depend upon the nature and number of particles in solution. It is also true that both are dependent upon the type, or types, of binding which are present in the solute particles.

Electrolytes, Weak Electrolytes, and Nonelectrolytes. Substances whose water solutions conduct an electric current are called *electrolytes*, and those substances whose water solutions will not carry an electric current are called *nonelectrolytes*. The difference is not only in kind but, in the case of electrolytes, also in degree. As a consequence, there is an intermediate group of substances whose water solutions are poor conductors, and these substances are loosely classified as *weak electrolytes*. Conductance of an electric current is due to migration of charged particles, called *ions*, in a solution to those electrodes of opposite charges. All but a few salts are strong electrolytes. Other strong electrolytes are the so-called strong acids and bases, namely, hydrochloric acid, nitric acid, sulfuric acid, perchloric acid, hydrobromic acid, hydriodic acid, sodium hydroxide, potassium hydroxide, strontium hydroxide, calcium hydroxide, and barium hydroxide.

The group of weak electrolytes includes those compounds usually referred to as weak acids and weak bases. Typical weak acids are acetic and nitrous acids; among the weak bases are ammonia water and pyridine.

Many molecular compounds, of which sugars and alcohols are representative, dissolve readily in water because of their chemical structures but do not produce charged particles in solution. These substances are nonelectrolytes, because their water solutions will not conduct an electric current.

Variation of Conductance with Concentration. The *equivalent conductance* of a solution of an electrolyte increases with progressive dilutions until a limiting value is reached in a very dilute solution. To understand the implications of this statement requires explanation of what is meant by equivalent conductance. Equivalent conductance is defined as the conductance (of electricity) of a solution containing 1 gram equivalent of an electrolyte, the solution being contained between two plane electrodes 1 cm apart. To verify by experiment that the equivalent conductance of a solution increases with dilution would require the use of a special electrolytic cell. This cell would be so constructed that the area of exposed electrodes would increase proportionally as the solution is diluted, the distance between electrodes always maintained as 1 cm. Such a cell may be constructed in a rectangular form with the two electrodes being of the same area as the two opposite sides of the cell, as shown in Fig. 2·4. The large size of this hypothetical cell would make it inconvenient for the determination of equivalent conductance. It is much simpler to calculate equivalent conductance from the following mathematical expression:

$$\Lambda = \frac{1,000 \ K}{C}$$

in which lambda is the equivalent conductance, K is the specific conductance, and C is the concentration of the solution. In this relation, specific conductance is the reciprocal of specific resistance, the latter being the resistance, in ohms, of a column of a solution 1 cm long and 1 sq cm in cross section. However, the quantitative determination of equivalent conductance is not pertinent to this discussion. On the other hand, the qualitative significance of the change of equivalent conductance with dilution is most interesting. Such measurements indicate that a given weight of an electrolyte in solution apparently produces more ions as it is diluted.

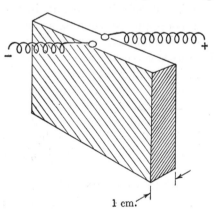

1 cm.

FIG. 2·4   Sketch of a hypothetical cell for the determination of equivalent conductance.

The increase in equivalent conductance with dilution takes place in solutions of both strong and weak electrolytes, as indicated in Table 2·2. In the case of strong electrolytes, of which sodium chloride is typical, the charged particles in solution exert an electrostatic attraction for charged particles of opposite charge. When the particles are close together, as in a concentrated solution, the coulombic forces of attraction are sufficiently strong to diminish the mobility of each ion involved. Consequently, the rate of migration of the ions between electrodes is decreased. If the solution is diluted, the electrostatic forces between the charged particles are weakened by distance, and the apparent or effective number of particles to carry electrical charges is increased.

TABLE 2·2 EQUIVALENT CONDUCTANCE OF AQUEOUS SOLUTIONS AT 25°C

Gram-formula weights per liter	HC$_2$H$_3$O$_2$	HCl	NH$_3$	NaOH	NaCl
1.0	.....	332	0.9	. . .	. . .
0.1	5.2	391	3.6	221	107
0.01	16.3	412	11.5	237	118
0.001	48.1	421	34	245	124
0.0001	127.7	426	93	. . .	126

In the case of weak electrolytes the increased conductance with dilution may be attributed to an increase in the solvation of the solute molecules. To illustrate, a weak acid, as acetic acid, becomes a weak electrolyte due to the reaction of the acetic acid molecules with water to produce charged particles, the hydronium and acetate ions.

$$HC_2H_3O_2 + H_2O \rightleftharpoons H_3O^+ + C_2H_3O_2^-$$

This reaction may be considered as a reversible reaction which goes to completion only at infinite dilution.

2·6 Colligative Properties. Certain physical properties of solutions depend quantitatively upon the number of particles of solute in solution. These properties are known as the *colligative properties* of the solution and are manifest as (1) a lowering of the vapor pressure, (2) a lowering of the freezing point, (3) an elevation in the boiling point, and (4) the development of an osmotic pressure. The number, not kind, of particles of solute determines the quantitative changes in these properties.

1. *Vapor-pressure Lowering.* The vapor pressure of water at a given temperature is the pressure exerted by the gaseous molecules in equilibrium with the liquid. Water has a vapor pressure of 17.5 mm at 20°C. (The height in millimeters refers to a column of mercury.) For a 1 *m* solution of a nonelectrolyte, as glucose, the vapor pressure of the water solution at 20°C is lowered 0.31 mm, and this value is called the *molal vapor-pressure lowering* of water. A 1 *m* solution of an electrolyte, as sodium chloride, causes a greater lowering of vapor pressure, which is dependent upon the number of ions produced by the electrolyte and its apparent extent of ionization. Although sodium chloride is completely ionized in water solution, the effective concentration of ions is somewhat less than twice that of the formula concentration. Therefore, a molal solution of NaCl causes a lowering of vapor pressure of the solution, which is slightly less than twice that of a molal solution of a nonelectrolyte.

2. *Freezing-point Depression.* The freezing point of any liquid is the temperature at which the liquid phase and the solid phase are in equilibrium under a pressure of 1 atm. The freezing point of pure water is 0°C. The presence of particles in solution lowers the freezing point of water. This depression is a colligative property which depends upon number and

not type of particle. It has been found by experiment that the *molal freezing-point* constant of water is 1.86°C. In other words, if 1 gfw of a nonelectrolyte is dissolved in 1,000 g of water, the freezing point of the solution will be −1.86°C. The freezing-point depression constant varies for different solvents; *e.g.*, it is 4.67°C for chloroform and 3.00°C for acetic acid. The freezing-point depression caused by an electrolyte in solution is abnormally large as compared with a nonelectrolyte. For instance, a 0.1 *m* solution of NaCl has a freezing point of −0.348°C, whereas the freezing point of a 0.1 *m* solution of a nonelectrolyte is −0.186°C.

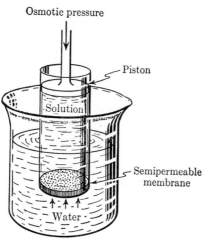

FIG. 2·5   Osmotic pressure exerted by a piston in preventing the passage of molecules of water through a semipermeable membrane into a solution.

3. *Boiling-point   Elevation.* The boiling point of a liquid is that temperature at which the vapor pressure of the liquid becomes equal to the atmospheric pressure. The boiling point of pure water at 1 atm pressure is 100°C. The addition of a nonvolatile solute raises the boiling point of a water solution. If the solute is a nonelectrolyte such as dextrose, a molal solution has a boiling point of 100.52°C, and the *molal boiling-point constant* for water solutions of nonelectrolytes is 0.52°C. Again, it is true that an electrolyte in aqueous solution produces a greater boiling-point elevation than does a nonelectrolyte in a comparable concentration. The boiling point of a molal solution of NaCl is 101.0°C.

4. *Osmotic Pressure.* If a solution is separated from pure water, or a less concentrated solution, by a semipermeable membrane, the molecules of water will pass through the membrane in the direction of the solution. On the other hand, the molecules or particles of the solute will not pass through the membrane to the water, or less concentrated solution. Consequently, this one-way diffusion results in the solution becoming more dilute. The transfer of solvent molecules through a semipermeable membrane to cause the dilution of a solution is called *osmosis*. The *osmotic pressure* of a solution is the external pressure which must be applied to the solution, when it is separated from the pure solvent by a semipermeable membrane, to prevent the passage of the solvent molecules through the membrane. Figure 2·5 illustrates the osmotic pressure exerted by a piston in preventing the passage of molecules of water through a semipermeable membrane into a solution.

The osmotic pressure of a solution is closely related to the lowering of vapor pressure and is proportional to the molal concentration of the solute. At 0°C the osmotic pressure of a 1 m solution of a nonelectrolyte is 22.4 atm. Again, this pressure is abnormally high for solutions of electrolytes; the osmotic pressure of a sodium chloride solution is nearly twice that of a solution of a nonelectrolyte in a comparable concentration.

2·7 Modern View of Ionization. In 1887 a young Swedish chemist, Svante Arrhenius, after working on the conductance of acid solutions for his doctor's thesis at the University of Stockholm, advanced the theory of ionization to account for the special properties of aqueous solutions of electrolytes. This theory revolutionized the thinking in inorganic chemistry and inspired extensive research in the field of solutions. The classical theory of Arrhenius, although still applicable with slight changes to the behavior of solutions containing weak electrolytes, has been modified considerably by recent theories and discoveries. Among the more important developments that have brought about modifications of the Arrhenius theory are the Debye-Hückel theory of complete ionization and interionic attraction, and Brønsted's definitions of acids and bases. Combining the classical theory with more recent developments, the modern view of ionization is summarized in the following postulates:

1. *Electrolytes, when dissolved in water or any other ionizing medium, produce electrically charged particles called ions.*

Electrolytes of the ionic type exist as ions, not only in solution but also in the crystal. X-ray analysis of the sodium chloride crystal indicates that alternate spacing of the sodium and chloride ions permits each sodium ion to be surrounded by six chloride ions, and each chloride ion to be surrounded by six sodium ions (see Fig. 1·4). In the process by which sodium chloride enters solution, water molecules, because of their dipole moments, orient their negative centers toward the sodium ions and their positive ends toward the chloride ions at the surface of the crystal. The dipole forces exerted by the oriented water molecules weaken the interionic attraction within the crystal so that some of the ions are pulled into solution. The removed ions wander away from the crystal, carrying their attached water molecules with them. If it is assumed that six water molecules are attached to each ion, then a schematic diagram of the solution process is indicated in Fig. 2·6.

Certain covalent compounds, of which HCl is typical, may react with water to produce ions in solution. The extent to which a reaction of this type proceeds depends upon the strength of the binding forces within the covalent molecule. In the case of hydrogen chloride, the reaction with water can be considered as going practically to completion, as indicated in the following equation:

$$HCl + H_2O \rightarrow H_3O^+ + Cl^-$$

2. *Electrolytes, in water solution, produce two kinds of ions. One of these ions, called the "cation," is positively charged, and the other, the "anion," is negatively charged. Since a solution is always electrically neutral, the two types of charges must occur in equivalent quantities. The total unit charge upon each ion is numerically equal to the valence of the ion as exhibited in its chemical reactions.*

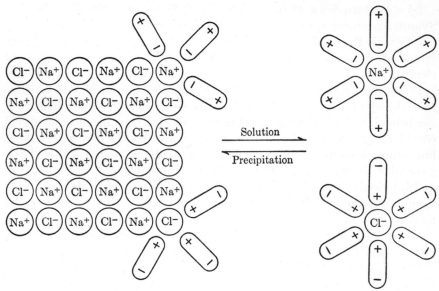

Fig. 2·6 Schematic diagram of the solution process of an ionic compound.

A gram-formula weight of silver ions reacts completely with a gram-formula weight of chloride ions to produce fairly insoluble silver chloride, leaving an excess of only enough of each ion in solution to satisfy the solubility product of silver chloride.

$$Ag^+ + Cl^- \rightarrow AgCl$$

The equation for this reaction indicates that silver and chloride ions are equivalent to each other electrically. However, a gram-formula weight of silver ions will not precipitate completely a gram-formula weight of chromate ions, in producing fairly insoluble silver chromate. Chromate ions are left in excess, and quantitatively only one-half of the total number of these ions are precipitated.

$$Ag^+ + \tfrac{1}{2}CrO_4^= \rightarrow \tfrac{1}{2}Ag_2CrO_4$$

Therefore, the chromate ion has an electrical charge which is twice that of the silver ion, and 2 gfw of silver ions are required to precipitate 1 gfw of chromate ions.

$$2Ag^+ + CrO_4^= \rightarrow Ag_2CrO_4$$

A knowledge of the type and number of electrical charges borne by all the common ions is indispensable in writing equations for the chemical reactions of inorganic chemistry.

3. *Conductance of an electric current by a solution is due to the presence of ions, and the extent of this conductivity is dependent upon the number and kind of ions between electrodes.*

When two electrodes, connected to a source of direct current, are placed in a solution of an electrolyte, those ions known as cations are attracted to the cathode, and those ions classified as anions are pulled to the anode. The process of electrolysis is, therefore, a transportation of matter from the solution to each of the electrodes. The arrival of the two different types of ions at their respective electrodes, under the influence of an electric current, produces chemical reactions at each electrode. The chemical reaction at the cathode is the result of electrons being removed when cations are discharged, and the chemical reaction at the anode is the result of the electrons being supplied when anions are discharged.

The conductivities of different electrolytes in solution vary greatly. Those electrolytes which have been classified as strong electrolytes are good conductors of electricity, whereas that group of electrolytes known as weak electrolytes are poor conductors. The equivalent conductance of an electrolytic solution, regardless of type, increases with dilution, reaching a maximum at infinite dilution. An explanation of this electrolytic behavior has been given in Sec. 2·5.

4. *Ions are chemically independent particles, which have specific chemical properties of their own.*

The formula of sodium chloride in the solid form is usually written as NaCl. A more correct formula is $(Na^+Cl^-)_x$, since solid sodium chloride is ionic rather than molecular. The ionic bond between the two ions is one of electrostatic attraction conforming to the laws of electrostatic forces. However, in dilute solutions, the sodium and chloride ions are so widely separated that there is very little electrical attraction between the two ions. Consequently, a solution of sodium chloride is made up of two separate identities, the sodium ion and the chloride ion. In solution, one of these ions may react chemically, leaving the other ion relatively unaffected. The unaffected ion is simply a spectator ion and should never be written into a chemical equation. If a solution containing 1 gfw of sodium chloride is added to a solution containing 1 gfw of silver nitrate, a chemical reaction takes place between the silver ion and the chloride ion to precipitate insoluble silver chloride. The nitrate and sodium ions are spectator ions and should not appear in the written equation for the chemical reaction.

$$Ag^+ + Cl^- \rightarrow AgCl$$

The same reasoning is true for all ionic reactions; the equations for reactions of this type should contain only the reacting ions and never the spectator ions.

5. *Electrolytes in water solution have a greater effect upon the colligative properties of the solution than have nonelectrolytes.*

Although these facts have been discussed in some detail in Sec. 2·6, it might be well to repeat that a gram-formula weight of an electrolyte produces more particles in solution than a gram-formula weight of a nonelectrolyte. An ionic compound, such as sodium chloride, never exists as molecules in a solution. As the formula, Na^+Cl^-, indicates, the substance contains two different kinds of ions; therefore, when a gram-formula weight of sodium chloride is dissolved in water there should be twice as many particles produced as in the case of a gram-formula weight of a nonelectrolyte such as cane sugar. Since the colligative properties of solutions are affected quantitatively by the number of particles in solution, it is reasonable to expect that a gram-formula weight of sodium chloride should produce twice the effect of a gram-formula weight of a nonelectrolyte. In the examples cited, twice as many particles are produced by sodium choride in solution as in the case of cane sugar, but the effect on the colligative properties is slightly less than twofold. Experiments show that the freezing point of a 0.1 *m* solution of cane sugar is −0.188°C, and the freezing point of a 0.1 *m* sodium chloride solution is −0.348°C. The discrepancy of the observed value for sodium chloride, or any other electrolyte, from the value expected, is examined in the next postulate.

6. *Electrolytes may be divided roughly into two classes: (a) strong electrolytes which are completely ionized, although the mobility of the ions produced by these compounds in solution is reduced by interionic attraction; and (b) weak electrolytes which produce comparatively few ions in solution.*

Although strong electrolytes, which includes most salts, are completely ionized in the crystal and also in solution, the effective concentration of ions in solution is less than the actual concentration. As has been pointed out in the previous section, the freezing point of a 0.1 *m* solution of cane sugar is −0.188°C as compared with −0.348°C, which is the freezing point of a 0.1 *m* solution of sodium chloride. Since the sodium chloride solution contains twice as many particles as the sugar solution, it is anticipated that sodium chloride should depress the freezing point of its water solution twice as much as sugar. Actually, each ion in solution is surrounded by an atmosphere, or cluster, of ions of opposite charge. The more concentrated the solution, the nearer the ions will be to each other, and the more compressed will be the atmosphere of ions around a central ion of opposite charge. The tendency of ions to form clusters around ions of opposite charge produces a retarding effect upon the rate of diffusion of the central ion.   This dragging effect also slows the rate of migration of ions between electrodes of a conductance cell (see Table 2·2).   The theory of interionic attraction was proposed by Debye and Hückel to account for the decrease in equivalent conductance, in solutions of strong electrolytes, with an increase in concentration.   This theory also offers an explanation for the observation that strong electrolytes do not produce as great an effect upon the colligative properties of solutions as is expected from known concentrations.   To compensate for apparent concentration being less than actual concentration of ions, the apparent or effective concentration is designated as the activity of the ionic solution.   The fraction that is used to convert actual concentration to effective concentration is called *activity coefficient*.   If the actual concentration is C, the effective concentration is A, and the activity coefficient is f, then the mathematical relationship of the three factors is

$$A = fC$$

or

$$\text{Activity} = \text{activity coefficient} \times \text{actual concentration}$$

The use of activity instead of concentration is necessary in the accurate calculations of more advanced chemistry.   However, the term activity coefficient is not a constant but is dependent upon the concentration and the nature of the solute, as well as other factors; therefore, few accurate values for this term are known.   Until more exact numerical data are available for activity coefficients, it is sufficient to use concentrations in the calculations of qualitative analysis.

The other class of electrolytes, which is designated as weak electrolytes, is made up largely of organic acids and bases.   These substances produce few ions in solution, and their effects upon the properties of solutions are intermediate between strong electrolytes and nonelectrolytes. For example, a 0.1 F solution of acetic acid exhibits an effective ionization of 1.34 per cent.   In contrast to this figure, a 0.1 F solution of potassium chloride, which is a strong electrolyte, presents an effective ionization of approximately 85 per cent.   It can be assumed that weak electrolytes are covalent compounds which exist as molecules in the pure compound.   Molecular acetic acid, which is a weak electrolyte, produces ions in aqueous solution by reaction with the solvent.

$$HC_2H_3O_2 + H_2O \rightleftharpoons H_3O^+ + C_2H_3O_2^-$$

This reaction takes place to only a slight extent but does increase with dilution.   The increase is evidenced by the fact that when a 0.1 F solution of acetic acid, which is 1.34 per cent ionized, is diluted to 0.01 F the ionization is increased to 4.2 per cent.

7. An acid is an ion or molecule which can donate one or more protons. A base is an ion or molecule which can accept protons. A strong acid loses protons more easily than a weak acid, and a strong base gains protons more readily than a weak base.

According to the Brønsted-Lowry theory of acid-base reactions, the reaction of an acid with a base produces another acid and base. This relationship is expressed by the equation

$$\text{Acid}_1 + \text{base}_2 \rightleftharpoons \text{acid}_2 + \text{base}_1$$

Therefore, any acid-base reaction involves two acids and two bases, and these acids and bases are called *conjugate pairs.* In the equation, given as a type example, the conjugate acid and base are designated by the same subscript; thus acid_1 and base_1 form a conjugate pair, and base_2 and acid_2 are a conjugate pair. To illustrate with specific examples, the compounds hydrogen chloride and hydrogen bromide in the liquid state are poor conductors of electricity and may be considered as covalent compounds, but in water solutions these compounds are strong electrolytes. Each of these substances is an acid, since each produces protons in water solution, and the water molecule can be considered to be a base inasmuch as water molecules accept protons to form hydronium ions. In the first equation of the following, the Cl^- ion is the conjugate base of the acid, HCl; and the H_3O^+ ion is the conjugate acid of the base, the water molecule.

$$\text{Acid}_1 + \text{base}_2 \rightleftharpoons \text{acid}_2 + \text{base}_1$$
$$HCl + H_2O \rightleftharpoons H_3O^+ + Cl^-$$
$$HBr + H_2O \rightleftharpoons H_3O^+ + Br^-$$

These two reactions illustrate the fact that certain covalent compounds may become strong electrolytes by solvation, and the reactions with water are acid-base reactions.

Ions may also act as acids, *e.g.*, the ammonium ion is an acid in aqueous solution. The equation for the reaction in this case is

$$\text{Acid}_1 + \text{base}_2 \rightleftharpoons \text{acid}_2 + \text{base}_1$$
$$NH_4^+ + H_2O \rightleftharpoons H_3O^+ + NH_3$$

However, the ammonium ion is a weak acid since comparatively few hydronium ions are produced in this reaction.

Acetic acid is another weak acid producing few hydronium ions in solution. The acetic acid molecule is a covalent compound which reacts with the base, water, to a slight extent according to the following equation:

$$\text{Acid}_1 + \text{base}_2 \rightleftharpoons \text{acid}_2 + \text{base}_1$$
$$HC_2H_3O_2 + H_2O \rightleftharpoons H_3O^+ + C_2H_3O_2^-$$

In the foregoing illustrative equations, the base which accepted protons was the molecule, water; however, from the original definition, any ion or molecule which accepts protons is a base, as indicated in the following equations:

$$Acid_1 + base_2 \rightleftharpoons acid_2 + base_1$$
$$HCl + NH_3 \rightleftharpoons NH_4^+ + Cl^-$$
$$H_2O + NH_3 \rightleftharpoons NH_4^+ + OH^-$$
$$H_3O^+ + OH^- \rightleftharpoons H_2O + H_2O$$
$$H_3O^+ + CO_3^= \rightleftharpoons HCO_3^- + H_2O$$

According to the Brønsted theory all negative ions, anions, are considered as bases, since they combine with protons. Those anions which form slightly dissociated substances with protons are considered as strong bases, and those which form weak linkages with protons are weak bases. Thus, in aqueous solution, the hydroxide ion is the strongest base, and the chloride ion is one of the weakest; the acetate ion is a fairly strong base, whereas the nitrate ion is a weak base. Strength of a base is measured by its ability to capture protons in competition with other bases.

Types of Exercises Relating to Chap. 2

Type 1. *Express in formality the concentration of a solution containing 36.9 per cent KOH with a density of 1.37 g/ml.*

By definition, formality = formula weights per liter. Therefore, 1 liter of solution contains

$$1{,}000 \text{ ml} \times 1.37 \text{ g/ml} \times 0.369 = 505.5 \text{ g of KOH}$$
$$\text{Formula weight of KOH} = 39.09 + 16.00 + 1.01 = 56.10$$

Consequently, formality is

$$\frac{505.5}{56.10} = 9.01 \ F$$

Type 2. *If 250 g of Na_2CO_3 is dissolved in sufficient water to give 500 ml of solution, what is the formality of the solution?*

250 g/500 ml is the same concentration as 500 g/liter. The formula weight of Na_2CO_3 is 106.0. Therefore, the formality of the solution is

$$\frac{500 \text{ g}}{106.0} = 4.71 \ F$$

Type 3. *How many milliliters of 6 F HCl are necessary to produce 200 ml of 0.5 F solution? How many milliliters of water are required in the dilution?*

For problems in dilution the following formula is generally true:

$$\underset{\text{before dilution}}{\text{Concentration}_1 \times \text{volume}_1} = \underset{\text{after dilution}}{\text{concentration}_2 \times \text{volume}_2}$$

Upon substitution into this general formula,

$$6 \ F \times \text{ml}_1 \text{ (of 6 } F \text{ HCl)} = 0.5 \ F \times 200 \text{ ml (of 0.5 HCl)}$$
$$\text{ml}_1 \text{ (of 6 } F \text{ HCl)} = {}^{100}\!\!/_{\!6} = 16.6 \text{ ml}$$
$$\text{Milliliters of } H_2O \text{ required for dilution} = 200 - 16.6 = 183.4 \text{ ml}$$

Type 4. *If 200 ml of 0.1 F $AgNO_3$ quantitatively precipitates Ag_2CrO_4 from 500 ml of K_2CrO_4, what is the formality of the potassium chromate solution?*

The equation for this reaction

$$2Ag^+ + CrO_4^= \rightarrow Ag_2CrO_4$$

indicates that two silver ions are required to precipitate each chromate ion. Therefore, one formula weight of $AgNO_3$ is chemically equivalent to one-half of a formula
weight of K_2CrO_4.

$$0.200 \text{ liter of } AgNO_3 \times 0.1 \ F = 0.02 \text{ gfw of } AgNO_3 \text{ in the solution}$$

Since 0.02 gfw of $AgNO_3$ is equivalent to 0.01 gfw of K_2CrO_4, then

$$0.500 \text{ liter of } K_2CrO_4 \times F \text{ of } K_2CrO_4 = 0.01 \text{ gfw}$$

and

$$\text{Formality} = \frac{0.01}{0.5} = 0.02 \ F$$

Type 5. *Calculate the formula weight of a nonelectrolyte, 20 g of which dissolved in
100 g of water gives a solution freezing at* $-1.56°C$.

The molal freezing-point constant for water solutions is $-1.86°C$ (for solutions
containing 1 gfw of a nonelectrolyte dissolved in 1,000 g of water). Therefore,

$$\text{Actual lowering} = \text{molal freezing-point constant} \times \text{gfw}$$

Since 20 g of solute per 100 g of solvent produces a solution which has the same concentration as 200 g of solute per 1,000 g of solvent, then

$$-1.56 = \frac{-1.86 \times 200}{\text{formula weight}}$$

and

$$\text{Formula weight} = \frac{-1.86 \times 200}{-1.56} = 238$$

Exercises

1. Explain the advantages of expressing concentrations of solutions in terms of
formality.

2. The use of normality as a method for expressing concentration is limited largely
to acids and bases. Why is the use of normality unsuited to the expression of concentrations for solutions of salts?

3. Percentage methods for expressing the concentrations of solutions are widely
used in chemical industries. Suggest why percentage methods might be preferable,
in industrial plants, to other methods for expressing concentrations.

4. Why are the liquids, carbon tetrachloride and water, immiscible? Why, then,
are the liquids, ethyl alcohol and water, miscible in all proportions?

5. Give an explanation for the fact that polar solids have a limit to their solubilities
in water, whereas polar liquids may be miscible in all proportions.

6. Explain why the ionization of water increases with a rise in temperature.

7. The grinding of a large crystal of a substance into smaller crystals increases the
rate of solution of the substance. Why?

8. Compare the advantages and disadvantages of methyl alcohol and glycerin as
antifreeze substances in automobile radiators.

9. Give equations showing how the following molecules and ions may act as acids:
(a) $HClO_4$, (b) HSO_4^-, (c) HCO_3^-, (d) H_2O, (e) $HPO_4^=$.

10. Give equations showing how the following molecules and ions may act as bases:
(a) $CO_3^=$, (b) H_2O, (c) $SO_4^=$, (d) NH_3, (e) HCO_3^-.

11. In water solutions, is HCO_3^- stronger as an acid or as a base? Why?

12. Express in formality the concentration of each of the following solutions:

(a) 28.4 per cent NH_3 by weight, having a density of 0.808 g/ml
(b) 36.0 per cent HCl by weight, having a density of 1.19 g/ml

(c) 69.5 per cent HNO_3 by weight, having a density of 1.42 g/ml

(d) 96.0 per cent H_2SO_4 by weight, having a density of 1.84 g/ml

(e) 99.5 per cent $HC_2H_3O_2$ by weight, having a density of 1.06 g/ml

13. How many grams of solute are in 500 ml of 6 F HCl?

14. If 100 g of NaOH is dissolved in water to give a solution with a volume of 250 ml, what is the formality of the solution?

15. How many milliliters of 3 F ammonia can be prepared from 100 ml of concentrated ammonia (28.4 per cent NH_3 by weight, having a density of 0.808 g/ml)?

16. How many gram-formula weights of H_2SO_4 are in 2 liters of 3 F H_2SO_4?

17. How many milliliters of 3 F KOH can be prepared from 100 g of KOH?

18. Calculate the number of gram-formula weights in the following weights of substances:

(a) 50 g of NaCl (b) 1 kg of lead

(c) 500 g of methyl alcohol, CH_3OH (d) 100 g of hydrated copper sulfate

19. To dilute 150 ml of 1 F $CaCl_2$ solution to 0.02 F would require how many milliliters of water?

20. Indicate how concentrated H_2SO_4, which is 18 F, may be diluted to produce 300 ml of 3 F H_2SO_4.

21. If 140 ml of 0.1 F $AgNO_3$ is required to precipitate, quantitatively, silver chloride from 120 ml of KCl solution, what is the formality of the KCl solution? The equation for this chemical reaction is

$$Ag^+ + Cl^- \rightarrow AgCl$$

22. If 220 ml of 1 F $AgNO_3$ is required to react quantitatively with 150 ml of KCN solution according to the reaction expressed by the equation

$$Ag^+ + 2CN^- \rightarrow Ag(CN)_2^-$$

what is the formality of the KCN solution?

23. Calculate the formula weight of a nonelectrolye, 5 g of which dissolved in 200 g of water gives a solution which has a freezing point of $-1.04°C$.

24. What is the boiling point of a solution of cane sugar, $C_{12}H_{22}O_{11}$, containing 100 g of the solute per kilogram of water?

25. If 8 liters of ethylene glycol, $C_2H_4(OH)_2$, density = 1.113 g/ml, is placed in an automobile radiator and diluted with 32 liters of water, what is the approximate freezing point of the solution in degrees Fahrenheit?

26. Calculate approximately how much methanol, CH_3OH, would be needed for an automobile radiator holding 4 gal to keep the radiator solution from freezing until a temperature of $-10.0°F$ is reached.

27. Determine the vapor pressure at 20°C of a cane-sugar solution, $C_{12}H_{22}O_{11}$, containing 10 g of sugar in 100 g of water.

28. Assuming that the following salt solutions have effective ion concentrations equal to the actual salt concentrations, determine the approximate freezing points of the solutions:

(a) A 0.1 F potassium sulfate solution

(b) A 0.1 F sodium chloride solution

(c) A 0.1 F aluminum sulfate solution

CHAPTER 3

CHEMICAL EQUILIBRIUM

Nearly all the chemical reactions which are pertinent to qualitative analysis are ionic, occurring in aqueous solution. As a general rule, reactions of this type proceed rapidly, but the extent to which they approach completion depends upon the nature of the reacting substances and the external conditions to which they are subjected. Those in which a precipitate is formed, a gas is released, or a slightly ionized molecule is produced, may be regarded as going nearly to completion, since the formation of these products removes reacting ions from solution. For example, ammonium chloride reacts with potassium hydroxide solution to liberate ammonia. If the mixture is heated and the ammonia allowed to escape, the hydroxide and ammonium ions are used up in the process. However, if the solution is not heated, all the ammonia is not driven off and the products and reactants establish an equilibrium. If the mixture is heated in a sealed container, again the ammonia is not driven off, resulting in a reversible system. Thus, by controlling the external conditions imposed upon the reactants, the latter may be converted completely into their corresponding products, or the components may exist together in the form of a reversible reaction.

$$OH^- + NH_4^+ \rightleftharpoons NH_3 + H_2O$$

3·1 Reversible Reactions. All ionic reactions may be considered to be reversible to some degree, inasmuch as the products, unless completely removed from the field of action, tend to react to produce the original substances. Therefore, any chemical reaction once initiated may be regarded as being the result of two opposing reactions: one proceeding toward the products, and the other, the products recombining to produce the initial reactants. If the external conditions of the system undergo no change the rates at which the two opposing reactions progress will eventually become equal. Such a condition is said to be a state of equilibrium, but this equilibrium is dynamic, implying that the two opposing reactions are still in progress. It is upon the basis of this concept of a dynamic equilibrium for a reversible chemical reaction that much of the fundamental theory of qualitative analysis is built.

3·2 Reaction Velocity. When two reacting substances are brought together, they are in their maximum concentrations only at the moment of contact. After the reaction commences, the concentrations of the original materials decrease in proportion to the concentrations of the products formed. The reaction velocity is the change in concentration in unit time. Since concentration is best expressed in gram-formula weights per liter, and time in seconds, then reaction velocity may be defined as the change in formality per second.

The time required for equilibrium to be established varies widely among different systems. Although all reactions require a definite interval of time for completion or attainment of equilibrium, some are so rapid that they appear to be instantaneous. For example, the reaction of hydronium ions with hydroxide ions, in the process of neutralization, takes place as rapidly as the two reacting solutions can be brought together. Other reactions are so slow that they may appear not to take place. For instance, a mixture of oxygen and hydrogen, at room temperature, may exist for years with no apparent reaction. Between these extremes there are many reactions which proceed with measurable velocities. The study of rates of chemical reactions and the factors which influence reaction velocities constitutes a special field known as *reaction kinetics*.

3·3 Factors Influencing Rate of Reaction. It is obvious that particles (ions, atoms, or molecules) of reacting substances must be brought together before reaction can take place. However, all collisions or contacts between reacting particles are not necessarily effective in the formation of reaction products. But any method or factor which increases the number of effective collisions between reacting particles also increases the reaction velocity. The three factors that have the greatest influence upon the rate of reaction are (1) the presence of catalysts, (2) temperature, and (3) concentration.

Presence of Catalysts. The speed of certain chemical reactions may be increased or decreased by the presence of catalysts which are themselves unaltered chemically. There are two types of positive catalysts. One type forms an intermediate compound with the reacting substances, from which it is subsequently regenerated without change. The catalytic action of nitrogen dioxide in the oxidation of sulfur dioxide offers a good example of this type. The other type is called a *contact catalyst* because it affords a surface upon which the reacting substances are adsorbed. In the process of adsorption, the energy contents of the molecules are so altered as to favor effective contacts to produce new products. Finely divided platinum is used as a contact catalyst in one of the processes for the production of sulfuric acid from sulfur dioxide.

Catalysts which accelerate reaction rates are positive catalysts, while those which retard reaction rates are designated as negative catalysts.

To illustrate the effects of these dissimilar catalysts upon a single reaction, a ferric salt will speed the decomposition of hydrogen peroxide, whereas the presence of a small amount of acetanilid will slow the same decomposition.

Temperature. Particles of substances which are chemically reactive must be brought in contact with each other before chemical reaction can take place. If this discussion is restricted to particles reacting in a solution, then the rate of reaction is dependent upon the rate of diffusion of the particles in the solvent. Moreover, the rate of diffusion is also dependent upon the kinetic energies of the particles of solute and the molecules of solvent. If the temperature of the solution is raised, the kinetic energies of the particles are increased, thereby augmenting their rates of diffusion. Consequently, the probability of the reacting particles coming into effective contact with each other is increased with a rise in temperature. For most reactions the speed is approximately doubled for each 10-degree rise in temperature. This increased rate is more easily demonstrated in certain redox reactions. If a solution containing highly colored permanganate ions is added to an acid solution of oxalate ions the reaction proceeds so slowly at room temperature that several minutes are required for the permanganate color to disappear. If the oxalate solution is heated nearly to boiling before the permanganate is added the rate of reaction is speeded up to such an extent that the permanganate color disappears almost instantaneously.

Concentration. The velocity of a reaction is dependent upon the effective contacts between reacting particles. For a simple reaction, in which one molecule of a reactant reacts with one molecule of another reactant, as in the case of

$$A + B \rightarrow \text{products}$$

if all other factors remain constant, the doubling of the number of particles for one reacting substance doubles the number of effective collisions and, therefore, doubles the velocity of the reaction. Again, if the concentrations of both of the reacting particles are doubled, the reaction speed is increased fourfold. But for those chemical changes in which the number of reacting molecules are not equal in the balanced equation, the change of reaction rate with concentration is not so simple. The effect of concentration upon reaction rate is discussed more completely in the explanation of the law of mass action.

3·4 Law of Mass Action. In 1864, two Norwegian chemists, Guldberg and Waage, after investigating the effect of concentration of a reactant upon the rate of reaction, enunciated the law of mass action as follows: *The rate of a chemical reaction is proportional to the active masses of the reacting substances present at the time.* The term *active mass* is usually interpreted as formula-weight concentration, and since some reactions involve multiple ions or molecules, a more complete statement of the law is: *The rate of a chemical reaction is directly proportional to the product of the formula-weight concentrations of the reacting substances, each raised to the power indicated by the number of ions or molecules appearing in the balanced equation for the reaction.*

Most of the reactions encountered in qualitative analysis take place quite rapidly. For this reason, the law of mass action, which deals with reaction rates, is not of itself particularly important in its application to ionic reactions. The importance of this law lies in the fact that there is a definite relationship between the concentrations of reactants and products *before* and *after* a state of equilibrium is reached. Therefore, a mathematical interpretation of the law of mass action is an excellent introduction to an understanding of the application of equilibrium constants to chemical equilibria, which is sometimes designated as the law of chemical equilibrium.

If two substances A and B of known formula-weight concentrations react, then

$$A + B \rightarrow \text{products}$$

and according to the law of mass action, the reaction velocity is proportional to the product of the formula-weight concentrations

$$v \propto [A] \times [B]$$

where one molecule of A and one molecule of B occur in the balanced equation for the chemical reaction. If the proportionality expression is converted to an equation, it becomes[1]

$$v = k \times [A] \times [B]$$

but if, in the balanced equation, m molecules of A react with n molecules of B as

$$mA + nB \rightarrow \text{products}$$

the over-all expression becomes

$$v = k \times [A]^m \times [B]^n$$

where the concentration of each reactant is raised to the power equal to the number of molecules of the reactant in the equation for the actual reaction.

---

[1] The term k is a proportionality constant which when inserted into a proportionality expression converts it into an equation. Thus k is understood to contain all factors, other than concentration, which may influence the speed of the chemical reaction.

3·5 Explanation of the Law of Mass Action. To illustrate the application of the law of mass action, consider a hypothetical reaction in which one molecule of A reacts with one molecule of B, or

$$A + B \rightarrow \text{products} \qquad (1)$$

The mathematical expression for the speed of this reaction is

$$v = k \times [A]^1 \times [B]^1 \qquad (2)$$

For definite concentrations of A and B at a given temperature, the velocity of the reaction becomes a finite value in terms of formula weights per second. If the concentration of A is doubled, then the probability of molecules of A coming into effective contact with molecules of B is also doubled, and the speed of the reaction is increased twofold. If the concentrations of both A and B are doubled, then the chance of effective contact is increased fourfold, and the velocity of the reaction is quadrupled. To make these illustrations more concrete, assume that the formula-weight concentrations of $A = 2$ and $B = 2$, and that the proportionality constant $k = 1$, then

$$v = 1 \times [2] \times [2] \qquad (3)$$
$$v = 4$$

If the formula-weight concentration of A is doubled, the reaction rate is increased twofold, or

$$v = 1 \times [4] \times [2] \qquad (4)$$
$$v = 8$$

Furthermore, if the formula-weight concentrations of both A and B are doubled, the reaction rate is increased fourfold, as

$$v = 1 \times [4] \times [4]$$
$$v = 16 \qquad (5)$$

Another method of illustrating the relation between reaction velocity and concentration is to determine the possible paths of collision between a given number of reacting molecules. If it is assumed that two molecules of A and two molecules of B are contained in a small space, then in order to react, a molecule of A must collide with a molecule of B. Since reaction rate depends upon effective collisions between the two different molecules per unit time, the number of possible paths between the different molecules will indicate the possible number of collisions. According to Fig. 3·1, the number of paths between two molecules of A and two molecules of B is four, and the reaction rate is proportional to this number.

If four molecules of A and two molecules of B are confined in the same space, the number of paths of collision are again equal to the product of the concentrations of the molecules. From Fig. 3·2, the possible number of paths is eight. Therefore, the reaction rate is directly proportional to this number of paths, or

$$v = k \times \text{possible paths between } A \text{ and } B$$

The possible paths of collisions between four molecules of A and four molecules of B are 16, as indicated in Fig. 3·3. This is again a verification of Eq. (5), assuming, of course, that the proportionality constant k is unity.

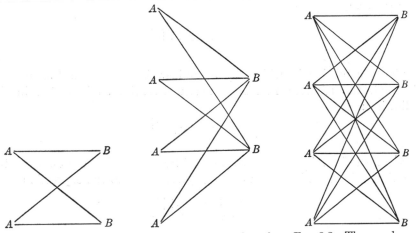

FIG. 3·1 The number of possible paths between two molecules of A and two molecules of B.

FIG. 3·2 The number of possible paths between four molecules of A and two molecules of B.

FIG. 3·3 The number of possible paths between four molecules of A and four molecules of B.

The effect of concentration becomes more complex for a reaction involving an unequal number of molecules in the balanced equation. For a general example, consider a reaction where two molecules of A react with one molecule of B, or

$$2A + B \rightarrow \text{products} \tag{6}$$

In a reaction of this type the probability of a "three-body collision" is slight. Usually, only two molecules collide at any instant. It seems more likely that this reaction takes place in steps, forming an intermediate product or products which, in turn, react to form the final products. If it is assumed that an intermediate product AB is formed, the over-all reaction may be considered as taking place in two steps, and the velocities of the two steps are proportional to the concentrations of the reactants.

$A + B \rightarrow AB$	and	$v \propto [A] \times [B]$
$A + AB \rightarrow \text{products}$	and	$v \propto [A]$
$2A + B \rightarrow \text{products}$	and	$v \propto [A] \times [A] \times [B]$

The velocity of the over-all reaction is proportional to the product of the formula-weight concentrations of all the reactants, each concentration being raised to the power indicated by the number of molecules in the balanced equation. The mathematical expression for this velocity is

$$v = k \times [A]^2 \times [B] \tag{7}$$

The influence of concentration upon the velocity of reaction (6) may be illustrated more effectively by the use of specific examples. If it is assumed that the formula-weight concentrations of $A = 2$ and $B = 2$ and that k is unity, then

$$v = 1 \times [2]^2 \times [2]$$
$$v = 8$$

Under a condition in which the formula-weight concentration of B is doubled, the reaction rate is increased twofold, as indicated in the following:

$$v = 1 \times [2]^2 \times [4]$$
$$v = 16$$

If the formula-weight concentrations of both A and B are doubled, the reaction velocity is increased eightfold, according to the expression

$$v = 1 \times [4]^2 \times [4]$$
$$v = 64$$

The importance of the factor of concentration becomes more significant as it is applied to reactions in equilibrium.

3·6 Law of Chemical Equilibrium. The law of chemical equilibrium is not a new law but simply a statement of the application of the law of mass action to a reversible chemical reaction which is in a state of dynamic equilibrium. From the previous discussion of a simple reaction of the type

$$mA + nB \rightarrow products$$

the reaction velocity was mathematically defined as

$$v = k \times [A]^m \times [B]^n$$

But unless the reactants are replenished as they are used up or the products are removed to prevent a reversible reaction, the reaction velocity is a maximum only at the beginning of the reaction; because, as the reactants are used up their concentrations diminish and the value for the reaction velocity decreases.

Up to this point, only the reactants have been considered in a hypothetical chemical reaction, but if the reaction is reversible—and all chemical transformations are reversible to some extent—then as the products are formed, the velocity for the reverse reaction must be taken into account.

In the original reaction under consideration m molecules of reactant A react with n molecules of reactant B to yield undesignated products. If the complete reaction is written, and if it is assumed that the products are o molecules of C and p molecules of D, then

$$mA + nB \rightleftharpoons oC + pD$$

In this reversible reaction the products C and D react to produce the initial reactants, and the expression for the velocity of the reverse reaction is

$$v = k \times [C]^o \times [D]^p$$

At the instant the original products are first brought together, the velocity of the forward reaction is a maximum and that of the reverse reaction is zero, but as the reaction proceeds, the rate of the reverse reaction increases since the concentrations of C and D are increasing. After a time, a condition is reached when the velocities of the two reactions to the right and left (backward and forward) are equal, and at this point the over-all reaction is said to be in a state of dynamic equilibrium. A graphical representation of the decrease of the rate of the forward reaction and the increase of the reverse reaction, until an equilibrium is attained, is shown in Fig. 3·4.

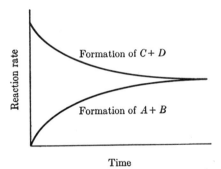

FIG. 3·4 The approach of a reaction toward equilibrium.

For the general reaction

$$mA + nB \rightleftharpoons oC + pD$$

the rate of the forward reaction is

$$k_1 \times [A]^m \times [B]^n$$

and the rate of the reverse reaction is

$$k_2 \times [C]^o \times [D]^p$$

When equilibrium is attained the reaction rates are equal to each other

$$k_1 \times [A]^m \times [B]^n = k_2 \times [C]^o \times [D]^p$$

or

$$\frac{[C]^o[D]^p}{[A]^m[B]^n} = \frac{k_1}{k_2} = K_e$$

This is the general expression for the equilibrium constant, where K_e is a definite value for a given temperature. The equilibrium constant K_e is independent of the concentration values of the reactants and products, and varies only with temperature. It is a matter of convention that, in the equilibrium expression for any reversible reaction, the formula-weight concentrations of the products, i.e., the substances on the right side of the written equation, are placed in the numerator.

Since the numerical value of K_e varies with the temperature of the reaction, it is necessary to specify temperature for each value of K_e. When the foregoing mathematical expression is converted into words, it is referred to as the law of chemical equilibrium. A general statement of this law is as follows: *For a reversible chemical reaction at a fixed temperature and in a state of equilibrium, the product of the formula-weight concentrations of the substances formed in the reaction divided by the product of the formula-weight concentrations of the reactants, each raised to the power indicated by the number of molecules or ions in the balanced equation, is equal to a constant.*

3·7 Principle of Le Chatelier. The law of chemical equilibrium is an expression indicating the quantitative effect of concentration upon chemical equilibria. This law can be considered as a special example of a more general law known as the principle of Le Chatelier. This principle, or rule, states that *when a stress is applied to a system in equilibrium, the equilibrium will shift in such a manner as to relieve or neutralize the stress.* Accordingly, a change in any of the factors which influence an equilibrium, such as temperature, pressure, and concentration, will cause the equilibrium to shift in a manner so as to neutralize the effect of the change. If the temperature of a system in equilibrium is raised, the equilibrium will be shifted in the direction which absorbs heat. For a gaseous equilibrium, an increase in pressure results in a shift to decrease the total number of molecules, if possible, thereby decreasing the pressure. The effect of changing the concentration of a reactant in a system in equilibrium obeys the rule of Le Chatelier, and is quantitatively defined in the law of chemical equilibrium.

3·8 Factors Influencing Equilibrium. The three factors which influence the equilibrium point, or proportion of reactants at equilibrium, are change in pressure, change in temperature, and change in concentration. It should be pointed out that, whereas changes in concentration and pressure (the latter applying only to gases) may shift the point of equilibrium, they do not change the value of the equilibrium constant. Only the factor of temperature may affect the value of the equilibrium constant.

Effect of Pressure Change. An increase of pressure, unless extremely large, has little effect upon equilibria reactions involving solids, liquids, and solutions. In the case of gases, the effect of a pressure change is dependent upon the volume changes produced by the reaction. If a reaction takes place without change in volume, any change in pressure upon the reaction equilibrium does not alter the equilibrium point. A reaction of this type is the union of one volume of nitrogen with one volume of oxygen to produce two volumes of nitric oxide as represented by the equation

$$N_2 + O_2 \rightleftarrows 2NO$$

But if there is an expansion or contraction of volume as a result of a chemical reaction, then according to the principle of Le Chatelier the stress of increased or decreased pressure will cause a shift in the equilibrium in the direction to relieve the stress. Thus, in the reaction of one volume of nitrogen with three volumes of hydrogen to produce two volumes of ammonia,

$$N_2 + 3H_2 \rightleftarrows 2NH_3$$

an increase in pressure will shift the reaction to the right, since four volumes of reactants produce two volumes of the product.

Effect of Temperature Change. In the statement of the law of chemical equilibrium, it was stipulated that the temperature must remain constant, otherwise the equilibrium constant would not remain unchanged. If the temperature is changed, the value of the equilibrium constant is altered, and according to Van't Hoff's law, which is a special application of the principle of Le Chatelier, the equilibrium is displaced in the direction which neutralizes the change in temperature. In the reaction of hydrogen with iodine to produce hydrogen iodide, heat is absorbed in the production of this substance.

$$H_2 + I_2 + heat \rightleftarrows 2HI$$

Consequently, an increase in the temperature of the reaction will cause the equilibrium point to shift to the right to form more hydrogen iodide. A decrease in temperature will produce a shift in the opposite direction.

Changes in temperature alter the velocities of reversible reactions in both directions, backward and forward, but not to the same extent. Therefore, the displacement of the equilibrium point with a change in temperature also involves a change in the equilibrium constant. This being so, any equilibrium reaction has different equilibrium constants for different temperatures.

Effect of Concentration Change. The principle of Le Chatelier predicts the effect of a change in concentration upon a system in chemical equilibrium. When stress in the form of increased concentration is applied to either the reactants or products, there is a shift of the point of equilibrium in the direction which relieves the stress. Both gaseous and solution equilibria are influenced by changes in concentration. Since the latter is of more interest in qualitative analysis, an example of this type is more appropriate as an illustration. When acetic acid is dissolved in water, hydronium and acetate ions are produced according to the following equation:

$$HC_2H_3O_2 + HOH \rightleftharpoons H_3O^+ + C_2H_3O_2^-$$

An increase of either of the products, hydronium ions or acetate ions, will cause a shift to the left, whereas an increase in either acetic acid or water increases the number of ions on the right, or a shift to the right.

Effect of Catalysts upon the Equilibrium Point. Although the presence of a catalyst may hasten the attainment of a condition of equilibrium, it has no influence upon the equilibrium point. The role of a catalyst is that of influencing reaction rate, and since a state of equilibrium is represented by a forward reaction and also a reverse reaction, the presence of a catalyst will influence both reaction rates to the same extent.

3·9 Application of the Law of Chemical Equilibrium. There are two general types of ionic equilibria to which the law of chemical equilibrium may be applied: the ionization of weak electrolytes, and the equilibrium of relatively insoluble substances with their ions. The first type is sometimes classified as homogeneous equilibria, and the second as heterogeneous equilibria. A homogeneous ionic system implies a condition where there is a uniform mixture of ions and undissociated molecules of a weak electrolyte in one phase, namely, in aqueous solution. A heterogeneous system is one in which more than one phase is present, as for example a saturated solution of ions in contact with excess of the solid solute. The application of the law of chemical equilibrium to a heterogeneous system is known as the *solubility product principle.* This principle is discussed in detail in Chap. 5.

Exercises

1. In determining the reaction velocity for the reaction

$$A + 2B \rightleftharpoons AB_2$$

why must the concentration of B molecules be squared?

2. Since reaction velocity is doubled for approximately each 10-degree rise in temperature, how much faster does a reaction proceed at 100°C than at 20°C?

3. Predict the effect of an increase in pressure upon each of the following gaseous equilibria:

(a) $2PH_3 + 6Cl_2 \rightleftharpoons 2PCl_3 + 6HCl$
(b) $2NO + O_2 \rightleftharpoons 2NO_2$
(c) $CO_2 + H_2 \rightleftharpoons CO + H_2O$
(d) $N_2 + O_2 \rightleftharpoons 2NO$
(e) $CH_4 + H_2O \rightleftharpoons CO + 3H_2$

4. Predict the effect of raising the temperature upon each of the following gaseous equilibria:

(a) $2NO + O_2 \rightleftharpoons 2NO_2 + heat$
(b) $H_2 + I_2 + heat \rightleftharpoons 2HI$
(c) $2SO_2 + O_2 \rightleftharpoons 2SO_3 + heat$
(d) $N_2 + O_2 + heat \rightleftharpoons 2NO$
(e) $CO + H_2O \rightleftharpoons CO_2 + H_2 + heat$

5. Write equilibrium expressions for the following reactions (reactants and products are all gases):

(a) $N_2 + 3H_2 \rightleftharpoons 2NH_3$
(b) $4HCl + O_2 \rightleftharpoons 2H_2O + 2Cl_2$
(c) $CH_4 + 2O_2 \rightleftharpoons CO_2 + 2H_2O$
(d) $3C_2H_2 \rightleftharpoons C_6H_6$
(e) $2CO_2 \rightleftharpoons 2CO + O_2$

6. Why does not the presence of a catalyst influence a chemical equilibrium?

7. Discuss the effects of the three factors that influence reaction rate.

8. Calculate K for the reaction

$$2A + B \rightleftharpoons C + D$$

if at equilibrium $A = 0.4$ formula weights/liter, $B = 0.5$ formula weights/liter, $C = 0.3$ formula weights/liter, and $D = 0.8$ formula weights/liter.

9. Give three examples of applications of Le Chatelier's principle to chemical equilibria.

10. Explain the effect, if any, of increasing the pressure upon a mixture of ice and water.

11. Derive the expression for the equilibrium constant for the reaction

$$2A + 4B \rightleftharpoons C + 3D$$

12. When ammonium acetate dissolves in water, the solution becomes cooler than the temperature of the water before solution. Is ammonium acetate more soluble at high or low temperatures?

13. When anhydrous sodium sulfate dissolves in water, the solution becomes warmer than the temperature of the water before solution. How will the solubility of anhydrous sodium sulfate vary with temperature?

14. What is the difference between a surface catalyst and a catalyst which enters solution?

15. In the following reaction at equilibrium

$$2NO + O_2 \rightleftharpoons 2NO_2 + 28.1 \text{ kcal}$$

state the effect upon the equilibrium of each of the following changes:

(a) An increase in pressure
(b) A decrease in temperature
(c) The addition of a positive catalyst
(d) The addition of more oxygen
(e) The addition of more nitric oxide

CHAPTER 4

IONIZATION OF WEAK ELECTROLYTES

As will be recalled from Chap. 2, weak electrolytes are substances whose water solutions contain comparatively few charged particles or ions; as a consequence, these solutions do not conduct an electric current to any great extent. The production of ions from the slightly dissociated molecules of a weak electrolyte is a reversible reaction to which the law of chemical equilibrium is applicable. However, this law does not apply to solutions of strong electrolytes, since the ionization of these substances is assumed to be complete.

In comparison to the total number of compounds which may be classified as nonelectrolytes, or to those compounds which are grouped as strong electrolytes, the total number of weak electrolytes is small. Very few weak acids and fewer weak bases are encountered in the analytical laboratory, but the application of the law of chemical equilibrium to the solutions of these compounds extends to broader fields than the study of qualitative analysis. The equilibria of weak acids (and their salts) are of great importance in controlling life functions in living organisms. Blood, milk, digestive juices, and other fluids which are produced, or used, in living tissues are highly buffered solutions, *i.e.*, solutions of weak acids and their salts. The control of hydronium-ion concentration in living protoplasm is necessary for the maintenance of life, and the mechanism of this control is the same for biological fluids as for inorganic solutions. For this reason some emphasis is placed upon the application of the law of chemical equilibrium to solutions of weak electrolytes.

4·1 Ionization of Weak Monoprotic Acids. In the production of ions by a strong acid, such as hydrochloric acid, it can be concluded that the reaction of hydrogen chloride with water to produce hydronium and chloride ions goes practically to completion. At least, the reversibility is of a negligible extent.

$$HCl + HOH \rightleftharpoons H_3O^+ + Cl^-$$

In terms of the Brønsted acid-base systems, the chloride ion can be considered as a very weak base in comparison with the strength of water as a base, so weak that the water molecules capture protons from the chloride ions to produce an irreversible reaction. Accordingly, a solution of

1 F HCl is also 1 F in respect to the concentration of hydronium and chloride ions. In that no equilibrium is involved, the law of chemical equilibrium cannot be applied to this reaction.

In the case of a weak electrolyte, such as acetic acid, the reaction of the acid with water to give hydronium ions and acetate ions proceeds to only a slight extent. This reaction is reversible, the reversibility being due to the comparative strengths of the conjugate acids and bases of the reaction.

$$HC_2H_3O_2 + HOH \rightleftharpoons H_3O^+ + C_2H_3O_2^-$$

The reaction may be considered as a competition between the two bases, water molecules and acetate ions, for protons. Since the acetate ion is a stronger base than the water molecule, the extent of the reaction to the left is greater than that to the right.

If the law of chemical equilibrium is applied to this reversible system, in which the product of the formula-weight concentrations of those substances indicated on the right of the equation is divided by the product of the formula-weight concentration of the reactants as denoted by the equation, the equilibrium expression is

$$\frac{[H_3O^+][C_2H_3O_2^-]}{[HC_2H_3O_2][H_2O]} = K_e$$

The majority of solutions used in qualitative analysis are quite dilute, usually of the order of 0.1 F or less. Therefore, the formula-weight concentration of water in these solutions varies only slightly from the formality of H_2O in pure water. Since formality is defined as the number of gram-formula weights per liter of solution, then the formality of H_2O in water is $1,000/18 = 55.5$ F. Substituting this value into the above equation,

$$\frac{[H_3O^+][C_2H_3O_2^-]}{[HC_2H_3O_2] \times 55.5} = K_e \quad \text{or} \quad \frac{[H_3O^+][C_2H_3O_2^-]}{[HC_2H_3O_2]} = K_e \times 55.5 = K_i$$

The new constant K_i is the ionization constant of the weak acid, acetic acid, in dilute solutions, and is in actuality the equilibrium constant for the ionization reaction with water multiplied by the formula-weight concentration of water in the dilute solution. It is obvious that this equation cannot be true for more concentrated solutions where the formality of water varies appreciably from 55.5 F.

The final equation also indicates that K_i is a constant for the ratio of the product of the concentration of the ions to the concentration of the undissociated acid in dilute solution.

By conductivity measurements, it has been determined that 0.1 F acetic acid, at 25°C, is 1.32 per cent ionized into its two ions. Therefore,

98.68 per cent of the acetic acid exists in the undissociated form.   Or, in terms of the Brønsted theory, 98.68 per cent of the acid does not react with water to form hydronium ions.   Converting percentage values to actual fractions and multiplying these fractions by the formality of the acid and its ions, the equilibrium expression containing these values is

$$\frac{(0.0132 \times 0.1)(0.0132 \times 0.1)}{(0.9868 \times 0.1)} = K_i = 1.75 \times 10^{-5}$$

The ionization constants of the common weak acids and bases have been determined by experiment, and values for these are found in the various chemistry handbooks.   Abbreviated tables of ionization constants for the most common weak acids and bases are given in Tables A·5 and A·6.

If it is assumed that the ionization constant value does not vary greatly with small differences in temperature, which is a valid assumption for rough calculations, then from the formality of a given weak electrolyte and its ionization constant, the concentration of the ions produced by the weak electrolyte in solution may be calculated.   The following problem provides an illustration of this statement: *If the ionization constant of acetic acid is* 1.75×10^{-5}, *determine the hydronium-ion concentration of a 0.050 F solution of acetic acid.*   The equation for the reversible reaction in which acetic acid reacts with water to produce ions is

$$HC_2H_3O_2 + HOH \rightleftharpoons H_3O^+ + C_2H_3O_2^-$$

and the K_i for this equilibrium is 1.75×10^{-5} at 25°C.   Therefore, the mathematical expression for this equilibrium is

$$\frac{[H_3O^+][C_2H_3O_2^-]}{[HC_2H_3O_2]} = 1.75 \times 10^{-5}$$

If the original concentration of $HC_2H_3O_2$, before the reaction takes place, is represented as C, then after acetic acid reacts with water to produce hydronium ions and acetate ions, the concentration of each of these ions may be designated as X, since there is one ion each of acetate and hydronium produced for each $HC_2H_3O_2$ molecule.   After equilibrium is reached the concentration of $HC_2H_3O_2$ can be indicated as $C - X$, and the equilibrium expression becomes

$$\frac{(X)(X)}{(C - X)} = 1.75 \times 10^{-5} \quad \text{or} \quad \frac{X^2}{0.050 - X} = 1.75 \times 10^{-5}$$

The foregoing equation is a quadratic and may be solved as such; however, it may be simplified and the quadratic avoided by discarding the value of X in the denominator.   From a mathematical viewpoint, X may be discarded only if it is a very small value in comparison with the value from which it is subtracted. In this particular illustrative problem, X can be ignored because it does not represent a significant number as compared with the concentration of acetic acid, given as $0.05\ F$. The validity of this approximation is verified by subsequent calculations. As a general rule, the value of X is insignificant for solutions of weak electrolytes, in which the concentrations of the weak electrolytes are not too dilute. When the K_i of the weak electrolyte is 10^{-4} or less, the term $C - X$ does not differ appreciably from C. By inspection, it can be seen that this estimation is true when C is not less than $0.1\ F$. On the other hand, this approximation is applicable to lower concentrations of those acids and bases whose ionization constants are less than 10^{-4}.

If the equation is solved as a quadratic,

$$\frac{X^2}{0.050 - X} = 1.75 \times 10^{-5}$$

or

$$X^2 + (1.75 \times 10^{-5})X - 8.75 \times 10^{-7} = 0$$

or

$$X = \frac{-1.75 \times 10^{-5} + \sqrt{(1.75 \times 10^{-5})^2 + 3.50 \times 10^{-6}}}{2}$$

and

$$X = 9.35 \times 10^{-4}\ F\ H_3O^+$$

If the equation is solved after assuming that $C - X$ does not differ appreciably from C, and upon discarding X in the denominator,

$$\frac{X^2}{0.050} = 1.75 \times 10^{-5} \qquad \text{or} \qquad X^2 = 0.050(1.75 \times 10^{-5})$$

and

$$X = 9.35 \times 10^{-4}\ F\ H_3O^+$$

Numerical values used in calculations of the law of chemical equilibrium are seldom of sufficient exactness to warrant the use of more than two significant figures. This is another justification for the assumption that the value of X, indicating the amount of dissociation, may be disregarded in expressing the concentration of an undissociated weak electrolyte.

In analyzing the behavior of weak acids and bases in water solution, it is well not to lose sight of the original Brønsted definitions for an acid and a base: *An acid is a substance that furnishes protons, and a base is a substance that accepts protons.* The present analysis deals with molecules which are largely covalent but have a slight tendency toward electrovalency. In Chap. 7 other groups of substances, cations and anions, which react with water to produce hydronium or hydroxide ions, will be examined.

4·2 Ionization of Weak Monoprotic Bases. In explaining the reaction of a weak acid with water to produce an equilibrium mixture containing hydronium ions, the discussion was limited to molecules of those weak electrolytes which are classified as weak acids. However, there are other molecules, or weak electrolytes, which react slightly with water to produce hydroxide ions, customarily called bases. Among the very few molecules of this type encountered in qualitative analysis, the most common is ammonia. This compound produces hydroxide ions by the reaction indicated in the following equation:

$$NH_3 + HOH \rightleftharpoons NH_4^+ + OH^-$$

Other molecules which react similarly with water are methylamine, CH_3NH_2, ethylamine, $C_2H_5NH_2$, and aniline, $C_6H_5NH_2$, but these weak electrolytes are rarely used in inorganic chemistry.

If the law of chemical equilibrium is applied to the reaction of ammonia with water, the following expression is obtained:

$$\frac{[NH_4^+][OH^-]}{[NH_3][H_2O]} = K_e \qquad \text{or} \qquad \frac{[NH_4^+][OH^-]}{[NH_3]} = K_e \times 55.5 = K_b$$

where K_b designates the ionization constant of the weak base.

Ammonia is a weak base with an ionization constant of 1.8×10^{-5} which is numerically almost the same as K_a for acetic acid. To solve for the formula-weight concentration of either ammonium ions or hydroxide ions, when the concentration of ammonia is given, the same mathematical procedure is followed as was given for obtaining the ion concentrations of a weak acid in a water solution.

4·3 Ionization of Water. Water may be considered as a weak electrolyte since the purest water obtainable will conduct an electric current to a measurable extent. Although water is the most widely used solvent, it cannot be considered as an inert medium for the physical solution of ions or molecules. As was pointed out in Chap. 2, there is no sharp demarcation between physical and chemical solutions, but it is a fairly safe assumption that water enters into some type of chemical combination in all its solutions. There is a variety of ways in which water may react with substances in its role as a solvent. It brings about the solution of certain organic compounds containing hydroxyl groups, such as sugars, by forming hydrogen bonds. It converts certain covalent compounds, as hydrogen chloride and acetic acid, into electrolytes by acting as a base to accept protons in forming hydronium ions. It may act as an acid with certain bases, such as ammonia, donating protons to leave an excess of hydroxide ions in solution. Water reacts as either an acid or a base with certain anions and cations to form conjugate acids and bases. The latter reactions are discussed more completely under the subject of Hydrolysis.

The bonding of atoms in water molecules is largely covalent, but the slight conductance of an electric current indicates the presence of some ions. Under appropriate conditions water may be regarded as either an acid or a base, since it may act as either a proton donor or a proton acceptor. This is due to the interaction of water molecules to produce an ionization reaction, similar to that of any other acid or base.

$$H_2O + H_2O \rightleftharpoons H_3O^+ + OH^-$$

The extent of this reaction to the right is small but of a definite quantity and dependent, as in all other ionization equilibria, upon temperature (see Table 4·1).

The equilibrium expression for the ionization of water is

$$\frac{[H_3O^+][OH^-]}{[H_2O]^2} = K_e$$

Since the formula-weight concentration of water is $1,000/18 = 55.5\ F$, this value can be considered as a constant, which results in an expression in which the product of the ions of water is equal to a new constant K_w, or

$$[H_3O^+][OH^-] = K_e \times [H_2O]^2 \quad \text{and} \quad [H_3O^+][OH^-]$$
$$= K_e \times (55.5)^2 = K_w$$

K_w is a special ionization constant, comparable to the K_a and K_b of weak acids and bases but differing in that it is an ion product in which the formal concentration of water is treated as a constant. K_w is usually referred to as *the ion product for water*, and at room temperature this constant has a value of 1×10^{-14}. Therefore, for pure water at 25°C, the H_3O^+ and OH^- concentration is $1 \times 10^{-7}\ F$.

$$[H_3O^+][OH^-] = 1 \times 10^{-14}$$

and

$$[H_3O^+] = [OH^-] = 1 \times 10^{-7}\ F$$

The ion product for water, K_w, increases with temperature as shown in Table 4·1. K_w is also affected by an increasing ion concentration, but

TABLE 4·1 CHANGE OF THE ION PRODUCT FOR WATER WITH TEMPERATURE

Temperature, °C	K_w	Temperature, °C	K_w
0	0.11×10^{-14}	50	5.5×10^{-14}
18	0.58×10^{-14}	75	19×10^{-14}
25	1.01×10^{-14}	100	48×10^{-14}

this is to be expected since the formality of water decreases as the concentration of dissolved ions increases. In view of the fact that most of the laboratory procedures in qualitative analysis are performed at room temperature with dilute solutions, the value of 1×10^{-14} can be considered as a constant for calculations involving K_w.

The equilibrium between water and its ions is important in calculating hydronium- or hydroxide-ion concentrations of aqueous solutions in that the ion product is practically the same for any dilute aqueous solution as that for pure water. In other words, the relationship of

$$[H_3O^+][OH^-] = 1 \times 10^{-14}$$

holds true for any dilute aqueous solution regardless of whether it is an acid, a base, or a salt solution. Moreover, since K_w does not change for a stated temperature, it follows that the formula-weight concentrations of either the hydronium or hydroxide ion may be varied but the product will always be the same. For example, in a 0.1 F solution of hydrochloric acid, the hydronium-ion concentration is 0.1 F, and the hydroxide-ion concentration is calculated as

$$0.1 \times [OH^-] = 1 \times 10^{-14}$$
$$[OH^-] = \frac{1 \times 10^{-14}}{0.1} = 1 \times 10^{-13} \, F$$

Similarly, the hydronium-ion concentration of a base may be calculated. In a 0.01 F solution of NaOH, assuming complete ionization of the base, the hydronium-ion concentration is

$$[H_3O^+] \times 0.01 = 1 \times 10^{-14}$$
$$[H_3O^+] = \frac{1 \times 10^{-14}}{0.01} = 1 \times 10^{-12} \, F$$

The repression of one ion of water by the increase in the formula-weight concentration of the other ion can never be carried to the extent that one ion becomes zero, since this would necessitate the concentration of the other ion being infinitely large.

4·4 pH and pOH Values. In dealing with hydronium-ion concentrations of aqueous solutions, quite often these values are very small numbers, usually written in the exponential form, which may vary through a wide concentration range. For example, the numbers 5×10^{-2}, 2×10^{-4}, and 7×10^{-5} might represent common hydronium-ion concentrations of solutions of weak acids. Numbers of this kind are almost impossible to plot in the form of a graph, and other modes of correlation are equally difficult to indicate. To avoid the awkwardness involved in comparing numbers varying through an extended range, Sörensen, a

Danish biochemist, devised a system by which such numbers are changed to their negative logarithms.

By the Sörensen system, a geometric progression of small numbers, as 1×10^{-2}, 1×10^{-3}, 1×10^{-4}, and 1×10^{-5}, is converted to an arithmetical progression of small numbers as 2, 3, 4, and 5. Through this mathematical device of reducing widely varying small numbers to slightly varying positive whole numbers, ordinary concentrations of hydronium ions may be converted to simple finite numbers usually ranging from 0 to 14.

By original definition pH is the negative logarithm, to the base 10, of the hydrogen-ion concentration. The formula for this statement is

$$pH = \log \frac{1}{[H^+]} = - \log [H^+]$$

In 1909, at the time Sörensen proposed this method of expressing hydrogen-ion concentrations, the term *hydronium ion*, which is a more accurate expression than hydrogen ion, was unknown. Also, the concepts of *activity* and *activity coefficient*, which relate actual concentration to effective concentrations, had not been developed. Although the foregoing formula is still widely used for pH conversion, the term pH by interpretation should be the negative logarithm of the activity of the hydronium ion. In qualitative analysis the assumption is made that for dilute solutions, formality does not differ greatly from activity; therefore, pH is the negative logarithm of the hydronium-ion concentration, or

$$pH = \log \frac{1}{[H_3O^+]} = - \log [H_3O^+]$$

To illustrate the use of this formula, suppose a solution has a hydronium-ion concentration of 2×10^{-9} F, what is the pH of the solution? The easiest way to produce the conversion is to take the exponent as a whole number, change its sign, and from it subtract the logarithm of the coefficient number. Thus, 10^{-9} becomes 9, and the logarithm of the coefficient number, 2, is .3. Subtracting .3 from 9 gives 8.7 which is the pH of the solution.

To calculate the hydronium-ion concentration from the pH of a given solution, the preceding process is reversed. For example, consider a solution with a pH value of 6.8, what is the hydronium-ion concentration? Since

$$pH = 6.8 = - \log [H_3O^+]$$

it follows that

$$[H_3O^+] = \text{antilog } .2 \times 10^{-7}$$

or

$$[H_3O^+] = 1.6 \times 10^{-7} \, F$$

Although rarely used, the hydroxide-ion concentration can be expressed as pOH, which is the negative logarithm of the hydroxide-ion concentration, or

$$pOH = \log \frac{1}{[OH^-]} = - \log [OH^-]$$

4·5 pK Values.   Occasionally it becomes convenient to express equilibrium constants as pK values which are analogous to pH values.   The pK value for an equilibrium constant of a weak acid or base is defined as the negative logarithm of the equilibrium constant, or

$$pK = \log \frac{1}{K_e} = - \log K_e$$

To illustrate with an example of a specific equilibrium, pK for the equilibrium constant of acetic acid, where $K_e = 1.75 \times 10^{-5}$, is

$$pK = - \log K_e = - \log (1.75 \times 10^{-5})$$
$$pK = 5 - \log 1.75 = 5 - .24 = 4.76$$

K_w for water represents a special equilibrium constant for dilute solutions, and since K_w has a value of 1×10^{-14} it is often advantageous to use the following equations in problems involving pH or pOH of aqueous solutions:

$$pH + pOH = pK_w$$
$$pH + pOH = 14$$

and in neutral aqueous solutions

$$pH = pOH = 7$$

4·6 Indicators.   The control of the hydronium-ion concentration is important in bacteriology, biochemistry, and industrial chemistry as well as in analytical chemistry.   In qualitative analysis the separation of some ions may be accomplished by strict control of pH during certain precipitations.   The pH of a solution may be determined either colorimetrically or electrometrically, and sometimes by a combination of the two methods.   The colorimetric method makes use of certain highly colored organic compounds, which have the property of changing color when the hydronium-ion concentration is changed over a certain range.   These compounds are known as *acid-base indicators.*

Each acid-base indicator has a definite pH range through which color change takes place.   The usual range of color change for a satisfactory indicator is approximately two pH units.   Inasmuch as each indicator has a characteristic pH range in which color change is produced, it is necessary to use a set of indicators to cover the pH range of 0 to 14 in order to determine the pH of any given solution.   By testing portions of the solution with each indicator from a set of this kind, the selection may be narrowed to one or two indicators which give a good approximation of the pH of the solution. Table 4·2 lists a set of indicators, covering the necessary range for pH determinations.

TABLE 4·2 INDICATORS

Indicator	Acid color	Base color	pH range
Cresol red	Red	Yellow	0.2– 1.8
Thymol blue (acid range)	Red	Yellow	1.2– 3.0
Red cabbage extract	Red	Green	2.4– 4.5
Bromphenol blue	Yellow	Blue	3.0– 4.6
Bromcresol green	Yellow	Blue	3.8– 5.4
Methyl red	Red	Yellow	4.2– 6.2
Bromcresol purple	Yellow	Purple	5.2– 6.8
Bromthymol blue	Yellow	Blue	6.0– 7.6
Phenol red	Yellow	Red	6.8– 8.4
Cresol red	Yellow	Red	7.2– 8.8
Thymol blue (base range)	Yellow	Blue	8.0– 9.6
Phenolphthalein	Colorless	Red	8.3–10.0
Thymolphthalein	Colorless	Blue	9.4–10.5
Alizarin yellow R	Yellow	Lilac	10.1–12.1
Trinitrobenzene	Colorless	Orange	12.0–14.0

Acid-base indicators are either weak organic acids or bases. In a two-color indicator it is generally assumed that one color is produced by the undissociated molecule of the indicator, and the other color is due to one of the ions produced by dissociation. If a weak acid indicator is given the general formula of HIn, it will react in water solution to give the following equilibrium:

$$\underset{\text{color } A}{HIn} + H_2O \rightleftharpoons H_3O^+ + \underset{\text{color } B}{In^-}$$

The equilibrium expression for this reaction is

$$\frac{[H_3O^+][In^-]}{[HIn]} = K_{ind}$$

where the equilibrium constant is usually designated as the indicator constant, K_{ind}. The above equation may be rearranged as

$$\frac{[H_3O^+]}{K_{ind}} = \frac{[HIn]}{[In^-]} \qquad \begin{array}{l}(\text{color } A)\\(\text{color } B)\end{array}$$

This equation shows that the ratio of the concentrations of the two colored forms is proportional to the ratio of the concentration of the hydronium ion to the indicator constant. In case the two colored forms are in equal concentration, so that $[HIn]/[In^-] = 1$, the $[H_3O^+]$ of the solution is equal to K_{ind}.

Assuming that the two-color indicator is a weak base, the ionization reaction is

$$InOH \rightleftharpoons In^+ + OH^-$$

and the equilibrium expression for this reaction is

$$[OH^-] = \frac{[InOH]}{[In^+]} \times K_{ind}$$

4·7　Common-ion Effect. The principle of Le Chatelier has been stated in effect that if any system which is in equilibrium is disturbed, the equilibrium will be readjusted in a manner so as to minimize the disturbance. This rule predicts the results that may be expected in disturbing the equilibrium mixture of a weak electrolyte and its ions by adding an excess of one of the ions. A system of this type is represented by the reaction of acetic acid molecules with water:

$$HC_2H_3O_2 + H_2O \rightleftharpoons H_3O^+ + C_2H_3O_2^-$$

If this equilibrium is altered by adding an excess of either one of the products or reactants, the equilibrium will be shifted in that direction to decrease the concentration of the substance added. Consequently, the addition of either water or acetic acid will shift the equilibrium to the right to produce more acetate and hydronium ions. On the other hand, in case either acetate ions or hydronium ions are added to the mixture, the equilibrium will be shifted to the left to decrease the concentration of the ion which is added, resulting in an increase in the concentrations of the substances on the left.

The law of chemical equilibrium is a quantitative expression of Le Chatelier's principle which may be restated in the following form: At a given temperature, any change in the formula-weight concentrations of either products or reactants of an equilibrium mixture will cause the system to readjust its formula-weight concentrations so as to produce values which will satisfy the equilibrium constant of the reversible reaction. For a more specific illustration, consider the mathematical expression for the reversible reaction of acetic acid with water, which has been previously derived as

$$\frac{[H_3O^+][C_2H_3O_2^-]}{[HC_2H_3O_2]} = K_a = 1.75 \times 10^{-5} \quad \text{(at 25°C)}$$

If the concentration of acetate ions is increased by the addition of a salt containing the acetate ion such as $NaC_2H_3O_2$, $NH_4C_2H_3O_2$, or $KC_2H_3O_2$, there is a shifting in concentrations of the other substances making up the equilibrium in the direction to diminish the acetate-ion concentration. Thus, the addition of acetate ions causes a corresponding formula-weight decrease in hydronium ions which, in turn, brings about an increase in the total concentration of the undissociated acetic acid.

The reaction of a weak electrolyte with water produces relatively few ions in solution, as is evidenced by the slight electrolytic conductance of the solution. Accordingly, in a solution of acetic acid, the formula-weight concentrations of hydronium ions and acetate ions are very small in comparison to the formula-weight concentration of the undissociated acetic acid. Therefore, it is evident that a large increase in acetate-ion concentration will produce a corresponding large decrease in hydronium-ion concentration but will not materially affect the total concentration of undissociated acetic acid, since the latter concentration is so large in comparison to the concentration of its ions. The effect of increasing the concentration of one ion in a solution of a weak electrolyte in order to decrease another ion of the equilibrium mixture is called the *common-ion effect*.

The mathematical expression for the equilibrium mixture of a weak electrolyte and its ions permits the quantitative calculation of the common-ion effect. For example, *what is the hydronium-ion concentration of a 0.050 F solution of acetic acid to which has been added 5.0 g of sodium acetate?*

$$\frac{5.0 \text{ g } NaC_2H_3O_2}{82 \text{ gfw } NaC_2H_3O_2} = 0.061 \text{ } F \text{ acetate ions}$$

assuming 100 per cent ionization of the $NaC_2H_3O_2$

Let X = hydronium-ion concentration

$0.061 + X$ = acetate concentration from $NaC_2H_3O_2 + HC_2H_3O_2$

Therefore

$$0.050 - X = \text{the concentration of undissociated } HC_2H_3O_2$$

Then

$$\frac{(X)(0.061 + X)}{(0.050 - X)} = 1.75 \times 10^{-5}$$

The value X which is added in the numerator to 0.061 and subtracted in the denominator from 0.050 may be discarded, since it is very small in comparison to the values to which it is added and from which it is subtracted. Consequently, the simplified equation becomes

$$\frac{(X)(0.061)}{(0.050)} = 1.75 \times 10^{-5}$$

$$X = \frac{(1.75 \times 10^{-5})0.050}{0.061} = 1.4 \times 10^{-5} \text{ } F \text{ } H_3O^+$$

4·8   Buffer Solutions.   A buffer solution is one which resists change in hydronium-ion concentration when an appreciable amount of either a strong acid or base is added to the solution.   Such a solution contains either a mixture of a weak acid and its salt, or a mixture of a weak base and its corresponding salt.   Typical examples of buffer mixtures are acetic acid with sodium acetate, and ammonia water with ammonium chloride.   In other words, a buffer solution is a mixture of a weak electrolyte and its salt, which by common-ion effect maintains a nearly constant hydronium-ion concentration, even when a strong acid or base is added.

The operation of a buffer solution depends upon the equilibrium between the molecules of the weak electrolyte and its ions.   An increase in the concentration of one of the ions results in a momentary decrease of the other ion; however, the two ions combine to form the undissociated electrolyte, and the original concentrations of the ions are not greatly changed.   This process can be explained more clearly by considering a specific example of a buffer mixture.   Assuming that a liter of solution is $0.5\ F$ with respect to acetic acid and $0.5\ F$ with respect to sodium acetate, then the hydronium-ion concentration may be calculated as

$$\frac{[H_3O^+][C_2H_3O_2^-]}{[HC_2H_3O_2]} = 1.75 \times 10^{-5} \quad \text{or} \quad \frac{[H_3O^+] \times 0.5}{0.5} = 1.75 \times 10^{-5}$$

and

$$[H_3O^+] = \frac{0.5}{0.5} \times 1.75 \times 10^{-5} \quad \text{or} \quad [H_3O^+] = 1.75 \times 10^{-5}$$

It should be recalled that a strong acid, *e.g.*, hydrochloric acid, is considered as completely ionized in water solution; therefore, a $0.1\ F$ solution of HCl should also be $0.1\ F$ in respect to hydronium ions.   If, however, 0.1 gfw of HCl is added to the preceding buffer mixture, the resulting hydronium-ion concentration is not $0.1\ F$ but is approximately one four-thousandths of this value, as is shown by the following calculations:

$$\underset{\text{from HCl}}{0.1 \text{ gfw } H_3O^+} + \underset{\text{from NaAc}}{0.5 \text{ gfw } C_2H_3O_2^-} = 0.1 \text{ gfw } HC_2H_3O_2$$

$$+ \underset{\text{in excess}}{0.4 \text{ gfw } C_2H_3O_2^-}$$

Therefore, after 0.1 gfw of hydrochloric acid is added to the buffer, assuming no change in volume,

Concentration of $HC_2H_3O_2$ = 0.5 gfw originally present + 0.1 gfw
formed in the reaction
$$[HC_2H_3O_2] = 0.6\ F$$
Concentration of $C_2H_3O_2^-$ = 0.5 gfw originally present − 0.1 gfw
$HC_2H_3O_2$ formed in the reaction
$$[C_2H_3O_2^-] = 0.4\ F$$

Therefore

$$[H_3O^+] = \frac{[HC_2H_3O_2]}{[C_2H_3O_2^-]} \times 1.75 \times 10^{-5}$$

$$[H_3O^+] = \frac{0.6}{0.4} \times 1.75 \times 10^{-5} = 2.6 \times 10^{-5} \, F$$

Consequently, the addition of 0.1 gfw of hydrochloric acid to a liter of the buffer mixture does not give a hydronium-ion concentration of 0.1 F but instead a concentration of $2.6 \times 10^{-5} \, F$, which is 3,800 times less than the $[H_3O^+]$ would be if this amount of HCl were added to a liter of pure water.

It can be seen that the buffer action is due to the reaction between the excess acetate ions and the added hydronium ions to increase the concentration of molecular acetic acid, or reserve acidity. In this adjustment, the actual hydronium-ion concentration is changed only slightly. In the illustrative problem, the change was from $1.75 \times 10^{-5} \, F$ to $2.6 \times 10^{-5} \, F$, or an increase of approximately 1.5 times.

To explain how a buffer mixture acts upon the addition of a strong base, suppose the preceding problem is changed to the extent that 0.1 gfw of NaOH is added to the buffer instead of hydrochloric acid. If it is assumed that sodium hydroxide in this dilution is completely ionized, then the addition of 0.1 gfw of NaOH to the liter of solution is in effect the addition of 0.1 gfw of OH^- ions, and the following reaction takes place:

0.1 gfw OH^- + 0.5 gfw $HC_2H_3O_2$ = H_2O + 0.1 gfw $C_2H_3O_2^-$
from NaOH

$$+ \, 0.4 \text{ gfw } HC_2H_3O_2$$
in excess

After 0.1 gfw of OH^- ions is added to the buffer, assuming no volume change,

Concentration of $HC_2H_3O_2$ = 0.5 F gfw originally present $-$ 0.1 gfw removed in the reaction

$$[HC_2H_3O_2] = 0.4 \, F$$

Concentration of $C_2H_3O_2^-$ = 0.5 F gfw originally present $+$ 0.1 gfw formed in the reaction

$$[C_2H_3O_2^-] = 0.6 \, F$$

Hence

$$[H_3O^+] = \frac{[HC_2H_3O_2]}{[C_2H_3O_2^-]} \times 1.75 \times 10^{-5}$$

$$[H_3O^+] = \frac{0.4}{0.6} \times 1.75 \times 10^{-5} = 1.2 \times 10^{-5} \, F$$

Therefore, the buffer solution "resists" the increase of hydroxide-ion concentration by decreasing the reserve acidity of molecular acetic acid, and the actual hydronium-ion concentration is decreased to only two-thirds of the original value.

A general formula for computing the hydronium-ion concentration of an acid buffer is

$$[H_3O^+] = \frac{C_{\text{acid}}}{C_{\text{salt}}} \times K_a$$

where C represents formula-weight concentration and K_a is the ionization constant of the acid in the buffer mixture.

A buffer solution produced by a mixture of a weak base and its salt operates in the same manner as an acid buffer, except it is more convenient to make the calculations in terms of hydroxide-ion concentrations, which may be converted to hydronium-ion concentration, or pH, if need be. An example of a buffer of this type is a mixture of ammonia water and ammonium chloride. A general formula for computing the hydroxide-ion concentration of a base buffer is

$$[OH^-] = \frac{C_{\text{base}}}{C_{\text{salt}}} \times K_b$$

where K_b is the ionization constant of the weak base. The addition of a strong base to an ammonia–ammonium-ion buffer produces a decrease in the ammonium-ion concentration and an increase in the ammonia concentration by the following reaction:

$$OH^- + NH_4^+ \rightarrow NH_3 + H_2O$$

The addition of an acid to the same buffer decreases the concentration of ammonia and increases the ammonium-ion concentration by the reaction:

$$H_3O^+ + NH_3 \rightarrow NH_4^+ + H_2O$$

To illustrate the action of a base buffer, consider a liter of solution which is 0.5 F in respect to both NH_3 and NH_4^+, and determine the effect upon the hydroxide concentration by the addition of 0.1 gfw of NaOH. Before the addition of NaOH, the hydroxide concentration of the solution is

$$[OH^-] = \frac{0.5\ F\ NH_3}{0.5\ F\ NH_4^+} \times 1.8 \times 10^{-5} \qquad (K_b \text{ for } NH_3)$$

or

$$[OH^-] = 1.8 \times 10^{-5}\ F$$

After 0.1 gfw of NaOH is added, assuming no volume change, the ammonium-ion concentration is reduced to 0.4 F and the ammonia is increased to 0.6 F. The formality of the hydroxide ion becomes

$$[OH^-] = \frac{0.6\ F\ NH_3}{0.4\ F\ NH_4^+} \times 1.8 \times 10^{-5}$$

and

$$[OH^-] = 2.7 \times 10^{-5}\ F$$

Therefore, the addition of 0.1 gfw of NaOH increases the hydroxide-ion concentration of this ammonia–ammonium-ion buffer to only 1.5 times its original value.

4·9 Ionization of Weak Polyprotic Acids. Polyprotic acids are those acids which react with water to give more than one hydronium ion per molecule of the original acid. Weak polyprotic acids are weak electrolytes which react with water stepwise to produce more than one hydronium ion. The protolysis of phosphoric acid occurs in three steps, in which the extent of reaction decreases with successive steps, as indicated by the values of the ionization constants, designated as K_1, K_2, and K_3. Equations for the ionization reactions of phosphoric acid are

$$H_3PO_4 + H_2O \rightleftharpoons H_2PO_4^- + H_3O^+ \qquad K_1 = 7.5 \times 10^{-3}$$
$$H_2PO_4^- + H_2O \rightleftharpoons HPO_4^= + H_3O^+ \qquad K_2 = 6.2 \times 10^{-8}$$
$$HPO_4^= + H_2O \rightleftharpoons PO_4^{3-} + H_3O^+ \qquad K_3 = 4.8 \times 10^{-13}$$

To imply that these reactions take place stepwise is to some extent a misrepresentation. It would be more exact to say that phosphoric acid has three protons which may be removed, but the amount of energy involved in the removal of the three protons increases successively as each is detached. It is apparent from the above equations that water enters largely into these reactions. In a concentrated solution, phosphoric acid may be considered as a monoprotic acid. This statement is approximately true for all polyprotic acids. The removal of the second proton to form hydronium ions becomes appreciable only in dilute solutions, and the extent of the removal of the third proton is always small.

The quantitative relationships of the law of chemical equilibrium are applicable to the reversible reactions represented by undissociated phosphoric acid reacting with water. Therefore, the removal of one proton, as indicated in the first equation, produces a concentration of hydronium ions which acts as a common ion to repress the secondary and tertiary ionization reactions. This explains the fact that the ionization of $H_2PO_4^-$ is much less in phosphoric acid solution than in the salt solution of NaH_2PO_4. The common-ion effect of the hydronium ions in a solution of phosphoric acid lowers the concentration of the phosphate ion to a value so small that phosphoric acid cannot be used as a precipitating agent for most of the heavy-metal phosphates.

The ionization constants for the three reactions of phosphoric acid with water to produce ions, $K_1 = 7.5 \times 10^{-3}$, $K_2 = 6.2 \times 10^{-8}$, and $K_3 = 4.8 \times 10^{-13}$, indicate the wide differences in the extent to which the three reactions may take place. Although the ionization of phosphoric acid is written as a stepwise reaction, this does not signify that one reaction or ionization has priority over another in a dilute solution.

On the contrary, at equilibrium all three reversible reactions must be considered as in action.

An aqueous solution of hydrogen sulfide, widely used in qualitative analysis, may be considered as a weak diprotic acid. Hydrosulfuric acid, as this solution is sometimes called, reacts with water to give two protons, one of which is much more easily removed than the other. Thus, again as in the case of phosphoric acid, this weak acid can be considered as reacting with water in a stepwise fashion to produce hydronium ions. And again it must be emphasized that the treatment of the reaction as taking place in two steps is simply a matter of convenience, since the removal of the two protons to form hydronium ions takes place at the same time, although one proton requires less energy for removal than the other.

$$H_2S + H_2O \rightleftharpoons H_3O^+ + HS^- \qquad K_1 = 5.7 \times 10^{-8}$$

and

$$HS^- + H_2O \rightleftharpoons H_3O^+ + S^= \qquad K_2 = 1.2 \times 10^{-15}$$

The extent of each reaction is slight, as indicated by the size of the ionization constants. The equilibrium expressions for the two reactions, considering the amount of water in the reactions as being constant, are as follows:

$$\frac{[H_3O^+][HS^-]}{[H_2S]} = 5.7 \times 10^{-8} = K_1 \qquad (1)$$

and

$$\frac{[H_3O^+][S^=]}{[HS^-]} = 1.2 \times 10^{-15} = K_2 \qquad (2)$$

Multiplying the two expressions for K_1 and K_2 gives an equation for the over-all ionization of hydrogen sulfide which may be designated as K_a:

$$\frac{[H_3O^+][HS^-]}{[H_2S]} \times \frac{[H_3O^+][S^=]}{[HS^-]} = (5.7 \times 10^{-8})(1.2 \times 10^{-15})$$

or

$$\frac{[H_3O^+]^2[S^=]}{[H_2S]} = 6.8 \times 10^{-23} \qquad (3)$$

4·10 Mathematical Application of the Law of Chemical Equilibrium to Polyprotic Acids. The expression for the over-all ionization of hydrogen sulfide, as given in the preceding section, is misleading in its mathematical implications. This equation might be interpreted to indicate that both the concentrations of hydronium ion and sulfide ion could be calculated for a water solution of hydrogen sulfide according to the chemical reaction

$$H_2S + 2H_2O \rightleftharpoons 2H_3O^+ + S^=$$

Accordingly, if the formula-weight concentration of $S^=$ were designated as X, then the formula-weight concentration of the hydronium ion, $2H_3O^+$, would appear to be $2X$, and the mathematical expression could be erroneously deduced as $4X^3/[H_2S] = 6.8 \times 10^{-23}$. Furthermore, since a saturated solution of H_2S at room temperature is approximately $0.1\ F$, this equation could be solved so that $X = 1.2 \times 10^{-8}\ F$, indicating a sulfide-ion concentration of this formality. However, experimental evidence proves that this concentration is far from the true value. The actual value of the $S^=$ ion in a saturated solution of H_2S at room temperature is approximately $1 \times 10^{-15}\ F$.

Consequently, Eq. (3) for the over-all ionization of H_2S cannot be used for computing the formalities of both the hydronium and sulfide ions. A reexamination of Eqs. (1) and (2) from which Eq. (3) is derived indicates that there is a wide difference in the formality of the two hydronium ions in the two equations; therefore, it would be a false deduction to substitute $2X$ for the value of the hydronium ion in Eq. (3). Actually, Eq. (3) is valid for a saturated solution of H_2S only when either the hydronium or sulfide concentration is known.

For any weak diprotic acid, the formula-weight concentration of the doubly charged anion is practically equal to the secondary ionization constant of the acid. The justification for this statement lies in the large difference between the primary and secondary ionization constants of the two ionization reactions. For example, in the ionization reaction,

$$H_2S + H_2O \rightleftharpoons H_3O^+ + HS^-$$

the equilibrium expression is

$$\frac{[H_3O^+][HS^-]}{[H_2S]} = 5.7 \times 10^{-8}$$

In this expression the formula-weight concentration of the hydronium ion is approximately equal to that of the bisulfide ion; therefore, in the expression for the secondary ionization, these terms can be canceled out, indicating the formula-weight concentration of the $S^=$ ion.

$$\frac{[\cancel{H_3O^+}][S^=]}{\cancel{[HS^-]}} = 1.2 \times 10^{-15} \qquad \text{or} \qquad [S^=] = 1.2 \times 10^{-15}$$

It is evident that the formula-weight concentration of the hydronium ion is slightly larger than the formula-weight concentration of the HS^- ion, but the difference is so small that mathematically it can be ignored, which causes no appreciable difference in the calculation of the sulfide-ion concentration.

The assumption that the sulfide-ion concentration is equal to the secondary ionization constant involves some error if the original concentration of hydrogen sulfide is not specified. Thus, this assumption could imply that in case one molecule of H_2S were dissolved in 1 liter of water, the resulting sulfide-ion concentration would be 1×10^{-15} F. To correct this obvious error, it should be stated that, in a saturated solution of hydrogen sulfide, the sulfide-ion concentration is approximately equal to the value of the secondary ionization constant.

Types of Exercises Relating to Chap. 4

Type 1. *If 0.06 F acetic acid exists as ions to the extent of 1.7 per cent, compute the ionization constant for acetic acid.*

$$\text{Concentration of } H_3O^+ = 0.017 \times 0.06 = 0.0010 \ F$$
$$\text{Concentration of } C_2H_3O_2^- = 0.017 \times 0.06 = 0.0010 \ F$$
$$\text{Concentration of } HC_2H_3O_2 = 0.06 - (0.017 \times 0.06) = 0.059 \ F$$

The ionization reaction is

$$HC_2H_3O_2 + H_2O \rightleftharpoons H_3O^+ + C_2H_3O_2^-$$

and the equilibrium expression for this reaction is

$$\frac{[H_3O^+][C_2H_3O_2^-]}{[HC_2H_3O_2]} = K_a$$

Upon substituting the known concentrations into this expression,

$$\frac{(0.0010)(0.0010)}{0.059} = K_a = 1.7 \times 10^{-5}$$

Type 2. *(a) Calculate the hydronium-ion concentration in a solution of 0.2 F HNO_2. The ionization constant of nitrous acid at 25°C is 4×10^{-4}.*

Let
$$X = \text{formula-weight concentration of } H_3O^+ \text{ ion}$$
Also
$$X = \text{formula-weight concentration of } NO_2^- \text{ ion}$$
Therefore
$$0.20 - X = \text{formula-weight concentration of molecular } HNO_2$$

The ionization reaction is
$$HNO_2 + H_2O \rightleftharpoons H_3O^+ + NO_2^-$$

and the equilibrium expression is

$$\frac{[H_3O^+][NO_2^-]}{[HNO_2]} = 4 \times 10^{-4}$$

Upon substitution into this expression, it becomes

$$\frac{(X)(X)}{(0.20 - X)} = 4 \times 10^{-4}$$

The X subtracted from 0.20 is so small in comparison to 0.20 that it can be discarded without affecting the validity of the equation. Therefore,

$$\frac{X^2}{0.20} = 4 \times 10^{-4}$$

and upon solving,

$$X = 9 \times 10^{-3} F \ H_3O^+$$

(b) *What is the degree of ionization of the nitrous acid in the 0.2 F solution?*
The degree of ionization is the extent (fractional or per cent) to which the weak acid reacts with water to produce ions. Therefore, the concentration of the hydronium ions formed in the reaction, divided by the concentration of molecular acid, gives the extent of ionization. Or

$$\frac{[H_3O^+]}{[HNO_2]} = \text{extent of ionization}$$

Since

$$[H_3O^+] = 9 \times 10^{-3} F \quad \text{and} \quad [HNO_2] = \text{approx } 0.2 \ F$$

then

$$\frac{9 \times 10^{-3}}{0.2} = 4.5 \times 10^{-2} = \text{degree of ionization}$$

and

$$(4.5 \times 10^{-2})100 = 4.5 \text{ per cent ionized}$$

Consequently, in a solution of this concentration, the HNO_2 has reacted with water to the extent of 9 per cent.

Type 3. *What is the formula-weight concentration of ammonia which reacts with water to produce ions to the extent of 2.0 per cent? The K_b for NH_3 at 25°C is 1.8×10^{-5}.*

Let

$$X = \text{the formula-weight concentration of } NH_3$$
$$0.02X = \text{formula-weight concentration of the } OH^- \text{ ion}$$
$$0.02X = \text{formula-weight concentration of the } NH_4^+ \text{ ion}$$

The ionization reaction is

$$NH_3 + H_2O \rightleftharpoons NH_4^+ + OH^-$$

and the equilibrium expression into which these values are substituted is

$$\frac{[NH_4^+][OH^-]}{[NH_3]} = K_b \quad \text{and} \quad \frac{(0.02X)(0.02X)}{(X - 0.02X)} = 1.8 \times 10^{-5}$$

or

$$\frac{4 \times 10^{-4}X^2}{0.98X} = 1.8 \times 10^{-5} \quad \text{and} \quad \frac{4 \times 10^{-4}X}{0.98} = 1.8 \times 10^{-5}$$

Therefore,

$$X = \frac{0.98(1.8 \times 10^{-5})}{4 \times 10^{-4}} = 0.044 \ F \ NH_3$$

Type 4. *What is the formula-weight concentration of hydronium ions in a solution which is 0.2 F in respect to HNO_2, and 0.5 F in respect to $NaNO_2$?*

$$K_a \text{ of } HNO_2 = 4 \times 10^{-4} \text{ at } 25°C$$

Let

$$X = \text{formula-weight concentration of } H_3O^+$$

Since $NaNO_2$ is assumed to be completely ionized,

$$\text{Concentration of } NO_2^- = 0.5 + X$$

where X is the NO_2^- from the dissociation of HNO_2.

$$\text{Concentration of undissociated } HNO_2 = 0.2 - X$$

The ionization reaction is

$$HNO_2 + H_2O \rightleftharpoons H_3O^+ + NO_2^-$$

and the equilibrium expression is

$$\frac{[H_3O^+][NO_2^-]}{[HNO_2]} = K_a \quad \text{and} \quad \frac{(X)(0.5 + X)}{(0.2 - X)} = 4 \times 10^{-4}$$

Simplifying the equation by discarding the X values which are not significant,

$$\frac{(X)(0.5)}{0.2} = 4 \times 10^{-4}$$

and upon solving,

$$X = 1.6 \times 10^{-4} \, F \, H_3O^+$$

Type 5. *Calculate the pH of a 0.08 F solution of HCN. The K_a for KCN is*

$$7.2 \times 10^{-10}$$

Let

$$X = \text{formula-weight concentration of } H_3O^+$$

also

$$X = \text{formula-weight concentration of the } CN^- \text{ ion}$$

Therefore,

$$0.08 - X = \text{formula-weight concentration of undissociated HCN}$$

The equilibrium expression is

$$\frac{[H_3O^+][CN^-]}{[HCN]} = K_a \quad \text{and} \quad \frac{X^2}{0.08 - X} = 7.2 \times 10^{-10}$$

Since the X in the denominator is not significant, it may be discarded, and

$$X^2 = 0.08(7.2 \times 10^{-10}) = 5.8 \times 10^{-11}$$
$$X = \sqrt{58 \times 10^{-12}} = 7.6 \times 10^{-6}$$

and

$$pH = - \log (7.6 \times 10^{-6}) = -(.88 - 6)$$

or

$$pH = 6 - .88 = 5.12$$

Type 6. *What is the hydronium-ion concentration which corresponds to a pH of 5.7?*

$$pH = - \log [H_3O^+] = \log \frac{1}{[H_3O^+]}$$

or

$$\log \frac{1}{[H_3O^+]} = 5.70 \quad \text{and} \quad \frac{1}{[H_3O^+]} = \text{antilog } 5.70 = 10^{5.7}$$

and

$$\frac{1}{[H_3O^+]} = 5 \times 10^5 \quad \text{or} \quad [H_3O^+] = \frac{1}{5 \times 10^5} = 2 \times 10^{-6}$$

Type 7. *What is the approximate hydronium-ion concentration of a saturated solution of H_2S? A saturated solution of H_2S is approximately 0.1 F at 25°C, and the primary ionization K_1 is 5.7×10^{-8}.*

In solving this problem, the over-all expression for the reaction of H_2S with water,

$$H_2S + 2H_2O \rightleftharpoons 2H_3O^+ + S^=$$

cannot be used because the stepwise reactions producing hydronium ions do not take place to the same extent. The primary ionization reaction of H_2S with water is

$$H_2S + H_2O \rightleftharpoons H_3O^+ + HS^-$$

Since the secondary ionization reaction takes place to such a small extent it may be ignored, and the equilibrium expression for determining the hydronium-ion concentration of a water solution of H_2S is

$$\frac{[H_3O^+][HS^-]}{[H_2S]} = K_1 \quad \text{and} \quad \frac{(X)(X)}{(0.1 - X)} = 5.7 \times 10^{-8}$$

where

$$X = [H_3O^+] = [HS^-]$$
$$0.1 - X = [H_2S]$$

Since X is small in comparison with 0.1, the expression may be simplified to

$$\frac{X^2}{0.1} = 5.7 \times 10^{-8}$$

and upon solving,

$$X = 7.6 \times 10^{-5} \, F \, H_3O^+$$

Type 8. *Hydrochloric acid is added to a saturated solution of H_2S at 25°C until the solution is 0.3 F in respect to hydronium ions. Compute the S^- ion concentration.*

In this problem the total hydronium-ion concentration is given; therefore, to solve for the S^- ion concentration, it is necessary to use the over-all ionization reaction of H_2S, which is

$$H_2S + 2H_2O \rightleftharpoons 2H_3O^+ + S^-$$

and the equilibrium expression for this reversible reaction is

$$\frac{[H_3O^+]^2[S^-]}{[H_2S]} = K_a \quad \text{and} \quad \frac{(0.3)^2[S^-]}{0.1} = 6.8 \times 10^{-23}$$

where $[H_3O^+] = 0.3 \, F$
$[H_2S] = 0.1 \, F$ (for a saturated solution at 25°C)
Solving,

$$[S^-] = \frac{0.1(6.8 \times 10^{-23})}{0.9 \times 10^{-1}} = 7.6 \times 10^{-23} \, F$$

Exercises

(Ionization constants for weak acids and bases are given in Table A·6.)

1. Nitrous acid, in a 0.1 F solution, is 6.5 per cent ionized. Calculate the ionizaton constant for this acid.

2. Compute the formula-weight concentration of NH_3 in a solution in which it is known to be 4.0 per cent ionized.

3. Calculate the degree of ionization of a 0.05 F solution of lactic acid.

4. Compute the ionization constant of hydrofluoric acid, if a 0.1 F solution is 8.13 per cent ionized.

5. What concentration of hydroxide ions exists in a 0.009 F solution of NH_3 at 25°C?

6. What is the hydronium-ion concentration of a 0.05 F HCN solution?

7. What concentration of nitrous acid has a hydronium-ion concentration of 0.01 F?

8. If a monoprotic acid is 3.8 per cent ionized in a 0.2 F solution, calculate its ionization constant. What is the percentage ionization of this acid in a 0.01 F solution?

9. What weight of lactic acid must be dissolved in a liter of solution to produce a hydronium-ion concentration of $1 \times 10^{-3} F$?

10. What is the hydronium-ion concentration of 1 g of acetic acid in 100 ml of water?

11. Calculate the hydroxide concentration of a solution that is 0.1 F with NH_3, and 0.25 F in respect to $(NH_4)_2SO_4$.

12. What concentration of $NaC_2H_3O_2$ must be added to 0.1 F $HC_2H_3O_2$ to give a hydronium-ion concentration of 2×10^{-6} gfw/liter?

13. If 5 g of acetic acid and 5 g of sodium acetate are dissolved to produce a liter of solution, what is the hydronium-ion concentration of this solution? What is the pH of the solution?

14. If 3 g of ammonium chloride and 2 g of ammonia are dissolved in sufficient water to produce 500 ml of solution, calculate the hydroxide-ion concentration of the solution. What is the pH of the solution?

15. If 50 ml of 1 F $HC_2H_3O_2$ is added to 100 ml of 1 F $NaC_2H_3O_2$, what is the hydronium-ion concentration of the resulting solution? Calculate the pH of the solution.

16. Approximately how many grams of ammonium chloride should be dissolved in a liter of 0.3 F NH_3 to reduce the concentration of hydroxide ions to one one-hundredth of its original value?

17. If 50 ml of 0.3 F HAc is mixed with 100 ml of 0.1 F KOH, what is the hydronium-ion concentration of the resulting solution? What is the pH of the solution?

18. If 20 ml of 3 F NH_3 and 5 g of $(NH_4)_2SO_4$ are added to 200 ml of water, what is the hydroxide-ion concentration of the resulting solution? Calculate the pOH of the solution.

19. Calculate the sulfide-ion concentration of a 0.5 F HCl solution which has been saturated with H_2S at 25°C.

20. Compute the sulfide-ion concentration of a 0.5 F $HC_2H_3O_2$ solution which has been saturated with H_2S at 25°C.

21. What is the hydronium-ion concentration of a 0.01 F solution of H_2CO_3, if only the primary ionization reaction is considered?

22. To 500 ml of 0.05 F H_2S solution is added 50 ml of 3 F acetic acid solution. What is the sulfide-ion concentration of the resulting solution?

23. Calculate the pH of a 0.1 F solution of $NaHSO_4$.

24. What is the HS^- ion concentration of a 0.1 F H_2S solution which is also 0.1 F in respect to $HC_2H_3O_2$?

25. The pH of a solution is 3.4. What is the concentration of hydroxide ions in the solution?

26. The pOH of a solution, which is 0.5 F with respect to a weak monoprotic acid, is 9.2. Calculate the ionization constant of the acid.

27. What concentration of nitrous acid is required to produce a solution with a pH of 2.6?

28. What concentration of NH_3 is required to make a solution with a pH of 10.2?

29. Calculate the pH of a solution which is 0.1 F in $HC_2H_3O_2$ and 0.1 F in HCl.

30. How much 0.1 F HCl is required to make 250 ml of solution with a pH of 1.7?

31. How much 0.1 F $HC_2H_3O_2$ is required to make 500 ml of solution with a pH of 4.0?

CHAPTER 5

THE SOLUBILITY PRODUCT PRINCIPLE

The discussion of chemical equilibria has hitherto been restricted to systems in which the active components were in one phase. The description as *one phase* indicates that the components exist in one physical state, and as a homogeneous body of uniform composition. Thus, any solution containing soluble molecules in equilibrium with ions is a one-phase system. A solution of acetic acid represents a homogeneous equilibrium of this type, in that the undissociated molecules of acetic acid are in equilibrium with hydronium and acetate ions, and the system is in one phase, namely, a liquid. On the other hand, any system in which the active components are in different physical states, involving a boundary or boundaries between states, is called a *heterogeneous* system. Therefore, a heterogeneous system is one involving substances in two or three possible physical states (solid, liquid, and gas). This chapter is devoted to the examination of heterogeneous systems produced by solids in equilibrium with ions in solution, or more specifically, to equilibria produced by saturated solutions of difficultly soluble electrolytes. The application of the law of chemical equilibrium to such solutions is known as the solubility product principle.

5·1 Solubility. Although the nature of solubility is still in the speculative state, it can be said that as a general rule salts dissolve more readily in solvents composed of molecules containing electrostatic dipoles. In the solid state, an ionic compound exists as ions and not as molecules, and these ions are arranged in a symmetrical fashion within the crystal lattice. The nature of the packing, or arrangement, of ions in the lattice is determined largely by the diameters of the ions. And the ions are held in their relative positions by strong electrostatic forces resulting from the charges upon the ions. To break down the architecture of the crystal, these electrostatic forces must be overcome. Moreover, the amount of energy necessary to cause the solution of a gram-formula weight of solid sodium chloride should be equivalent to the amount of energy required to melt a gram-formula weight of solid sodium chloride. In the process of bringing an electrolyte into solution, it is generally assumed that there is an interaction between the polar molecules of water and the ions of the crystal, in which the dipoles of the water molecules are oriented to exert a pulling force to overcome the attractive forces between the ions within the crystal. For a substance to be readily soluble, more energy must be available to break down the crystal than was liberated in building up the ionic lattice. In other words, the energy of solvation must be of greater magnitude than the lattice energy. Now, energy of solvation may come from two sources: the dipole attraction of solvent molecules for the ions in the crystal, and the chemical reaction between the ions and water molecules to form hydrated ions with a resulting liberation of energy. Since these two sources of energy, for bringing ions into solution, are not easily distinguishable, it is more convenient to consider them collectively as the energy of solvation. Then it may be said that the solubility of a salt is proportional to the magnitude of two energy factors: lattice energy and energy of solvation.

Electrolytes in which the lattice energies of the crystals are relatively large usually are not very soluble. Such compounds are never totally insoluble, although some have low solubilities because of great differences between the lattice energies and the energies released by solvation. Difficultly soluble electrolytes do, produce some ions in solution. The reaction to produce ions from the solid solute is a reversible one, and in a saturated solution there is an equilibrium between the ions in solution and the undissolved solute. As in all reversible chemical reactions, this equilibrium is dynamic, since there is one reaction in progress to detach ions at the surface of the crystal, and a reverse reaction in which ions are deposited upon the crystal. An equilibrium of this kind may be shifted either by a change in temperature, or by changes in the concentration of the ions involved in the equilibrium. If a difficultly soluble salt, composed of monovalent ions, is designated as MA, the reversible reaction produced in a saturated solution of the salt may be indicated as

$$MA(s) + XH_2O \underset{\text{crystallization}}{\overset{\text{solution}}{\rightleftharpoons}} M(H_2O)_x{}^+ + A(H_2O)_x{}^-$$

where X is the unknown number of water molecules which may combine with the ions produced.

5·2 Derivation of Solubility Product Expression. In a saturated solution of an electrolyte, the equilibrium between the solid and its ions is in a dynamic state of balance between two opposing reactions. The dissolving reaction is that reaction in which the ions are pulled away from the crystal to form soluble hydrated ions, and the precipitation reaction is the reverse reaction, in which the dissolved ions with different electrical charges come into contact with each other, and as a result of the contact may lose their water of hydration and precipitate upon the surface of the crystal. The solubility product principle is only valid for fairly insoluble electrolytes. A good illustration of a reversible equilibrium of this type is a saturated solution of silver chloride. Most ions are assumed to be hydrated in water solution, and certainly the silver and chloride ions should be no exceptions. However, to simplify the derivation of the solubility product principle, the hydration of these particular ions is ignored.

Solid silver chloride forms a cubic lattice, similar to NaCl, in which there is an alternate spacing of silver and chloride ions. A surface view of one face of the cubic crystal is indicated diagrammatically in Fig. 5·1.

A positive silver ion must be deposited above a negative chloride ion and vice versa, in order to continue the crystal lattice. The rate at which an ion leaves the surface is proportional to the number in the surface layer, whereas the rate of deposition of an ion is proportional to its concentration in solution and also to the number of places at the surface to which it can be attached. Equilibrium is attained when equal numbers of silver and chloride ions are dissolved and deposited in the same time.

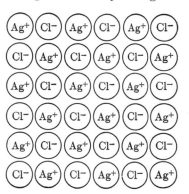

FIG. 5·1 Diagram of the surface of a silver chloride crystal.

The total surface of the solid phase, exposed within the saturated solution, may be represented as unity. If X is the fraction of the surface covered with silver ions, then $1 - X$ is the fraction covered by chloride ions. The rate V_1 at which silver ions leave the surface may be expressed as K_1X, in which K_1 is a proportionality constant, or

$$V_1 = K_1X \qquad (1)$$

The rate V_2 at which silver ions are deposited on the surface is proportional to the concentration of the silver ions in the solution and to the number of available spaces at the surface for attachment. The concentration of silver ions is $[Ag^+]$, and $1 - X$ denotes the number of places where silver ions may be attached. Therefore,

$$V_2 = K_2(1 - X)[Ag^+] \qquad (2)$$

At equilibrium, the rates of solution and deposition are equal, or $V_1 = V_2$, and

$$K_1X = K_2(1 - X)[Ag^+] \qquad (3)$$

Equation (3) may be rearranged as

$$[Ag^+] = \frac{K_1X}{K_2(1 - X)} \qquad (4)$$

In a similar fashion, the solution of chloride ions may be expressed as $K_3(1 - X)$, and the deposition of chloride ions at the surface as $K_4X[\text{Cl}^-]$. At equilibrium, these expressions are equal to each other, or

$$K_3(1 - X) = K_4X[\text{Cl}^-] \tag{5}$$

and upon rearrangement, to indicate the chloride concentration,

$$[\text{Cl}^-] = \frac{K_3(1 - X)}{K_4X} \tag{6}$$

If Eqs. (4) and (6) are multiplied together,

$$[\text{Ag}^+][\text{Cl}^-] = \frac{K_1X}{K_2(1 - X)} \times \frac{K_3(1 - X)}{K_4X}$$

the unknown factors of X are eliminated to give

$$[\text{Ag}^+][\text{Cl}^-] = \frac{K_1K_3}{K_2K_4}$$

Since all the K values are constant, they may be equated to a single constant, which is the *solubility product constant*.

$$[\text{Ag}^+][\text{Cl}^-] = K_{\text{s.p.}} \tag{7}$$

In the foregoing derivation, the difficultly soluble salt chosen for an illustration forms only two ions in solution; therefore, Eq. (7) indicates that the product of the concentration of the ions in solution is the solubility product constant. However, if the fairly insoluble salt produces more than two ions, e.g., $\text{Pb}_3(\text{PO}_4)_2$ releases five ions in solution when it dissolves, or

$$\text{Pb}_3(\text{PO}_4)_2(s) \rightleftharpoons 3\text{Pb}^{++} + 2\text{PO}_4{}^{3-}$$

then the solubility product expression for this compound is

$$[\text{Pb}^{++}]^3[\text{PO}_4{}^{3-}]^2 = K_{\text{s.p.}}$$

Therefore, the solubility product principle may be generally stated as: *In a saturated solution of a difficultly soluble electrolyte, the product of the formal concentrations of the ions, each ion raised to the power equal to the number of times it occurs in the formula, is a constant at a given temperature.*

5·3 Relationship of Solubility Product to Solubility. The solubility product principle is an application of the law of chemical equilibrium, and the solubility product constant is a special form of an equilibrium constant. In spite of its name, the solubility product constant is not in itself a quantitative value in terms of weight and volume. For example, AgCl and Ag_3PO_4 are soluble in water to the extent of 1.5×10^{-3} and 6.5×10^{-3} g/liter, respectively, signifying that silver phosphate is approximately four times as soluble as silver chloride. The solubility product constants of AgCl and Ag_3PO_4 are 1.5×10^{-10} and 1.8×10^{-18}, respectively, or, in relative numerical terms, the $K_{s.p.}$ of AgCl is one hundred million times larger than the $K_{s.p.}$ of Ag_3PO_4. From these examples, it is obvious that the numerical values of the solubility products cannot be compared in relation to the solubility of the two salts. The reason for the wide difference in the size of these solubility product values is indicated by the mathematical expressions for them:

$$[Ag^+]^3[PO_4{}^{3-}] = K_{s.p.} \text{ of } Ag_3PO_4$$
$$[Ag^+][Cl^-] = K_{s.p.} \text{ of } AgCl$$

The concentration of the silver ion is cubed in the expression for the $K_{s.p.}$ for Ag_3PO_4, whereas in the expression of the $K_{s.p.}$ of AgCl, the silver-ion concentration is not taken to a power.

To better indicate the relative solubility of these different type salts, the concentration of the silver ion in a saturated solution of each salt is calculated as follows:

$$[Ag^+][Cl^-] = 1.5 \times 10^{-10}$$
$$(X)(X) = 1.5 \times 10^{-10}$$
$$X = \sqrt{1.5 \times 10^{-10}} = 1.2 \times 10^{-5} F$$

Concentration of Ag^+ in saturated AgCl solution $= X = 1.2 \times 10^{-5} F$

$$[Ag^+]^3[PO_4{}^{3-}] = 1.8 \times 10^{-18}$$
$$(3X)^3(X) = 1.8 \times 10^{-18}$$
$$27X^4 = 1.8 \times 10^{-18}$$
$$X = 1.6 \times 10^{-5} F$$

Concentration of Ag^+ in saturated solution of Ag_3PO_4
$$= 3X = 4.8 \times 10^{-5} F$$

Therefore, the silver-ion concentration in a saturated solution of silver phosphate is four times greater than in a saturated solution of silver chloride.

Since the numerical value of the solubility product constant depends upon the concentration of ions produced by the relatively insoluble salt, this value is a rough qualitative indication of solubility. Consequently, a very small solubility product value indicates a very insoluble compound, and a large one denotes a more soluble substance. To illustrate this qualitative significance with two extremes, the solubility product constants of Ag_2S and $AgC_2H_3O_2$ are 1.6×10^{-49} and 1.8×10^{-3}, respectively, and from these values it may be deduced that silver sulfide is a very insoluble substance and that silver acetate is comparatively soluble. Only when two insoluble salts produce the same number of ions may the numerical values of their solubility products be directly compared; even under these conditions, the comparison is somewhat relative because of the difference in the formula weights of the two compounds. For example, AgBr and AgI have solubility product constants of 7.7×10^{-13} and 1.5×10^{-16}, respectively, indicating that silver iodide is less soluble than silver bromide, but these relative values are not quantitative because the formula weights of the two compounds are different.

5·4   Calculation of Solubility Product Constant from Solubility. To illustrate the calculation of the solubility product constant from a known value for solubility, *consider the compound* $PbSO_4$, *which has a solubility of* 4.2×10^{-2} *g/liter:*

$$\text{Gram-formula weight of } PbSO_4 = 303$$

Therefore,

$$\text{Formal solubility of } PbSO_4 = \frac{4.2 \times 10^{-2}}{303} \approx 1.4 \times 10^{-4} \text{ gfw/liter}$$

The equation for the production of ions is

$$PbSO_4(s) \rightleftharpoons Pb^{++} + SO_4^{=}$$

The mathematical expression for $K_{s.p.}$ is

$$[Pb^{++}][SO_4^{=}] = K_{s.p.}$$

Substituting the formal concentration of the ions into this expression,

$$(1.4 \times 10^{-4})(1.4 \times 10^{-4}) = K_{s.p.} = 2 \times 10^{-8}$$

If the relatively insoluble salt produces more than two ions, each ion is taken to the power equal to the number of times that it occurs in the formula of the salt. For example, *calculate the solubility product constant of* Ag_3PO_4, *if the solubility of this salt is* 6.5×10^{-3} *g/liter.*

$$\text{Gram-formula weight of } Ag_3PO_4 = 418.7 \text{ g}$$

$$\text{Formal solubility of } Ag_3PO_4 = \frac{6.5 \times 10^{-3}}{418.7} = 1.6 \times 10^{-5} \text{ gfw/liter}$$

The equation for the production of ions is

$$Ag_3PO_4(s) \rightleftharpoons \quad 3Ag^+ \quad + \quad PO_4^{3-}$$
$$1.6 \times 10^{-5} F \quad 3 \times 1.6 \times 10^{-5} F \quad 1.6 \times 10^{-5} F$$

The expression for $K_{s.p.}$ is

$$[Ag^+]^3[PO_4^{3-}] = K_{s.p.}$$

Substituting the solubility values of the ions into this expression,

$$(3 \times 1.6 \times 10^{-5})^3(1.6 \times 10^{-5}) = K_{s.p.}$$
$$K_{s.p.} = 1.8 \times 10^{-18}$$

5·5 Calculation of Solubility from Solubility Product Constant. As stated elsewhere, the numerical value of a solubility product constant is not a quantitative term and is only a rough qualitative approximation of solubility. However, from solubility product constants can be calculated solubility values if the ionization reactions and the formula weights are known. By way of illustration, *calculate the solubility of* SrC_2O_4 *in gram-formula weights per liter, and in grams per liter, if the* $K_{s.p.}$ *is* 1.4×10^{-7}.

The equation for the ionization reaction is

$$SrC_2O_4(s) \rightleftharpoons Sr^{++} + C_2O_4^{=}$$

The expression for $K_{s.p.}$ is

$$[Sr^{++}][C_2O_4^{=}] = K_{s.p.}$$

The formal solubility of $SrC_2O_4 = X$ and, therefore, each of its ions $= X$. Accordingly,

$$(X)(X) = K_{s.p.} = 1.4 \times 10^{-7}$$
$$X^2 = 1.4 \times 10^{-7}$$
$$X = 3.7 \times 10^{-4} \text{ gfw/liter}$$

The solubility in grams per liter is

$$3.7 \times 10^{-4} \text{ gfw} \times 176 \text{ (gfw of } SrC_2O_4) = 0.065 \text{ g/liter}$$

The calculations involving solubility product constants become more complex for a relatively insoluble salt which produces several ions in solution. The following problem illustrates this type: *If the solubility product constant of lead phosphate is* 1.5×10^{-32}, *what is the formal solubility of this compound? What is the solubility in grams per* 100 ml?

The equation for the production of ions from this compound is

$$\underset{X}{Pb_3(PO_4)_2(s)} \rightleftharpoons \underset{3X}{3Pb^{++}} + \underset{2X}{2PO_4^{3-}}$$

If the formal solubility of $Pb_3(PO_4)_2$ is designated as X, then from the equation for the production of ions, the formality of the Pb^{++} ion is $3X$ and that of the PO_4^{3-} ion is $2X$. Hence, the expression for $K_{s.p.}$ of lead phosphate is

$$[Pb^{++}]^3[PO_4^{3-}]^2 = K_{s.p.}$$

Upon substituting the X values into this expression, it becomes

$$(3X)^3(2X)^2 = 1.5 \times 10^{-32}$$
$$108X^5 = 1.5 \times 10^{-32}$$
$$X^5 = 13.8 \times 10^{-35}$$
$$X = 1.7 \times 10^{-7}$$

The gram-formula weight of lead phosphate is 811.6 g; therefore, the solubility in grams per 100 ml is

$$1.7 \times 10^{-7} \times 811.6 \times 0.1 = 1.4 \times 10^{-5} \text{ g/100 ml}$$

5·6 Solubility Product Constant and Temperature. Under the discussion of chemical equilibrium (Sec. 3·8), it was stated that the only factor which appreciably changes the value of an equilibrium constant is temperature. Inasmuch as the solubility product constant is a special form of an equilibrium constant, it is to be expected that temperature changes will produce the same effect upon either constant. As has been pointed out, also, the speed of a reaction is increased by a rise in temperature, and since a saturated solution of a difficultly soluble salt, MA, may be represented by the equilibrium,

$$MA(s) \underset{\text{crystallization}}{\overset{\text{solution}}{\rightleftharpoons}} M^+ + A^-$$

a rise in temperature will speed both the rate of solution and the rate of precipitation. However, the increases in the two rates of the opposing reactions are not the same; therefore, for each different temperature, there will be a different solubility product constant.

The solubilities of most substances increase with rising temperatures. This is true for fairly insoluble substances as well as soluble ones. As a consequence, the values for the solubility product constants also increase with rises in temperature. Evidence to this statement are the changes of the solubility product constants for $Pb(IO_3)_2$ and $AgCl$ with temperatures:

CHANGE OF $K_{s.p.}$ WITH TEMPERATURE

Substance	$K_{s.p.}$	Temperature, °C
Lead iodate	5.3×10^{-14}	9.2
	1.2×10^{-13}	18
	2.6×10^{-13}	25.8
Silver chloride	2.1×10^{-11}	4.7
	3.7×10^{-11}	9.7
	1.56×10^{-10}	25
	1.32×10^{-9}	50

5·7 Influence of a Common Ion on Solubility. The effect of a common ion upon a precipitate in equilibrium with its ions is analogous to the effect of a common ion upon a weak electrolyte in equilibrium with its ions, which was discussed in Sec. 4·7. Accordingly, if a solution contains a sparingly soluble salt in equilibrium with its ions, it is to be expected that an increase in the concentration of one of the ions will cause a corresponding decrease in the other ion to satisfy the value of the solubility product constant, or, in other words, to maintain the constant value of the solubility product. For instance, in a saturated solution of silver chloride at room temperature, the concentration of the chloride ion is $1 \times 10^{-5} F$. This value is obtained from the solubility product expression as

$$[Ag^+][Cl^-] = 1 \times 10^{-10}$$

where
$$X = [Ag^+] = [Cl^-]$$
$$X^2 = 1 \times 10^{-10}$$
$$X = 1 \times 10^{-5} F$$

If the concentration of the silver ion is increased, by adding excess silver ions, to $10^{-3} F$, this increase causes a corresponding decrease in the chloride-ion concentration to 1×10^{-7} to satisfy the solubility product constant.

$$[Ag^+][Cl^-] = K_{s.p.} = 1 \times 10^{-10}$$
$$(1 \times 10^{-3})(1 \times 10^{-7}) = 1 \times 10^{-10}$$

A decrease in the chloride-ion concentration can be accomplished only by the precipitation of more silver chloride; consequently, the addition of a common ion produces a decrease in the solubility of the solid phase.

The decrease in solubility of a precipitate by common-ion effect is utilized in quantitative analysis to lower the concentration of an ion, under analysis, which remains in solution. It is common practice to add a slight excess of a precipitating reagent to produce a more nearly complete precipitation of the ion undergoing analysis. On the other hand, a large excess of the common ion is to be avoided, because such an excess may cause increased solubility either by neutral salt effect or by the formation of a soluble complex ion.

The common-ion effect is illustrated by the following problem: *What is the solubility of silver chromate, Ag_2CrO_4, in grams per liter, in a 0.1 F solution of K_2CrO_4? The $K_{s.p.}$ for Ag_2CrO_4 is 9×10^{-12}.*

The equation for the production of ions is

$$\underset{X}{Ag_2CrO_4(s)} \rightleftharpoons \underset{2X}{2Ag^+} + \underset{0.1 + X}{CrO_4^=}$$

If
$$X = \text{gfw of } Ag_2CrO_4 \text{ entering solution}$$

then
$$\text{Concentration of } Ag^+ = 2X$$

and
$$\text{Concentration of chromate ion} = 0.1 + X$$

Solubility product expression is

$$[Ag^+]^2[CrO_4^=] = K_{s.p.}$$

Substituting the known values into this expression, it becomes

$$(2X)^2(0.1 + X) = 9 \times 10^{-12}$$

But the value of X which is added to 0.1 is small in comparison to 0.1, and, consequently, may be discarded. Thus, the equation becomes

$$(2X)^2(0.1) = 9 \times 10^{-12}$$
$$4X^2 = \frac{9 \times 10^{-12}}{0.1} \quad \text{and} \quad X^2 = 22.5 \times 10^{-12}$$

Therefore,

$$X = 4.8 \times 10^{-6} \, F \quad \text{(or gfw/liter)}$$

Since the formula weight of Ag_2CrO_4 is 331.8, then

$$4.8 \times 10^{-6} \times 331.8 = 1.6 \times 10^{-3} \text{ g/liter for the solubility of } Ag_2CrO_4$$

5·8 Solubility Product Principle and Salt Effect. From solubility data obtained in pure water, the calculation of the solubility product constant is fairly accurate for a sparingly soluble salt. But such a condition as a difficulty soluble salt existing in pure water is rarely encountered in ordinary laboratory procedures. Precipitations of most compounds occur usually in solutions containing other ions. Also, the presence of other ions which are not common to a precipitate increases its solubility and, in consequence, the value of its solubility product constant. The same effect is obtained by the presence of a large excess of a common ion. This increase in the solubility of a relatively insoluble salt and consequent increase in the value for its solubility product, due to the presence of either uncommon or common ions, is referred to as the *salt effect*.

The salt effect increases with the number of electrical charges upon the ions involved in the effect. Accordingly, the effect of ions from $MgSO_4$ upon the solubility of $BaSO_4$ is greater than the effect of ions from KCl upon the solubility of $AgCl$. Table 5·1 shows how the solubility of thallous chloride changes in the presence of certain uncommon ions. The presence of ions from either KNO_3 or K_2SO_4 increases the solubility of $TlCl$, and as a result, the value for its solubility product. But the increase is greater in the presence of ions from K_2SO_4 than of ions produced by KNO_3. This difference is attributed to the doubly charged sulfate ions, which have more effect upon solubility than the nitrate ion with a single charge.

The evidence of a salt effect upon the solubility of a sparingly soluble electrolyte, by either the presence of uncommon ions or by a large concentration of common ions, indicates the obvious fact that, in a saturated solution of a fairly soluble salt, the solubility of the salt is affected by the presence of its own ions. As a consequence, the solubility product principle is only valid for difficulty soluble salts.

Since the calculations of solubility products are only accurate for sparingly soluble salts in pure water, the deviations from this principle, produced by increased ionic concentrations, may be ascribed to a change in the nature of the solvent. Hence, a salt solution may be considered as

TABLE 5·1 SOLUBILITY AND SOLUBILITY PRODUCT CONSTANTS OF THALLOUS CHLORIDE AT 25°C IN THE PRESENCE OF OTHER SALTS*

Normality of added salt	Solubility of TlCl in KNO$_3$	$K_{s.p.}$ of TlCl in KNO$_3$	Solubility of TlCl in K$_2$SO$_4$	$K_{s.p.}$ of TlCl in K$_2$SO$_4$
0.00	0.0161 N	2.6 × 10^{-4}	0.0161 N	2.6 × 10^{-4}
0.02	0.0172 N	3.0 × 10^{-4}	0.0178 N	3.2 × 10^{-4}
0.05	0.0183 N	3.4 × 10^{-4}	0.0194 N	3.8 × 10^{-4}
0.10	0.0196 N	3.9 × 10^{-4}	0.0214 N	4.7 × 10^{-4}
0.30	0.0231 N	5.3 × 10^{-4}	0.0260 N	6.9 × 10^{-4}
1.00	0.0307 N	9.4 × 10^{-4}	0.0340 N	12.0 × 10^{-4}

* W. C. Bray and W. J. Winninghoff, *J. Am. Chem. Soc.*, **33**, 1663 (1911).

having different solvent properties than pure water. This difference is due to the interionic attraction between the excess ions and those ions in equilibrium with the solid phase. In a saturated solution of an ionic compound, there is a dynamic equilibrium between the ions going into solution from the surface of a crystal and the ions returning to the crystal. The equilibrium may be indicated as

$$\text{MA}(s) \underset{\text{crystallization}}{\overset{\text{solution}}{\rightleftharpoons}} \text{M}^+ + \text{A}^-$$

The rate of ions leaving the crystal is not influenced by the addition of excess ions to the solution, but the presence of excess ions does change the rate of ions returning to the crystal surface. Each positive ion involved in the equilibrium is attracted by excess negative ions, and each negative ion is attracted by excess positive ions. This interionic attraction, caused by an excess of ions in solution, amounts to a dragging effect upon the movement of the ions throughout the solution. Consequently, the decrease in the rate of diffusion of those ions in solution also decreases the rate of ions returning to the solid phase. In other words, the salt effect causes a decrease in the rate of precipitation but has no effect upon the rate of solution in the dynamic equilibrium produced by a slightly soluble electrolyte and its ions. As a result of the difference of solution and precipitation, there is a shift of equilibrium, which is expressed by a new solubility product constant. Accordingly, for each different concentration of excess ions there is a different solubility product constant. The change in solubility product constant with an increase in ionic concentration is somewhat analogous to the effect of temperature upon equilibrium constants.

The salt effect is produced by a comparatively small concentration of uncommon ions, as evidenced in the values in Table 5·1. The same effect is produced by a large concentration of common ions. Therefore, it is evident that the solubility product expression is a more or less inexact approximation for a difficultly soluble salt in the presence of an appreciable concentration of ions.

5·9   Fractional Precipitation.   To precipitate a difficultly soluble salt from solution, the product of the concentrations of the ions of the salt must exceed the solubility product constant, at a given temperature. Conversely, to prevent the precipitation of a sparingly soluble salt, the concentrations of the ions must be kept below the values which exceed the solubility product of the salt. There are occasions in qualitative analysis when it is necessary to precipitate one or more ions from a mixture, leaving other ions in solution, which are precipitated later by the same reagent in a different concentration. For example, in the conventional scheme of cation analysis, the cations of Group II are precipitated by the sulfide ion in an acid solution containing a hydronium-ion concentration of 0.3 F, but the concentration of the sulfide ion in this solution is too low to permit the precipitation of Group III cations. However, if the concentration of the sulfide ion is increased, by making the solution basic, the cations of Group III are precipitated. Thus, by controlling the concentration of the sulfide ion, which is the precipitating agent, the two groups of cations may be precipitated separately. This separation is made possible by the wide difference in the values of the solubility product constants of the two groups of sulfides. The possibility of fractional precipitation brings up certain questions regarding the conditions necessary for separating two ions by means of the same precipitating reagent. To consider these questions and their answers, suppose that a solution contains a mixture of barium ions and lead ions, and that the concentration of each of these ions is 0.001 F. If a solution of sulfate ions is added to this mixture in successive small portions, what will be the composition of the precipitate first formed? Will the compound having the smallest solubility product precipitate first, and if so, will it precipitate completely before the other compound begins to precipitate? Under what conditions will simultaneous precipitation of both compounds take place? To answer these questions, examine Table 5·2, which indicates what happens in a solution containing such a mixture of barium and lead ions when the sulfate ion is added, first in a concentration of 10^{-9} F, and then increased in successive steps to a concentration of 10^{-4} F.

The solubility product constants of $BaSO_4$ and $PbSO_4$ are 1×10^{-10} and 1×10^{-8}, respectively.

TABLE 5·2   FRACTIONAL PRECIPITATION OF $BaSO_4$ AND $PbSO_4$

$10^{-3} F\ Ba^{++} \times 10^{-9} F\ SO_4^- = 1 \times 10^{-12}$	No pptn of $BaSO_4$, less than $K_{s.p.}$
$10^{-3} F\ Pb^{++} \times 10^{-9} F\ SO_4^- = 1 \times 10^{-12}$	No pptn of $PbSO_4$, less than $K_{s.p.}$
$10^{-3} F\ Ba^{++} \times 10^{-8} F\ SO_4^- = 1 \times 10^{-11}$	No pptn of $BaSO_4$, less than $K_{s.p.}$
$10^{-3} F\ Pb^{++} \times 10^{-8} F\ SO_4^- = 1 \times 10^{-11}$	No pptn of $PbSO_4$, less than $K_{s.p.}$
$10^{-3} F\ Ba^{++} \times 10^{-7} F\ SO_4^- = 1 \times 10^{-10}$	Pptn of $BaSO_4$ begins, $K_{s.p.}$ exceeded
$10^{-3} F\ Pb^{++} \times 10^{-7} F\ SO_4^- = 1 \times 10^{-10}$	No pptn of $PbSO_4$, less than $K_{s.p.}$
$10^{-4} F\ Ba^{++} \times 10^{-6} F\ SO_4^- = 1 \times 10^{-10}$	Pptn of $BaSO_4$, $K_{s.p.}$ exceeded
$10^{-3} F\ Pb^{++} \times 10^{-6} F\ SO_4^- = 1 \times 10^{-9}$	No pptn of $PbSO_4$, less than $K_{s.p.}$
$10^{-5} F\ Ba^{++} \times 10^{-5} F\ SO_4^- = 1 \times 10^{-10}$	Pptn of $BaSO_4$, $K_{s.p.}$ exceeded
$10^{-3} F\ Pb^{++} \times 10^{-5} F\ SO_4^- = 1 \times 10^{-8}$	Pptn of $PbSO_4$ begins, $K_{s.p.}$ exceeded
$10^{-6} F\ Ba^{++} \times 10^{-4} F\ SO_4^- = 1 \times 10^{-10}$	Pptn of $BaSO_4$, $K_{s.p.}$ exceeded
$10^{-4} F\ Pb^{++} \times 10^{-4} F\ SO_4^- = 1 \times 10^{-8}$	Pptn of $PbSO_4$, $K_{s.p.}$ exceeded

Since the concentrations of barium and lead ions are equal in the original mixture, the successive addition of sulfate ions causes $BaSO_4$ to precipitate first, because its solubility product constant is exceeded first. Continued addition of sulfate ions precipitates $BaSO_4$ until the solubility product constant of $PbSO_4$ is exceeded, and then both compounds precipitate together. However, the concentration of Ba^{++} ions is reduced from $10^{-3}\ F$ to $10^{-5}\ F$ before Pb^{++} ions begin to precipitate as $PbSO_4$. Therefore, when Ba^{++} and Pb^{++} are in equal concentrations, there is a definite range of concentration for the two ions in which $BaSO_4$ can be precipitated alone. In practice, this range of concentration is difficult to attain for these two ions. The concentrations of $BaSO_4$ and $PbSO_4$ in the solid phase, as well as the concentrations of Ba^{++} and Pb^{++} ions in the solution, are not equal after the solubility products are exceeded. If a ratio is made of the two solubility product expressions for these compounds, it becomes

$$\frac{[Pb^{++}][SO_4^-]}{[Ba^{++}][SO_4^-]} = \frac{1 \times 10^{-8}}{1 \times 10^{-10}} = \frac{[Pb^{++}]}{[Ba^{++}]} = 1 \times 10^2$$

This ratio shows that the solid phase contains $BaSO_4$ and $PbSO_4$ in a concentration ratio of 100 to 1, whereas in the solution the ratio of the concentrations of Ba^{++} to Pb^{++} ions is $1:100$.

Separation of two ions from a solution by a common precipitating reagent is practical only when the equilibrium ratio between the two substances in the solid phase is quite large. To make a fairly clean separation by fractional precipitation requires a ratio as high as one million to one. By way of illustration, the iodide ion may be separated from the chloride ion satisfactorily when the silver ion is used as the precipitating agent. The solubility product expressions, in the form of a ratio, for the two silver halides are

$$\frac{[Ag^+][Cl^-]}{[Ag^+][I^-]} = \frac{1.56 \times 10^{-10}}{1.5 \times 10^{-16}} \quad \text{or} \quad \frac{[Cl^-]}{[I^-]} = 1.04 \times 10^6$$

The equilibrium ratio of the two precipitates, AgCl to AgI, in the solid phase is 1,040,000:1, and such a separation can be regarded as complete.

5·10　Solubility and Particle Size. The solubility of very small crystals of a sparingly soluble salt is greater than that of larger crystals of the same salt. This difference is more pronounced for substances which form hard crystals than for those which produce soft crystals. The effect of particle size upon the solubility of hard crystals may be illustrated by crystals of barium sulfate. Particles of this salt with an average diameter of 0.0018 mm have a solubility of 0.00229 g/liter, whereas particles with an average diameter of 0.0011 mm are soluble to the extent of 0.00415 g/liter. In other words, for the particular dimensions, the smaller crystals of $BaSO_4$ are approximately 80 per cent more soluble than the larger crystals. From experimental data[1] it has been calculated that barium sulfate particles with an average diameter of 0.00004 mm are about 1,000 times more soluble than larger crystals. On the other hand, substances which form soft crystals show little difference in solubility with decrease in particle size. For instance, particles of PbI_2 with an average diameter of 0.00004 mm are only 1.4 times as soluble as large crystals. Other examples of soft crystals with solubilities independent of crystal size are the halides of silver.

For substances which form hard crystals, the decrease in solubility with crystal growth is explained in terms of reduced surface energy. The surface tension which exists at the boundary surfaces of the solid and liquid phases tends to decrease the total surface to the smallest possible area. This reduction in surface area is accomplished by small crystals going into solution, to reprecipitate upon the surface of larger crystals. Usually, when a precipitate is first formed, the solid phase consists of particles of varying sizes. Also, the first precipitated particles are more imperfect in terms of lattice structure. If the precipitate is of the type which may form hard crystals with closely packed ions, the imperfect or irregular crystals will dissolve more readily than perfect crystals. Again, this may be attributed to the larger surface area of the imperfect crystals.

A finely divided precipitate is difficult to filter or centrifuge; conse-

[1] M. L. Dundon and E. Mack, *J. Am. Chem. Soc.*, **45**: 2479 (1923.)

quently, a precipitate of this nature is usually allowed to age before attempting these operations. The aging of a precipitate is customarily called *digestion*, which amounts to letting the precipitate stand until the average particle size has increased sufficiently for easy filtering or centrifuging. Heating increases the rate of digestion because it speeds up the rate of solution of the solid phase for most substances. Stirring also favors crystal growth by keeping the concentration of the solution uniform throughout.

Since the solubility of small crystals is greater than that of large crystals, it follows that the solubility product of a difficulty soluble substance, existing as very small crystals, is a larger value than if the solid phase were composed of particles of larger dimensions. However, solubility product constants are not calculated from the solubility of very small crystals but from ionic concentrations of solutions which have stood in contact with the solid phase during an interval sufficient for complete digestion.

5·11 Hydrogen Sulfide as a Precipitating Agent. The classical scheme of qualitative analysis depends largely upon the use of hydrogen sulfide as a reagent for the precipitation of the majority of the heavy-metal cations. The successful use of this fundamental reagent may be attributed to the general insolubility of most of the metal sulfides, and the convenient control of the sulfide-ion concentration by regulation of the hydronium-ion concentration. This permits the precipitation and separation of two sulfide groups by fractional precipitation. Hydrogen sulfide is a gas of fairly low solubility. A saturated solution at 25°C is approximately 0.1 F, and this small solubility permits a solution of the gas to be treated as a slightly soluble electrolyte with an ion product constant, corresponding in some respects to a solubility product constant.

At 25°C the over-all ionization constant of hydrogen sulfide is 6.8 $\times$ 10^{-23}, and the mathematical expression for this ionization is

$$\frac{[H_3O^+]^2[S^=]}{[H_2S]} = 6.8 \times 10^{-23}$$

Assuming that the solubility of H_2S is fairly constant at ordinary temperatures, the formality of a saturated solution, 0.1 F, can be treated as a constant. When this value is substituted into the above expression, it becomes

$$\frac{[H_3O^+]^2[S^=]}{0.1} = 6.8 \times 10^{-23} \quad \text{or} \quad [H_3O^+]^2[S^=] = 6.8 \times 10^{-24}$$

The last equation can be considered as an ion product expression which applies to saturated solutions of hydrogen sulfide at room temperature. However, the concentrations of the two ions in this expression represent two unknown concentrations which cannot be resolved into terms of each other as is done with solubility product expressions. The explanation of this statement was given in Sec. 4·10. Therefore, the ion product expression cannot be used for computing the formality of both the hydronium and sulfide ions, if both are unknown. On the other hand, if the formal concentration of either of the ions is known, the concentration of the other ion may be obtained from the ion product expression. In view of the fact that the hydronium-ion concentration in this expression is squared, the concentration of the sulfide ion varies inversely as the square of the hydronium-ion concentration.

A solution of hydrogen sulfide is a weak acid, and the concentration of the sulfide ion in a saturated solution is approximately equal to the value of the secondary ionization constant, or 1.2×10^{-15} F. If hydronium ions, in the form of a strong acid, are added to a saturated solution of hydrogen sulfide, the increase of these ions will cause a decrease in the concentration of the sulfide ion. Since the concentration of the hydronium ion is known from the amount of strong acid added, the concentration of the sulfide ion may be calculated from the ion product expression. For example, if sufficient acid is added to produce a 0.01 F solution of hydronium ions, the concentration of sulfide ions is calculated as follows:

$$[H_3O^+]^2[S^=] = 6.8 \times 10^{-24} \quad \text{and} \quad (0.01)^2[S^=] = 6.8 \times 10^{-24}$$

Therefore,

$$[S^=] = \frac{6.8 \times 10^{-24}}{1 \times 10^{-4}} = 6.8 \times 10^{-20}$$

If the acidity of hydrosulfuric acid is neutralized and an excess of base added, such that the concentration of the hydroxide ions in the solution is 0.001 F, the sulfide-ion concentration increases to a comparatively large value. The hydronium-ion concentration can be obtained from the expression for K_w:

$$[H_3O^+][OH^-] = K_w = 1 \times 10^{-14} \quad \text{and} \quad [H_3O^+](0.001) = 1 \times 10^{-14}$$

Therefore,

$$[H_3O^+] = 1 \times 10^{-11}$$

Substituting the hydronium-ion concentration into the ion product for H_2S gives an expression from which the sulfide-ion concentration may be determined.

$$(1 \times 10^{-11})^2[S^=] = 6.8 \times 10^{-24}$$

$$[S^=] = \frac{6.8 \times 10^{-24}}{1 \times 10^{-22}} = 6.8 \times 10^{-2} F = 0.068 \ F$$

5·12 Hydrogen Sulfide as a Reagent for Fractional Precipitation.
Although the sulfides of the heavy-metal cations are fairly insoluble in
water, the range of their solubility product constants is quite wide (see
Table A·9).   To illustrate with two extremes, the $K_{s.p.}$ of MnS is approximately 10^{-15}, and that of HgS is approximately 10^{-54}.   Since the values
of these solubility product constants indicate roughly their comparable
solubilities, it may be said that mercuric sulfide is quite insoluble, and
manganese sulfide is only fairly insoluble.   In the preceding section, calculations were given to illustrate how the concentration of the sulfide ion
can be controlled within certain limits.   In fact, the concentration of the
sulfide ion can be regulated so closely that the solubility product constants of certain sulfides are exceeded and consequently precipitated,
whereas the solubility product constants of other sulfides are not attained,
and therefore, the cations of these sulfides remain in solution.   In the
qualitative scheme of analysis, the sulfides of eight cations are precipitated as Group II in a hydronium-ion concentration of 0.3 F.   After the
precipitated sulfides are removed from the supernatant liquid by filtering
or centrifuging, the remaining solution is made basic with ammonia,
thereby increasing the sulfide-ion concentration to a value that exceeds
the solubility product constants of the five sulfides which occur in Group
III.   The value of the hydronium-ion concentration in this separation is
an arbitrary value, which has been found by experiment to be most satisfactory for analytical purposes.   If a different hydronium-ion concentration were selected, the number of cation sulfides falling into the two
different groups would be changed.   The following problem illustrates
the separation of cations of these two groups of sulfides.   *Calculate the
concentrations of* Cd^{++} *and* Zn^{++} *which will remain unprecipitated by
hydrogen sulfide in a 0.3 F solution of hydronium ions.*   The $K_{s.p.}$ of CdS
is 3.6×10^{-29}, and the $K_{s.p.}$ of ZnS is 1.2×10^{-23}.

The concentration of the sulfide ion in a 0.3 F solution of hydronium
ions may be calculated as

$$[H_3O^+]^2[S^=] = 6.8 \times 10^{-24} \qquad \text{or} \qquad (0.3)^2[S^=] = 6.8 \times 10^{-24}$$

and

$$[S^=] = \frac{6.8 \times 10^{-24}}{0.09} = 7.5 \times 10^{-23} \, F$$

Substituting this value into the solubility product expression for CdS,

$$[Cd^{++}][S^=] = 3.6 \times 10^{-29} \qquad \text{and} \qquad [Cd^{++}](7.5 \times 10^{-23}) = 3.6 \times 10^{-29}$$

Therefore

$$[Cd^{++}] = \frac{3.6 \times 10^{-29}}{7.5 \times 10^{-23}} = 4.8 \times 10^{-7} \, F$$

This concentration value for the unprecipitated cadmium ions indicates that the precipitation of these ions as the sulfide is practically complete.

Substituting the value of the sulfide-ion concentration into the solubility product expression for ZnS,

$$[Zn^{++}][S^=] = 1.2 \times 10^{-23} \quad \text{and} \quad [Zn^{++}](7.5 \times 10^{-23}) = 1.2 \times 10^{-23}$$

Consequently

$$[Zn^{++}] = \frac{1.2 \times 10^{-23}}{7.5 \times 10^{-23}} = 0.16 \, F$$

Since the concentrations of solutions commonly used in qualitative analysis are of the order of 0.1 F, it may be said that Zn^{++} is not precipitated in the above solution. This problem illustrates the fact that, by careful control of hydronium-ion concentration, cadmium ions can be precipitated fairly completely in Cation Group II, leaving zinc ions in solution.

5·13 Solubility of Sulfides in Hydronium-ion Solutions. The solubility of sulfides in nonoxidizing acids varies widely. Some sulfides dissolve readily in very dilute hydrochloric acid, some dissolve in fairly dilute acid, others dissolve only in concentrated acid, and still others are insoluble in concentrated hydrochloric acid. The same principles that were applied in determining whether a sulfide would form in an acid solution may be applied to dissolving the precipitate. If a sulfide is represented by the formula, MS, it may, or may not, dissolve in hydronium ions, and if it does dissolve, the equation for the reaction is

$$MS + 2H_3O^+ \rightleftharpoons M^{++} + H_2S + 2H_2O$$

Whether the sulfide goes into solution depends upon the value of the solubility product constant of the sulfide, the value of the ionization constant of hydrogen sulfide, and the concentration of hydronium ions in the solution. In other words, the sulfide cannot go into solution unless the sulfide ion is removed sufficiently to reduce the concentration of the ions of the salt (the sulfide) below the values which satisfy the solubility product constant. Furthermore, the extent to which sulfide ions are removed depends upon the over-all ionization constant of hydrogen sulfide and the concentration of the hydronium ions in the solutions. Therefore, the solubility of a sulfide may be determined from the solubility product expression for the sulfide and the over-all ionization expression for hydrogen sulfide. These two expressions may be combined into the form of a ratio as

$$\frac{\dfrac{[M^{++}][S^=]}{[H_3O^+]^2[S^=]}}{[H_2S]} = \frac{K_{s.p.}}{6.8 \times 10^{-23}} \tag{1}$$

This ratio combination may be simplified to

$$\frac{[M^{++}][H_2S]}{[H_3O^+]^2} = \frac{K_{s.p.}}{6.8 \times 10^{-23}} \tag{2}$$

The following problem serves to illustrate the use of the foregoing ratio: *Calculate the theoretical formality of hydronium ions necessary to dissolve 0.01 gfw of ZnS in a liter of solution. Perform the same calculations for 0.01 gfw of PbS and 0.01 gfw of CuS.*

The solubility product constant of ZnS is 1.2×10^{-23}. After 0.01 gfw of ZnS dissolves in a liter of solution the concentration of Zn^{++} ions will be 0.01 F, and the concentration of H_2S produced by the reaction will also be 0.01 F. These values are indicated by the equation

$$ZnS \quad + 2H_3O^+ \rightleftharpoons Zn^{++} \quad + \quad H_2S \quad + 2H_2O$$

0.01 gfw   0.01 gfw   0.01 gfw

Substituting these values into the expression [Eq. (2)] for determining the solubility of the sulfide,

$$\frac{(0.01)^2}{[H_3O^+]^2} = \frac{1.2 \times 10^{-23}}{6.8 \times 10^{-23}}$$

$$[H_3O^+]^2 = \frac{(0.01)^2(6.8 \times 10^{-23})}{1.2 \times 10^{-23}} = \frac{6.8 \times 10^{-27}}{1.2 \times 10^{-23}} = 5.7 \times 10^{-4}$$

$$[H_3O^+] = 2.4 \times 10^{-2} \text{ or } 0.024 \; F$$

Therefore, ZnS is readily soluble in dilute HCl.

The solubility product constant for PbS is 3.4×10^{-28}. The concentration of hydronium ions necessary to dissolve 0.01 gfw of PbS in 1 liter of solution is

$$\frac{(0.01)^2}{[H_3O^+]^2} = \frac{3.4 \times 10^{-28}}{6.8 \times 10^{-23}}$$

$$[H_3O^+]^2 = \frac{(0.01)^2(6.8 \times 10^{-23})}{3.4 \times 10^{-28}} = \frac{6.8 \times 10^{-27}}{3.4 \times 10^{-28}} = 20$$

$$[H_3O^+] = 4.3 \; F$$

This value indicates that PbS is insoluble in dilute HCl but will dissolve fairly readily in concentrated HCl. (Concentrated HCl is 12 F.)

The solubility product constant of CuS is 8.5×10^{-45}. The theoretical concentration of hydronium ion necessary to dissolve 0.01 gfw of CuS in 1 liter of solution is

$$\frac{(0.01)^2}{[H_3O^+]^2} = \frac{8.5 \times 10^{-45}}{6.8 \times 10^{-23}}$$

$$[H_3O^+]^2 = \frac{(0.01)^2(6.8 \times 10^{-23})}{8.5 \times 10^{-45}} = \frac{6.8 \times 10^{-27}}{8.5 \times 10^{-45}} = 8 \times 10^{17}$$

$$[H_3O^+] = 9 \times 10^9 \; F$$

Inasmuch as a hydronium-ion concentration of 9×10^9 is impossible to attain, this value indicates that CuS is insoluble in both dilute and concentrated hydrochloric acid.

Exercises

(Consult Table A·9 for physical constants needed.)

1. The solubility of AgI is 2.9×10^{-6} g/liter. Calculate its solubility product constant.

2. A saturated solution of $BaSO_4$ is $1.1 \times 10^{-5} F$ at room temperature. Calculate the solubility product constant of barium sulfate.

3. The solubility of strontium fluoride at room temperature is 2.3×10^{-1} g/liter. Calculate its solubility product constant.

4. The solubility of silver chromate is 0.0014 g/100 ml. What is the solubility product constant of this salt?

5. The solubility of $Fe(OH)_3$ is 4.8×10^{-9} g/100 ml at room temperature. Calculate its solubility product constant.

6. The solubility of $Ca_3(PO_4)_2$ is 0.03 g/liter. Calculate its solubility product constant.

7. The solubility product constant for barium carbonate at 18°C is 8.1×10^{-9}. What is the solubility of $BaCO_3$ in grams per 100 ml at this temperature?

8. The solubility product constant for AgBr at 25°C is 7.7×10^{-13}. What is the solubility of AgBr in grams per liter at 25°C?

9. The solubility product constant of cupric iodate is 1.4×10^{-7} at 25°C. Calculate its formal solubility.

10. The solubility product constant of silver carbonate at 25°C is 6.2×10^{-12}. Calculate the solubility of silver carbonate in grams per liter.

11. The solubility product of $MgNH_4PO_4$ is 2.5×10^{-13}. Calculate its solubility in gram-formula weights per liter.

12. What would be the sulfide-ion formality in a saturated solution of Bi_2S_3, if the $K_{s.p.}$ of this compound is 1.6×10^{-72}?

13. Calculate the solubility in grams per liter of silver chloride in 0.01 F hydrochloric acid. (Assume that no complex ion is formed.)

14. What weight of barium sulfate will remain in solution when 250 ml of 0.10 F barium nitrate solution is added to 600 ml of 0.10 F potassium sulfate solution?

15. A solution is 0.01 F with respect to Mg^{++} ions. What concentration of hydroxide ions in formula weights per liter will be needed to precipitate $Mg(OH)_2$? The $K_{s.p.}$ of $Mg(OH)_2$ is 1.2×10^{-11}.

16. What is the solubility in grams per liter of ferric hydroxide in 0.2 F KOH solution? Ferric hydroxide has a $K_{s.p.}$ of 1.1×10^{-36}.

17. What is the maximum concentration in gram-formula weights per liter of calcium ions in a 0.01 F carbonate solution? The $K_{s.p.}$ of $CaCO_3$ is 8.7×10^{-9}.

18. The $K_{s.p.}$ of PbI_2 is 1.39×10^{-8}. Calculate the solubility in grams per 100 ml in a 0.1 F solution of CaI_2.

19. The solubility of $Mn(OH)_2$ in water is 0.0002 g/100 ml. What is the solubility in gram-formula weights per liter in a solution which is 0.01 F with respect to hydroxide ions?

20. What is the maximum concentration of Mg^{++}, in formula weights per liter, that can exist in a solution which is 0.5 F with respect to NH_4Cl and 0.1 F with respect to NH_3?

21. A 0.6 F solution of NH_3 is made 0.1 F with respect to Mg^{++} ions. What is the minimum concentration of NH_4^+ ions necessary to prevent precipitation of magnesium hydroxide?

22. If 100 ml of a solution containing 0.01 g of Fe^{3+} is mixed with 1 ml of 0.1 F NH_3, calculate whether or not a precipitate will form.

23. If K_2CrO_4 is added to a solution containing 10 g each of Ag^+ and Pb^{++} per liter, which ion will precipitate first?

24. If K_2CrO_4 is added to a solution containing 10 g of Ag^+ and 1 g of Pb^{++} per liter, which ion will precipitate first?

25. To a solution containing 10 g each of Ba^{++} and Pb^{++} per liter, potassium chromate solution is added dropwise. Which ion will precipitate first?

26. What concentration of Br^- is necessary to precipitate AgBr from a saturated solution of AgCl?

27. Hydrogen sulfide is passed into a solution which is 0.1 F with respect to both Pb^{++} and Mn^{++} ions until no more precipitate forms. What concentration of each ion is left in the final solution?

28. A solution is 0.01 F with respect to Co^{++} and 0.3 F in H_3O^+ ions. If the solution is saturated with H_2S, indicate calculations as to whether or not a precipitate of CoS will be formed.

29. The $K_{s.p.}$ of NiS is 1.4×10^{-24}. What must be the concentration of hydronium ions to dissolve 0.01 gfw of NiS in a liter of solution?

30. The $K_{s.p.}$ of PbS is 3.4×10^{-28}. What must be the hydronium-ion concentration to produce a solution which is 0.005 F with respect to Pb^{++} ions?

31. The $K_{s.p.}$ of ZnS is 1.2×10^{-23}. Calculate the formula-weight solubility of ZnS in a solution where the final hydronium-ion concentration is 0.3 F.

32. How many Hg^{++} ions are in a liter of a saturated solution of mercuric sulfide? (Avogadro's number is 6.023×10^{23}.)

33. A solution is 0.01 F with respect to both Mn^{++} and Ac^- ions. What formality of HAc is necessary to prevent the precipitation of MnS when the solution is saturated with H_2S?

34. A solution contains 0.1 F Mn^{++} and 0.05 F HAc. The solution is saturated with H_2S, and some solid NH_4Ac is added. What must be the formality of the Ac^- ion to start the precipitation of MnS?

35. Calculate the solubility of ZnS in 1 F acetic acid.

36. A solution contains H_3O^+ and Pb^{++} ions, and is 0.1 F with respect to each. If the solution is saturated with H_2S, calculate the concentration of Pb^{++} remaining in solution. (Do not neglect the H_3O^+ ion concentration produced by the reaction.)

37. How many grams of Pb^{++} may go into solution when a PbS precipitate is treated with a liter of 0.5 F HCl? (Assume that the concentration of H_3O^+ ions remains unchanged in the dissolving process.)

38. A liter of solution contains 0.01 g of Pb^{++} ions. What must be the pH of the solution to prevent precipitation of PbS when the solution is saturated with H_2S?

CHAPTER 6

HYDROLYSIS

Pure water is 1×10^{-7} F with respect to H_3O^+ and OH^- ions at room temperature. Therefore, water must be regarded as a weak electrolyte. The reaction by which these ions are produced may be expressed as

$$H_2O + H_2O \rightleftharpoons H_3O^+ + OH^-$$

and since the concentration of H_2O in the reaction can be considered a constant, the product of the ions must also be a constant, or

$$[H_3O^+][OH^-] = K_w = 1 \times 10^{-14} \qquad \text{(at 25°C)}$$

The ion product K_w can change only with temperature; consequently, at a given temperature, any shift in the equilibrium point of the reversible reaction does not alter the value of K_w but does result in a change in concentration of the two ions in the equilibrium expression. The ion product expression of water states that the concentration of the hydronium ion is inversely proportional to the concentration of the hydroxide ion.

A shift in the water equilibrium

$$H_2O + H_2O \rightleftharpoons H_3O^+ + OH^-$$

may be accomplished by adding hydronium ions or hydroxide ions in the form of an acid or base, or by adding a substance which will react with water to change the relative concentration of H_3O^+ and OH^- ions in the resulting solution. Such a substance may be an ion produced by the solution of a salt. The reaction between water and the ions of a salt is termed *hydrolysis*.

The term hydrolysis is a carry-over from older definitions of acids and bases. For years, the word hydrolysis has conveyed the meaning of the reverse of neutralization. With the increasing use of the Brønsted acid-base definitions, this word is losing its significance. To review the Brønsted-Lowry definitions, an acid is a proton donor, and a base is a proton acceptor. The fundamental relationship between an acid and a base is indicated by the following three equations:

$$\text{Acid}_1 \rightleftharpoons H^+(\text{proton}) + \text{base}_1$$
$$\text{Base}_2 + H^+(\text{proton}) \rightleftharpoons \text{acid}_2$$

The sum of these two equations is

$$\text{Acid}_1 + \text{base}_2 \rightleftharpoons \text{acid}_2 + \text{base}_1$$

To use a specific example, acetic acid reacts with sodium hydroxide solution to give water and acetate ions according to the following equation:

$$\underset{\text{acid}_1}{HC_2H_3O_2} + \underset{\text{base}_2}{OH^-} \rightleftharpoons \underset{\text{acid}_2}{HOH} + \underset{\text{base}_1}{C_2H_3O_2^-}$$

This equation represents a reversible reaction which is an acid-base reaction to the right, and also an acid-base reaction in the reverse direction. Accordingly, the reaction of the acetate ion with water to produce acetic acid molecules and hydroxide ions is an acid-base reaction. Therefore, it is apparent that if the word hydrolysis is to be used at all, it must signify an acid-base reaction. Hydrolytic reactions are largely confined to ions which may act as proton donors or proton acceptors.

6·1 Hydrolysis of Ions. Chapter 5 is devoted to a discussion of the reactions of weakly electrovalent molecules with water to produce reversible acid-base equilibria. The present chapter is restricted to an interpretation of the reversible reactions resulting from the solution of strongly electrovalent compounds, other than compounds commonly referred to as strong acids and bases, in water. These strong electrolytes, called *salts*, are completely ionized in water solution, producing positively charged metal ions called *cations* and negatively charged ions called *anions*. To simplify the discussion of hydrolysis, salts are divided into four classes with respect to their reactions with water. These four classes are:

1. *Salts whose ions are aprotic.* These are ions, cations or anions, which apparently do not gain or lose protons, and, therefore, do not affect the equilibrium concentration of H_3O^+ and OH^- in the solvent, water. Examples of such salts are $NaCl$ and KNO_3.

2. *Salts which produce anions that are proton acceptors.* Such anions, according to Brønsted interpretations, are defined as bases. In consequence of protons being accepted by the anions, there is a decrease in the hydronium-ion concentration of the solution to make it basic. Examples of such salts are $NaAc$, KCN, Na_2CO_3, and Na_2S.

3. *Salts which produce cations that are proton donors.* In accordance with Brønsted definitions, such cations may be considered as acids. These cations are of two types: unhydrated cations as exemplified by the ammonium ion, and hydrated cations such as the aluminum and ferric ions.

4. *Salts which produce cations that are acids, and anions that are bases.* Since the cation is a proton donor and the anion is a proton acceptor, it is obvious that a solution of a salt of this type will be acidic, neutral, or

basic, depending upon the relative strength of the cation as an acid and the anion as a base.   Examples of this type of salt are ammonium acetate and ammonium cyanide.

6·2   Hydrolysis Constant.   The reaction of an ion with water is comparable to an ionization reaction of a weak electrolyte.   Both types of reactions are reversible, and as a general rule, but with some exceptions, the extent of such reactions is comparatively small.   Therefore, the law of chemical equilibrium may be applied to reactions involving the hydrolysis of ions in a manner similar to the reactions for the ionization of weak electrolytes.   The equilibrium constants for hydrolytic reactions are customarily called *hydrolysis constants*, but, in terms of the Brønsted acid-base concept, such constants are equivalent to ionization constants of weak electrolytes.   However, since the term hydrolysis constant is so deeply entrenched in the classical expositions of solution chemistry, this term is retained in the following discussion.   The student should recognize that there is no fundamental difference between the meaning of K_a for acetic acid and K_h for the acetate ion.   To illustrate the use of K_h for the hydrolysis of an ion, assume that a salt, designated as MA, reacts with water to produce a basic solution.   This indicates that the anion is a base, and the hydrolytic reaction may be written in the form of an equation as

$$A^- + HOH \rightleftharpoons HA + OH^-$$

Since the concentration of water is practically constant for dilute solutions, the equilibrium expression for the hydrolysis reaction is

$$\frac{[HA][OH^-]}{[A^-]} = K_h$$

where K_h is the hydrolysis constant.   This example represents a simplified case of hydrolysis, which can better be understood by considering the four possible types or reactions between salts and water.

6·3   Hydrolysis of Salts Whose Ions Are Aprotic.   Salts enter solution as ions because of electrostatic forces acting between the electrically charged ions and the electrostatic dipoles of the water molecules, or because of chemical reaction between the ions and water molecules to produce hydrated ions.   The difference between the two types of solubilities, physical and chemical, is not always pronounced.   In the solution of a salt which produces aprotic ions, the extent of hydration must be slight since the presence of these ions does not produce any measurable change in the pH of the resulting solution.   Therefore, in a solution of this type of salt, the ions from the salt are simply spectator ions to the extent that they do not affect the ion product of water.   A solution of sodium chloride in water may be represented in the form of an equation as

$$Na^+ + Cl^- + 2H_2O \rightleftharpoons Na^+ + Cl^- + H_3O^+ + OH^-$$

and if the spectator ions are canceled from the equation, there remains the water equilibrium

$$2H_2O \rightleftharpoons H_3O^+ + OH^-$$

No apparent hydrolysis takes place between the ions of a salt of this type and water; consequently, no hydrolysis equilibrium can be set up for the solution of such a salt, other than the water equilibrium.

6·4 Hydrolysis of Anions That Are Bases. *Hydrolysis of a Monoprotic Anion.* Examples of salts that produce monoprotic anions are sodium acetate and potassium cyanide. These salts dissolve in water to give solutions which are strongly basic. Since the sodium and potassium ions neither gain nor lose protons and are therefore aprotic, it must be concluded that the acetate and cyanide ions are bases. The reaction of the acetate ion, acting as a base, is represented in the following equation:

$$C_2H_3O_2^- + HOH \rightleftharpoons HC_2H_3O_2 + OH^-$$

The equilibrium expression for this reaction is

$$\frac{[HC_2H_3O_2][OH^-]}{[C_2H_3O_2^-][HOH]} = K_e \tag{1}$$

where K_e is the equilibrium constant. In dilute solutions the concentration of water may be considered as constant, and the equation becomes

$$\frac{[HC_2H_3O_2][OH^-]}{[C_2H_3O_2^-]} = K_h \tag{2}$$

where K_h is the hydrolysis constant. If the extent of hydrolysis is small, this constant is similar to the equilibrium constant of a weak acid or weak base, K_a or K_b.

Additional significance for Eq. (2) may be obtained by substituting equivalent values for certain terms in the expression. For example,

$$[H_3O^+][OH^-] = K_w$$

or

$$[OH^-] = \frac{K_w}{[H_3O^+]} \tag{3}$$

and substituting expression (3) into expression (2),

$$\frac{[HC_2H_3O_2]K_w}{[C_2H_3O_2^-][H_3O^+]} = K_h \tag{4}$$

Since the reciprocal of the ionization constant for acetic acid is

$$\frac{[HC_2H_3O_2]}{[C_2H_3O_2^-][H_3O^+]} = \frac{1}{K_a} \tag{5}$$

therefore, upon substituting $1/K_a$ into Eq. (4), the following expression is obtained:

$$\frac{K_w}{K_a} = K_h \tag{6}$$

This equation states that the extent of hydrolysis is a ratio between the ion product of water and the ionization constant of the weak acid, which is acetic acid in this particular example. If the ratio K_w/K_a is substituted into Eq. (2), it becomes

$$\frac{[HC_2H_3O_2][OH^-]}{[C_2H_3O_2^-]} = \frac{K_w}{K_a} \tag{7}$$

In the original equation for the reaction of the salt with water

$$C_2H_3O_2^- + HOH \rightleftharpoons HC_2H_3O_2 + OH^-$$

there is one OH^- ion produced for each $HC_2H_3O_2$ molecule; therefore, the concentration of $[HC_2H_3O_2] = [OH^-]$, and Eq. (7) may be converted to

$$\frac{[OH^-]^2}{[C_2H_3O_2^-]} = \frac{K_w}{K_a} \tag{8}$$

Since the majority of salts may be assumed to be completely ionized in solution, the concentration of the salt and the concentration of the anion, $C_2H_3O_2^-$, are approximately the same.   Equation (8) also assumes that the extent of hydrolysis is so slight that the decrease in concentration of the acetate ion, due to hydrolysis, can be ignored.   Therefore, the value of the acetate ion can be denoted as C, where C is equal to the concentration of the salt in gram-formula weights per liter, and the equation may be written

$$\frac{[OH^-]^2}{C} = \frac{K_w}{K_a} \qquad \text{or} \qquad [OH^-] = \sqrt{\frac{K_w C}{K_a}} \tag{9}$$

The $[OH^-]$ may be converted to $[H_3O^+]$, since $[OH^-] = K_w/[H_3O^+]$

$$\frac{K_w}{[H_3O^+]} = \sqrt{\frac{K_w C}{K_a}} \qquad \text{or} \qquad [H_3O^+] = \sqrt{\frac{K_w K_a}{C}} \tag{10}$$

Equation (10) becomes useful in calculating the hydronium-ion concentration and pH of an aqueous solution of a salt that produces an anion which reacts as a base.   Equation (7) may be used to calculate the degree or percentage of hydrolysis.   To illustrate with a specific example, *suppose 0.2 gfw of sodium acetate is dissolved in sufficient water to produce a liter of solution.   Calculate the hydronium-ion concentration and pH of the solution.   Also compute the degree of hydrolysis of the acetate ion in this concentration.* (Given that K_a for HAc is 1.75×10^{-5} and K_w for water is 1×10^{-14}.)

$$[H_3O^+] = \sqrt{\frac{K_w K_a}{C}} = \sqrt{\frac{(1 \times 10^{-14})(1.75 \times 10^{-5})}{0.2}}$$

$$[H_3O^+] = \sqrt{\frac{1.75 \times 10^{-19}}{0.2}} = \sqrt{88 \times 10^{-20}} = 9.4 \times 10^{-10}$$

$$\text{pH} = -\log (9.4 \times 10^{-10}) = 10.00 - .97 = 9.03$$

The degree of hydrolysis may be calculated from Eq. (7)

$$\frac{[HC_2H_3O_2][OH^-]}{[C_2H_3O_2^-]} = \frac{K_w}{K_a} = K_h$$

which is the equilibrium expression for the equation representing the hydrolysis reaction

$$C_2H_3O_2^- + HOH \rightleftharpoons HC_2H_3O_2 + OH^-$$
$$0.2 - X \qquad\qquad X \qquad X$$

If

$$\text{Concentration of } [HC_2H_3O_2] = [OH^-] = X$$

and

$$\text{Concentration of } [C_2H_3O_2^-] = 0.2 - X$$

then

$$\frac{X^2}{0.2 - X} = \frac{1 \times 10^{-14}}{1.75 \times 10^{-5}}$$

In comparison with 0.2, the value of X in the denominator is small and may be discarded; therefore,

$$\frac{X^2}{0.2} = \frac{1 \times 10^{-14}}{1.75 \times 10^{-5}} \qquad \text{or} \qquad X = \sqrt{\frac{2 \times 10^{-15}}{1.75 \times 10^{-5}}}$$

$$X = 1.07 \times 10^{-5} \text{ gfw/liter} = [HC_2H_3O_2] = [OH^-]$$

$$\text{Degree of hydrolysis} = \frac{1.07 \times 10^{-5}}{0.2} = 5.3 \times 10^{-5}$$

$$\text{Per cent of hydrolysis} = (5.3 \times 10^{-5})100 = 0.0053 \text{ per cent}$$

Hydrolysis of a Diprotic Anion. A salt of this type produces an anion in solution, which may theoretically accept two protons. For example, sodium carbonate gives carbonate ions in solution which may react with water in two steps:

$$CO_3^= + HOH \rightleftharpoons HCO_3^- + OH^- \tag{11}$$
$$HCO_3^- + HOH \rightleftharpoons H_2CO_3 + OH^- \tag{12}$$

The extent to which these two reactions take place depends upon the relative values of the ionization constants of the acids produced, compared with the ion product of water, as evidenced by Eq. (6), where $K_h = K_w/K_a$. In the case of the carbonate ion, reaction (11) takes place to a much greater extent than reaction (12), since the ionization constant of HCO_3^-, 5.6×10^{-11}, is much smaller than the ionization constant for H_2CO_3, 4.3×10^{-7}. Therefore, to calculate the extent of hydrolysis of the normal salt, Na_2CO_3, only Eq. (11) is used. Equation (12) may be used for determining the degree of hydrolysis of the acid salt, sodium bicarbonate.

The equilibrium expression for the hydrolysis of sodium carbonate is

$$\frac{[HCO_3^-][OH^-]}{[CO_3^=]} = \frac{K_w}{K_a} = K_h$$

where K_a is the ionization constant of the HCO_3^- ion. Accordingly, the equation for determining the extent of hydrolysis of sodium carbonate is identical with expression (10), or

$$[H_3O^+] = \sqrt{\frac{K_w K_a}{C}}$$

The following example illustrates the essential calculations involved in determining the extent of hydrolysis of a diprotic anion: *What is the* pH *of a 0.2 F solution of sodium carbonate and the per cent hydrolysis, if the ionization constant of the* HCO_3^- *ion is* 5.6×10^{-11}?

$$[H_3O^+] = \sqrt{\frac{(1 \times 10^{-14})(5.6 \times 10^{-11})}{0.2}} = \sqrt{2.8 \times 10^{-24}}$$
$$[H_3O^+] = 1.7 \times 10^{-12}$$
$$pH = -\log [H_3O^+] = (12 - .22) = 11.78$$

To calculate the degree of hydrolysis,

$$\frac{[HCO_3^-][OH^-]}{[CO_3^=]} = \frac{1 \times 10^{-14}}{5.6 \times 10^{-11}} = K_h$$

where $[HCO_3^-] = [OH^-] = X$
$[CO_3^=] = 0.2 - X$

Since X is small in comparison to 0.2, it may be discarded, and the equation becomes

$$\frac{X^2}{0.2} = \frac{1 \times 10^{-14}}{5.6 \times 10^{-11}} \quad \text{and} \quad X^2 = \frac{2 \times 10^{-15}}{5.6 \times 10^{-11}} = 3.6 \times 10^{-5}$$
$$X = 6 \times 10^{-3}$$
$$\text{Per cent of hydrolysis} = \frac{(6 \times 10^{-3})100}{0.2} = 3 \text{ per cent}$$

The sulfide ion from a salt such as Na_2S is hydrolyzed to a greater extent than either the acetate ion or the carbonate ion. Therefore, calculations for the hydrolysis of the sulfide ion are more rigorous than for the other ions. An example of this hydrolysis is: *What is the degree of hydrolysis of a 0.1 F solution of sodium sulfide?*

The equation for the hydrolysis of the sulfide ion is

$$S^= + HOH \rightleftharpoons HS^- + OH^-$$

The hydrolysis of the HS^- ion

$$HS^- + HOH \rightleftharpoons H_2S + OH^-$$

takes place to such a small extent in comparison with the first hydrolysis reaction that it can be ignored. Therefore, the equilibrium expression for the hydrolysis of the sulfide ion is

$$\frac{[HS^-][OH^-]}{[S^=]} = K_h = \frac{K_w}{K_a}$$

where K_a is the ionization constant of the HS^- ion, which is 1.2×10^{-15}.

The concentration of $[HS^-] = [OH^-] = X$, and the concentration of $[S^=] = 0.1 - X$. Therefore, the equation becomes

$$\frac{X^2}{0.1 - X} = \frac{1 \times 10^{-14}}{1.2 \times 10^{-15}} \quad \text{and} \quad \frac{X^2}{0.1 - X} = 8.3$$

Since the value of K_h (8.3) is large, X in the denominator is large in comparison to 0.1 F and cannot be discarded.

$$X^2 = 0.83 - 8.3X \quad \text{or} \quad X^2 + 8.3X - 0.83 = 0$$

and

$$X = 0.099 \text{ gfw/liter} = [HS^-] = [OH^-]$$

Per cent of hydrolysis $= \dfrac{0.099 \times 100}{0.1} = 99$ per cent

6·5 Hydrolysis of Cations That Are Acids. *Hydrolysis of Unhydrated Cations.* There are a number of unhydrated ions belonging to the ammonium-ion family, such as the methyl ammonium ion, the phenyl ammonium ion, and the dimethyl ammonium ion, which react with water to give acid solutions. These ions are proton donors and are, therefore, acids. An aqueous solution of ammonium chloride is used as an example. Salts of the ammonium chloride type react with water in the following manner:

$$NH_4^+ + HOH \rightleftharpoons NH_3 + H_3O^+ \tag{13}$$

Since the concentration of water may be considered as a constant, the equilibrium expression for the reaction is

$$\frac{[NH_3][H_3O^+]}{[NH_4^+]} = K_h \tag{14}$$

But $[H_3O^+] = K_w/[OH^-]$, and substituting this ratio into Eq. (14) produces

$$\frac{[NH_3]K_w}{[NH_4^+][OH^-]} = K_h \tag{15}$$

The reciprocal of the ionization constant expression for ammonia in water is

$$\frac{[NH_3]}{[NH_4^+][OH^-]} = \frac{1}{K_b}$$

therefore, substituting $1/K_b$ into Eq. (15) reduces it to

$$\frac{K_w}{K_b} = K_h \tag{16}$$

The original equilibrium expression (14) may now be written as

$$\frac{[NH_3][H_3O^+]}{[NH_4^+]} = \frac{K_w}{K_b} \tag{17}$$

In the chemical reaction (13), one H_3O^+ ion is produced for each NH_3 molecule; therefore, $[H_3O^+] = [NH_3]$, and

$$\frac{[H_3O^+]^2}{[NH_4^+]} = \frac{K_w}{K_b} \tag{18}$$

Since the salt is completely ionized, $C - [H_3O^+]$ does not differ appreciably from C. Consequently, Eq. (18) may be written as

$$\frac{[H_3O^+]^2}{C} = \frac{K_w}{K_b} \tag{19}$$

and the latter equation may be converted into the form

$$[H_3O^+] = \sqrt{\frac{K_w}{K_b} C} \tag{20}$$

The following is an illustrative problem of a salt of this type: *What is the K_b for an aqueous solution of ammonia, if 0.1 F ammonium chloride has a pH of 5.13?* $(K_w = 1 \times 10^{-14}.)$

$$pH = -\log[H_3O^+] \quad \text{or} \quad 5.13 = -\log[H_3O^+]$$
and
$$[H_3O^+] = 7.5 \times 10^{-6} F$$

Substituting the known values into Eq. (18),

$$\frac{(7.5 \times 10^{-6})^2}{0.1} = \frac{1 \times 10^{-14}}{K_b}$$

Solving,

$$K_b = 1.8 \times 10^{-5}$$

Hydrolysis of Hydrated Cations. Certain salts produce hydrated cations in aqueous solution which are proton donors. In fact, most metal ions in water solution are hydrated. The extent of hydration and the strength of the bonds holding the water molecules to the cation depend largely upon the diameter and electronic structure of the cation. These aspects of hydration are discussed more completely in Chap. 7. If it is assumed that an ion of this type has a definite number of water molecules coordinated around the central cation, the ion as a whole may act as a proton donor, in which the proton splits away from one of the water molecules. As an example, the hydrated aluminum ion may react with water in the following fashion:

$$Al(H_2O)_6{}^{3+} + HOH \rightleftharpoons Al(H_2O)_5(OH)^{++} + H_3O^+ \tag{21}$$

The ion, $Al(H_2O)_5(OH)^{++}$, may produce other protons by stepwise reactions, but the extent of these reactions is small in comparison with the first ionization reaction.

The equilibrium expression for the above reaction (21), considering the concentration of water as constant, is

$$\frac{[Al(H_2O)_5(OH)^{++}][H_3O^+]}{[Al(H_2O)_6{}^{3+}]} = K_h = \frac{K_w}{K_b} \tag{22}$$

In the case of hydrated ions the value of the hydrolysis constant K_h is also the ionization constant K_a of the ion as an acid. In other words, the ionization reaction of the hydrated ion to produce hydronium ions is the same as the hydrolysis of the ion. The value for K_a or K_h of the hydrated aluminum ion is 1.4×10^{-5} at room temperature. In the Brønsted acid-base terminology the K_h of any salt is also the ionization constant of the salt as an acid or base. Thus, K_h can always be considered as equivalent to a K_a or K_b value.

A typical problem illustrating the effect upon the acidity of a solution by certain hydrated cations is as follows: *If the hydrated aluminum ion is considered as a monoprotic acid, what is the* pH *of a solution which is* 0.1 *F with respect to aluminum chloride?* ($K_h = K_a = 1.4 \times 10^{-5}$.)

If

$$[H_3O^+] = [Al(H_2O)_5(OH)^{++}] = X \quad \text{and} \quad [Al(H_2O)_6{}^{3+}] = 0.1 - X$$

then

$$\frac{[Al(H_2O)_5(OH)^{++}][H_3O^+]}{[Al(H_2O)_6{}^{3+}]} = K_h = \frac{K_w}{K_b}$$

or

$$\frac{X^2}{0.1 - X} = 1.4 \times 10^{-5}$$

Since the X in the denominator is small in comparison with 0.1 it may be discarded and

$$\frac{X^2}{0.1} = 1.4 \times 10^{-5} \quad \text{or} \quad X = \sqrt{1.4 \times 10^{-6}}$$

$$X = 1.2 \times 10^{-3} F = [H_3O^+]$$
$$pH = - \log [H_3O^+] = (3 - .08) = 2.92$$

6·6   Hydrolysis of Salts Whose Cations Are Acids and Whose Anions Are Bases.   Certain salts produce in aqueous solutions cations which are acids and anions which are bases.   Typical examples are ammonium cyanide and ammonium acetate.   The pH of the resulting solution is determined by the relative extent of the hydrolysis reactions of the two ions composing the salt.   When ammonium acetate is dissolved in water, the following reversible reactions are present in the solution:

$$NH_4^+ + HOH \rightleftharpoons NH_3 + H_3O^+$$
$$C_2H_3O_2^- + HOH \rightleftharpoons HC_2H_3O_2 + OH^-$$
$$2H_2O \rightleftharpoons OH^- + H_3O^+$$

The equilibrium expression for the first equation is the same as (14), or

$$\frac{[NH_3][H_3O^+]}{[NH_4^+]} = K_h = \frac{K_w}{K_b}$$

and the equilibrium expression for the second equation is the same as (7), which is

$$\frac{[HC_2H_3O_2][OH^-]}{[C_2H_3O_2^-]} = K_h = \frac{K_w}{K_a}$$

and the third equation is the ion product of water, or

$$[H_3O^+][OH^-] = K_w$$

The extent of hydrolysis of a salt of this type depends upon the relative strength of the acid and base, the NH_4^+ and $C_2H_3O_2^-$ ions, which in turn is relative to the removal of H_3O^+ and OH^- ions which constitute the ion product of water, K_w.   This relation is shown by dividing the ion product of water by the other two expressions:

$$\frac{[H_3O^+][OH^-]}{\dfrac{[NH_3][H_3O^+]}{[NH_4^+]} \times \dfrac{[HC_2H_3O_2][OH^-]}{[C_2H_3O_2^-]}} = \frac{K_w}{\dfrac{K_w}{K_b} \times \dfrac{K_w}{K_a}}$$

and upon simplifying,

$$\frac{[NH_3][HC_2H_3O_2]}{[NH_4^+][C_2H_3O_2^-]} = \frac{K_w}{K_b K_a} = K_h \tag{23}$$

If the ionization constants K_a and K_b are of approximately the same magnitude and if the salt is completely ionized, the following assumptions may be made:

$$[NH_3] = [HC_2H_3O_2] \qquad \text{and} \qquad [NH_4^+] = [C_2H_3O_2^-] = C$$

With these assumptions, the equation may be written as

$$\frac{[HC_2H_3O_2]^2}{C^2} = \frac{K_w}{K_a K_b} \tag{24}$$

or

$$[HC_2H_3O_2] = C\sqrt{\frac{K_w}{K_a K_b}} \tag{25}$$

The following relation comes from the expression for the ionization constant of acetic acid:

$$[HC_2H_3O_2] = \frac{[H_3O^+][C_2H_3O_2^-]}{K_a}$$

Upon substituting equivalent values into Eq. (25), it becomes

$$\frac{[H_3O^+][C_2H_3O_2^-]}{K_a} = C\sqrt{\frac{K_w}{K_a K_b}} \tag{26}$$

The concentration C may be substituted for $[C_2H_3O_2^-]$, changing Eq. (26) to

$$\frac{[H_3O^+] \times C}{K_a} = C\sqrt{\frac{K_w}{K_a K_b}} \tag{27}$$

and Eq. (27) may be simplified to

$$[H_3O^+] = \sqrt{\frac{K_w K_a}{K_b}} \tag{28}$$

Equation (28) is unique in that the factor of concentration does not appear in it. Therefore, from this equation, it may be concluded that the pH of a solution containing a salt of this type is independent of the concentration of the salt. A problem involving such a solution is given in the following example: *What is the* pH *of a solution which is 0.1 F in respect to* NH_4CN? *Calculate the per cent hydrolysis of the* NH_4CN. (K_b for NH_3 is 1.8×10^{-5}, K_a for HCN is 7.2×10^{-10}, and K_w is 1×10^{-14}.)

$$[H_3O^+] = \sqrt{\frac{K_wK_a}{K_b}} = \sqrt{\frac{(1 \times 10^{-14})(7.2 \times 10^{-10})}{1.8 \times 10^{-5}}}$$

$$[H_3O^+] = 6.3 \times 10^{-10}$$

$$pH = -\log (6.3 \times 10^{-10}) = (10 - .8) = 9.2$$

Equation (23) is the equilibrium expression for the hydrolysis of this type of salt. The equilibrium expression for the hydrolysis of ammonium cyanide is

$$\frac{[NH_3][HCN]}{[NH_4^+][CN^-]} = \frac{K_w}{K_aK_b} = K_h$$

Assuming that

$$\text{Concentration of } [NH_3] = [HCN] = X$$

then

$$\text{Concentration of } [NH_4^+] = 0.1 - X$$

and

$$\text{Concentration of } [CN^-] = 0.1 - X$$

Substituting these known values into the above equation,

$$\frac{X^2}{(0.1 - X)^2} = \frac{1 \times 10^{-14}}{(1.8 \times 10^{-5})(7.2 \times 10^{-10})}$$

The X in the denominator is too large to be discarded because the value of K_h is large, as indicated by the following equation:

$$\frac{X^2}{(0.1 - X)^2} = 0.77$$

where 0.77 is the value of K_h. Extracting the square root of both sides of this equation produces

$$\frac{X}{0.1 - X} = 0.88$$

Therefore,

$$1.88X = 0.088 \quad \text{and} \quad X = \frac{0.088}{1.88} = 0.047 \ F$$

which is the formality of NH_3 and HCN produced by the hydrolysis of ammonium cyanide.

$$\text{Per cent hydrolysis} = \frac{0.047}{0.1} \times 100 = 47 \text{ per cent}$$

Exercises

(Consult the Appendix for physical constants needed.)

1. Derive the hydrolysis constant of potassium nitrite.

2. Calculate the concentration of hydroxide ions in a 0.1 F solution of potassium nitrite.

3. Calculate the pH of a 2 F solution of sodium formate.

4. What are the pH value and percentage hydrolysis at 25°C in a 0.1 F solution of sodium cyanide?

5. What concentration of potassium acetate has a pH of 8.9?

6. A certain weak acid, designated as HA, forms a sodium salt, NaA. If a 0.1 F solution of NaA has a pH of 9.2, calculate the ionization constant of HA.

7. How many gram-formula weights per liter of potassium acetate are necessary to produce a solution with a hydroxide-ion concentration of $1 \times 10^{-4} F$?

8. How many grams of sodium cyanide must be added to 1 liter of water to give a hydroxide-ion concentration equivalent to a 0.05 F NH_3 solution?

9. Derive the hydrolysis constant of methyl ammonium chloride. (The formula of this salt is CH_3NH_3Cl.)

10. Ammonium chloride in 0.001 F solution is 0.076 per cent hydrolyzed. Calculate the ionization constant of NH_3 from these values.

11. Calculate the pH of a 1 F solution of methyl ammonium chloride.

12. Calculate the grams of ammonium nitrate which must be added to a liter of aqueous solution to produce a pH of 5.4.

13. Calculate the percentage hydrolysis and pH of a 0.1 F solution of NH_4Cl.

14. How many grams of NH_4Cl must be added to 1 liter of aqueous solution to give the same pH as a saturated solution of hydrogen sulfide?

15. Calculate the pH and percentage hydrolysis of a 0.1 F solution of $NaHCO_3$.

16. Calculate the percentage hydrolysis and pH of a 0.1 F solution of Na_2CO_3.

17. Calculate the percentage hydrolysis and pH of a 0.1 F solution of NaH_2PO_4.

18. Calculate the concentration of an aqueous solution of Na_2SO_3 which is 0.020 per cent hydrolyzed.

19. What is the pH of a 0.1 F solution of ferric chloride? (K for the primary hydrolysis is 6×10^{-3}.)

20. Calculate the percentage hydrolysis of a 0.1 F solution of aluminum chloride. (K for the primary hydrolysis is 1.4×10^{-5}.)

21. What is the concentration of hydronium ions in a 0.5 F solution of zinc chloride? (K for the primary hydrolysis is 2.5×10^{-10}.)

22. Derive the hydrolysis constant of ammonium borate.

23. Calculate the percentage hydrolysis and pH of a 0.1 F solution of ammonium borate.

24. Calculate the pH of a 0.01 F solution of ammonium benzoate.

25. Calculate the concentration of hydroxide ions in a 0.2 F solution of ammonium cyanide.

CHAPTER 7

COMPLEX IONS

The symbol for the hydronium ion is generally accepted as H_3O^+. This indicates that a proton, H^+, has combined with one molecule of water to form the hydrated ion, $H \cdot H_2O^+$. There is considerable experimental evidence to justify the use of this formula. Certainly, the idea of a bare proton existing in a water solution is untenable. The same may be said concerning the possibility for the existence of other unhydrated ions in solution. Unquestionably, all ions that exist in water solution are hydrated to some degree. In fact, the solubility of salts in water is due, in part, to the formation of hydrated ions. Therefore, the use of symbols indicating simple ions as Li^+, Mg^{++}, Al^{3+}, Cl^-, and $SO_4^=$ is not justified upon the basis of the true composition of these ions. On the other hand, the use of chemical symbols, formulas, and equations is essentially a "shorthand" method for expressing elements, ions, compounds, and reactions. The symbol H^+ could indicate the hydrated proton, and Cr^{3+} might indicate the hydrated chromic ion. Instead of writing a symbol such as $Cr(H_2O)_6^{3+}$ for the hydrated chromic ion, it might be easier to conceive of the simpler symbol Cr^{3+} as indicating the hydrated ion. The use of hydrated ions adds to the complexity of equation writing and may not be entirely plausible until the determination of the extent of hydration has passed the experimental stage.

7·1 Introduction. There are certain theoretical aspects of solution chemistry that can best be presented by the use of hydrated forms of those ions involved. Beyond question, the presence of hydrated ions may affect the acidity of a solution. Likewise, certain oxidation-reduction reactions occurring in basic solutions can be indicated in equation form more rationally by means of hydrated ions.

It is logical that hydrated ions should be one of the topics discussed under the general heading of Complex Ions. The term *complex ions* has been a catchall for so many meanings that it seems worthwhile to define or at least restrict its usage. Since the existence of a simple ion as an entity in a water solution is highly improbable, all ions might conceivably be classed as complex ions. For the purpose of simplification in the present discussion, a complex ion will be defined as an ion resulting from the union of a simple ion with an atom, molecule, or another ion, which is fairly stable in water solution.

Such ions as $SO_4^=$, ClO_3^-, and NO_3^- will be regarded as simple ions, although in a broad sense they may be regarded as complex ions. Lattice complexes consisting of certain double salts such as $FeSO_4 \cdot (NH_4)_2 \cdot SO_4 \cdot 6H_2O$ and alums such as $KAl(SO_4)_2 \cdot 12H_2O$ are complex substances only in the solid state, since they break down in water solution into simpler substances.

7·2 Werner's Theory of Coordination Compounds. The theory of valence developed during the nineteenth century provided, for that period, a satisfactory explanation for the formation and properties of most organic compounds and the simple salts of the metals. But this early, nonelectronic theory of valence offered no adequate explanation for the union of neutral molecules with ions to form such compounds as $CuSO_4 \cdot 5H_2O$ and $CoCl_3 \cdot 6NH_3$. To account for the entrance of neutral molecules into chemical reactions, Albert Werner introduced in 1893 his concept of auxiliary valence. This concept, generally known as Werner's coordination theory, was stated as follows:

Even when, to judge by the valence number, the combining power of certain atoms is exhausted, they still possess in most cases the power of participating further in the construction of complex molecules with the formation of very definite atomic linkages. The possibility of this action is to be traced back to the fact that, besides the affinity bonds designated as principal valencies, still other bonds on the atoms, called auxiliary valences, may be called into action.

According to Werner, the combining power of an atom is divided into two spheres of attraction: the inner or coordinate sphere, and the outer or ionization sphere. Neutral molecules or oppositely charged ions are coordinated around a central ion in the inner sphere. The number of such groups which may be arranged around the central ion is the coordination number of that ion. He recognized that this arrangement of molecules or ions around the central ion was such as to produce a symmetrical spatial grouping. The coordination numbers which permit spatial symmetry are 2, 3, 4, 6, and 8, of which the values 4 and 6 are most common. On the basis of his auxiliary valence theory, Werner assigned to $CoCl_3 \cdot 6NH_3$ the structural formula

$$\left[\begin{array}{ccc} & NH_3 & \\ NH_3 & | & NH_3 \\ & \diagdown \; | \; \diagup & \\ & Co & \\ & \diagup \; | \; \diagdown & \\ NH_3 & | & NH_3 \\ & NH_3 & \end{array} \right] Cl_3$$

The addition of six molecules of ammonia takes place by means of auxiliary valencies. In this complex union, the chemical characteristics not only of the ammonia but also of the cobalt ion are lost. On the other hand, the chloride ions retain their typical physical and chemical properties.

Werner's theory was satisfactory at the time it was propounded, when the theory of the electronic structure of matter was unknown. To make the Werner theory compatible with the electronic concept of valence, Sidgwick introduced the idea of a dative bond, sometimes called the *coordinate bond*. According to Sidgwick, the auxiliary valence conceived by Werner is a special form of a covalent bond, in which the paired electrons of the bond are furnished by one and only one of the atoms concerned. The atom furnishing the electrons is called the donor, and the ion accepting the electrons is called the acceptor. Once the bond is formed it is not different from a covalent bond—the only difference is the mode of formation. For example, the cobaltic ammonia complex is formed by the cobaltic ion accepting 12 electrons from six ammonia molecules. (Each arrow in the structural formula indicates the transfer of two electrons.)

$$\left[\begin{array}{ccc} & NH_3 & \\ H_3N & \downarrow & NH_3 \\ & \searrow \downarrow \swarrow & \\ & Co & \\ & \nearrow \uparrow \nwarrow & \\ H_3N & \uparrow & NH_3 \\ & NH_3 & \end{array} \right]^{3+}$$

Not only may neutral molecules be coordinated around a central ion, but ions may also be coordinated in a like manner. Therefore, the total electrovalent charge on the complex varies with the number of charged ions and neutral molecules within the coordination sphere. Coordinated molecules may be partially or completely replaced by ions, resulting in a change in the electrovalence of the complex ion. The ammines of quadrivalent platinum illustrate these variable combinations. Quadrivalent platinum has a coordination number of 6, and the ammine groups may be replaced by chloride ions to change the valence and nature of the complex in successive steps as indicated in Table 7·1.

TABLE 7·1 SOME COMPLEX IONS CONTAINING PLATINUM

Formula	Cation	Anion
$[Pt(NH_3)_6]Cl_4$	$[Pt(NH_4)_6]^{4+}$	$4Cl^-$
$[Pt(NH_3)_5Cl]Cl_3$	$[Pt(NH_3)_5Cl]^{3+}$	$3Cl^-$
$[Pt(NH_3)_4Cl_2]Cl_2$	$[Pt(NH_3)_4Cl_2]^{++}$	$2Cl^-$
$[Pt(NH_3)_3Cl_3]Cl$	$[Pt(NH_3)_3Cl_3]^{+}$	Cl^-
$[Pt(NH_3)_2Cl_4]$	nonelectrolyte	
$[Pt(NH_3)Cl_5]K$	K^+	$[Pt(NH_3)Cl_5]^-$
$[PtCl_6]K_2$	$2K^+$	$[PtCl_6]^-$

When an ion replaces a neutral molecule in the "inner sphere" of a complex, the ion loses its electrovalent character and is attached to the central ion by a coordinate bond, which may be considered as identical with a covalent bond. This fact may be verified by precipitating the electrovalent chloride ions with silver ions. In the first complex listed in Table 7·1, there are four chloride ions which may be precipitated by silver ions. In the second complex only three of the chlorides are precipitated by silver ions, and in the third and fourth complexes only two and one electrovalent chloride ions remain. Complex five is a nonelectrolyte, which is almost insoluble in water and, consequently, produces no ions in solution. In complexes six and seven, the chlorine atoms are tied up with covalent bonds and cannot be precipitated as simple ions.

NATURE OF THE LINKAGE IN COMPLEX IONS AND COMPOUNDS

The foregoing discussion may have left the impression that the components of complex ions are held together only by covalent or coordinate covalent bonds. This is far from true, since many complex ions are formed without the exchange or sharing of electrons. Such ions result from electrostatic forces between their constituents. Consequently, complex compounds may be classified rather loosely into those resulting from electrostatic forces, and those held together by covalent or dative bonds.

7·3 Complexes Resulting from Electrostatic Forces between Constituents. A large group of complexes contain ion-dipole bonds. Those hydrated ions which are isoelectronic with the inert gases contain bonds of this type. For example, the ions, $Mg(H_2O)_6^{++}$ and $Al(H_2O)_6^{3+}$, result from the electrostatic attraction between the positively charged cations and the electric dipole charges of the water molecules. The polarity of the water molecule is due to its distortion from a linear to a triangular form. Such a molecule can be visualized as triangular in shape, with the negative oxygen forming an apex to the triangle.

Because of the polar character of water molecules, they may be oriented and attracted by ions in water solution. Positive ions are usually smaller than negative ions; therefore, cations attract and bind water molecules more tightly to themselves than do anions. The number of water molecules attached to a cation is called its *coordination number,* and this number is determined by the size of the cation. The hydrated aluminum ion is indicated symbolically in Fig. 7·1.

The electrostatic force existing between a positive ion and a coordinated polar molecule obeys Coulomb's law of electric force. This law states that the magnitude of the electric force between two charged bodies is proportional to the product of the charges, and inversely proportional to the square of the distance between them. Accordingly, the electrostatic force between a positive ion and a water molecule is proportional to the product of the charge of the ion and the electric dipole of the molecule, and inversely proportional to the square of the distance between the two charges. If it is assumed that the ion and the oxygen atom are charged spheres in contact with each other, then the distance between the charges is the sum of the radii of the positive ion and the negative oxygen atom in the water molecule.

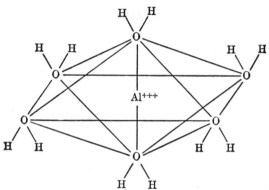

FIG. 7·1   Symbolic representation of the aluminum ion.

In comparing binding forces of various cations in hydrates, the radius of the oxygen atom and the electric dipole charge in the water molecule can be considered as constants. Therefore, in predicting stability of a hydrate, the charge of the central ion and its radius are most significant. As a general rule, stable hydrates are formed by those ions with large charges and small radii.

Since ions such as cesium, rubidium, and potassium are comparatively large with small charges, they are either loosely hydrated or not hydrated at all. Conversely, the aluminum ion is small and has a large charge, and as a result, is strongly hydrated in water solution. Table 7·2 shows a comparison of typical ions, isoelectronic with the inert gases, as to their ionic radii, ionic potential, and extent of hydration.

The number of water molecules that are oriented around the central ion is the coordination number of the hydrated ion and is dependent upon the size of the ion. The determination of absolute hydration numbers is still in the experimental stage, but it is obvious that a small ion, such as the beryllium ion, has a smaller coordination number than a larger ion, as for example the barium ion.

7·4 Complexes Resulting from the Formation of Coordinate Bonds.

The dative bond, or coordinate bond, is also called the *semipolar bond* in that such a bond appears to be partly ionic and partly covalent. The bond may be considered as consisting of an electron pair, but the electron

TABLE 7·2 EXTENT OF HYDRATION AS RELATED TO IONIC RADIUS AND POTENTIAL

Ion	Ionic radius, angstroms	Ionic potential, charge/radius	Extent of hydration
Cs^+	1.69	0.59	May not be hydrated
Rb^+	1.48	0.68	
K^+	1.33	0.75	
Na^+	0.95	1.05	Loosely hydrated
Ba^{++}	1.35	1.48	
Li^+	0.60	1.70	Definitely hydrated
Sr^{++}	1.13	1.78	
Ca^{++}	0.99	2.00	
Mg^{++}	0.65	3.1	Strongly hydrated
Al^{3+}	0.50	6.0	
Be^{++}	0.31	6.5	

pair is furnished by one atom or ion in a donor-acceptor relationship. Ions which are isoelectronic with the inert gases do not form the "Werner-type" complexes. Such ions may form hydrates due to electrostatic forces, but there is little evidence that the coupling is brought about by the completion of incomplete orbitals.

Ions of the transition and posttransition elements have a tendency toward the formation of complexes containing coordinate bonds, and these complexes are apparently more stable than those formed by electrostatic forces. As a general rule, the radii of the transition metal cations are less than the radii of those cations which are isoelectronic with the inert gases. This may account, in part, for the greater stability of the transition-ion complexes. An examination of the electronic orbitals of the first transition elements and posttransition elements from Sc through Zn, with atomic numbers 21 to 30, shows that the transition elements have incomplete $3d$ orbitals, and these are progressively filled in passing through the range of these elements. In general, an atom or ion entering chemical reaction tends to add a sufficient number of electrons to fill incomplete orbitals, within spatial limitations. Ions of the transition elements may accept electrons in pairs from donor atoms. According to Pauling,[1] the inner $3d$ orbitals of the transition elements

[1] Linus Pauling, "The Nature of the Chemical Bond," p. 93, Cornell University Press, Ithaca, New York, 1940.

have about the same energy as the 4s and 4p orbitals of the valence shell, and if they are not completely occupied by unshared electron pairs they play a very important part in bond formation.

Singly occupied electronic orbits may be detected by measuring the magnetic moments of various ions in aqueous solution. An electron spinning about its own axis and an electron revolving in an orbit are equivalent to an electric current in a circuit. Electrons so described behave as micromagnets, and as such possess magnetic moments. The total magnetic moment of an electron is, therefore, dependent on the spin quantum number s and the orbital revolution quantum number l. In a completed orbital the magnetic moments of the two coupled electrons compensate for each other, since they have opposite angular momentums as predicted by the Pauli exclusion principle; thus, only atoms and ions with incomplete electron levels are paramagnetic. Substances which are paramagnetic, when placed in a magnetic field, have a greater magnetization than a vacuum, and tend to crowd lines of force together. Magnetic measurements, therefore, provide a means of detecting the presence of unpaired electrons in atoms, ions, or molecules.

In the transition metal ions the incomplete electron shells are the two outermost shells. In these ions the contribution to the total magnetic moment by the orbital angular momentum may be neglected, since this component is largely canceled by interaction with other ions in solution or in crystals. Hence, only spin magnetism need be considered because this moment is unaffected by the electrical field of ions but does respond to a magnetic field. In the ions of the transition elements the 3d shell contains five orbitals. In passing from vanadium to copper, the first five electrons enter one into each of these five orbitals to produce singly occupied orbits. Above five, the additional electrons go into orbitals already containing one electron to form paired electrons with opposed spins. Consequently, the number of uncoupled electrons rises to five and then falls to zero as the 3d shell is completed. Table 7·3 indicates values in magnetons (the natural unit of magnetic moment) for the magnetic moments of the transition metal ions in solution as compared with the number of unpaired electrons in these ions.

Magnetic data may serve to distinguish between ionic and covalent bonding. The transition metals form many octahedral complex ions (in such an ion the six coordinated particles are arranged around the central ion to produce the spatial structure of an octahedron), and magnetic measurements indicate that in some of these complexes the bonding is ionic and in others covalent. For example, the magnetic moment of the ion $Fe(CN)_6{}^{3-}$ indicates the presence of one unpaired electron whereas the magnetic moment of the ion $FeF_6{}^{3-}$ indicates five unpaired electrons. Obviously, the bonding in the first complex is covalent and in the second it must be ionic.   This conclusion is reached by examining the distribution of electrons in the ferric and ferricyanide ions.

TABLE 7·3   MAGNETIC MOMENTS OF VARIOUS IONS IN AQUEOUS SOLUTION

Ion	Number of $3d$ electrons	Number of unpaired electrons	Moment, magnetons	
			Calculated	Observed
K^+, Ca^{++}, Sc^{3+}, Ti^{4+}	0	0	0.00	0.00
Ti^{3+}, V^{4+}	1	1	1.73	1.7
V^{3+}	2	2	2.83	2.4
V^{++}, Cr^{3+}	3	3	3.88	3.8–3.9
Cr^{++}, Mn^{3+}	4	4	4.90	4.8–4.9
Mn^{++}, Fe^{3+}	5	5	5.92	5.9
Fe^{++}, Co^{3+}	6	4	4.90	5.3
Co^{++}	7	3	3.88	5.0–5.2
Ni^{++}	8	2	2.83	3.2
Cu^{++}	9	1	1.73	1.9–2.0
Cu^+, Zn^{++}, Ga^{3+}	10	0	0.00	0.00

The iron atom consists of a nucleus surrounded by successive shells of planetary electrons having in them 2, 8, 14, and 2 electrons, respectively. The energy levels and orbitals of the iron atom may be indicated as

Each circle represents an orbital which may contain a pair of electrons of opposite spins, the electrons being signified by dots.   This representation indicates that the iron atom has four unpaired electrons in the $3d$ orbitals. In forming the ferric ion the iron atom loses its two $4s$ electrons and one $3d$ electron, thereby producing an electronic structure containing five singly occupied $3d$ orbitals, which may be indicated symbolically as

Therefore, when the ferric ion accepts 12 electrons (indicated by small crosses) from six cyanide ions to form six covalent bonds, the resulting ion $Fe[CN]_6^{3-}$ contains only one unpaired $(3d)$ electron:

In this ion, six stable $3d$, $4s$, and $4p$ orbitals are completed in attaining the octahedral structure.

In the case of the FeF_6^{3-} ion, the presence of five singly occupied orbitals indicates that the electronic distribution is the same as in the simple ferric ion. Thus the bonding is ionic, in which the fluoride ions are held in the octahedral structure by electrostatic forces.

The formation of complex ions by coordinate bonds appears to follow two general rules:

1. The central ion tends to accept electrons to fill incomplete stable orbitals, and each completed orbital contains a pair of electrons of opposite spins.

2. The central ion tends to accept sufficient coordinated molecules, or ions, to produce a symmetrical structure of molecules packed around the central ion. This structure may be planar, tetrahedral, octahedral, or cubic.

The tendency to attain the inert gas structure, with completed shells, is significant but not always possible. In some cases the electron shells of inert gases are attained. In other elements which form complexes, the total number of electrons may either not attain or may even exceed the number in the inert gas shell. Examples illustrating these various electron shells are given in Table 7·4.

TABLE 7·4   VARIABILITY OF ELECTRON SHELLS IN COMPLEX IONS OF TYPICAL TRANSITION ELEMENTS

Element	Atomic number	Electrons lost in ion formation	Electrons gained in coordination	Total shell
Co(ic)	27	3	12	36
Zn	30	2	8	36
Pt	78	4	12	86
Cr	24	3	12	33
Fe(ic)	26	3	12	35
Ni	28	2	12	38

The production of hydrated ions by the transition elements is a more complex process than for simple ions with inert gas structures. In such an ion as the hydrated aluminum ion, the binding force producing the complex is an electrostatic one obeying Coulomb's law of electric force. In a hydrated ion of a transition element, not only is an ion-dipole bond possible, but there is also the tendency toward coordinate bond formation to fill incomplete stable orbitals of the central ion. Since two processes may be involved in the formation of a hydrated transition ion, it would seem that such an ion should be more stable than a hydrated ion in which only the ion-dipole forces are in operation. Such a comparison necessarily assumes that the ions are approximately the same size and have equal charges.

An index of the strength of the bond between the central ion and a coordinated water molecule is the ease with which a proton is lost from the complex. The effect of hydrated ions on the pH of their aqueous solutions is illustrated by the following equations:

$$Al(H_2O)_6{}^{3+} + H_2O \rightleftharpoons Al(H_2O)_5(OH)^{++} + H_3O^+$$
$$Fe(H_2O)_6{}^{3+} + H_2O \rightleftharpoons Fe(H_2O)_5(OH)^{++} + H_3O^+$$

If it is assumed that protons split off more easily from strongly hydrated ions, then the magnitude of the acid constants of these ions should represent their relative stabilities. This assumption must be regarded as speculative since the determination of acid constants of hydrated-ion acids is still in the experimental stage. In Table 7·5 are given two examples of such constants which have been determined.

TABLE 7·5   ACID CONSTANTS FOR TWO DIFFERENT TYPES OF HYDRATED IONS

Ion	Electronic structure	Radius, angstroms	Acid constant
Al^{3+}	Inert gas structure	0.50	1.4×10^{-5}
Fe^{3+}	Incomplete $3d$ orbitals	0.60	6×10^{-3}

GENERAL TYPES OF COMPLEX IONS

All ions in aqueous solution may be regarded as complex ions. These ions may be hydrates, or the complexes may result from the union of a central ion with other ions, atoms, or molecules. A study of the numerous possible combinations to produce complex ions is beyond the scope of this book. Consequently, the discussion will be limited to those complex ions of most common occurrence in qualitative analysis. One broad classification of complex ions divides them into three general types:

1. Complex ions formed by the union of cations with inorganic molecules. The ammoniates and hydrates are familiar examples of this type of complex.

2. Complexes formed by the union of cations with inorganic anions in which the anions are usually in excess of the number to satisfy the electrovalence of the cations. Among the many anions which, in excess, may produce such complex ions are the cyanide, hydroxide, thiocyanate, sulfide, thiosulfate, and halide ions.

3. Complexes resulting from the union of inorganic cations with organic anions or molecules.

7·5 Complex Ions Formed by the Union of Cations with Inorganic Molecules.

Hydrated Ions. The majority of ions are hydrated to some extent in aqueous solution. The stability of such ions varies with many factors, as has been explained in the preceding pages. Familiar examples of these ions are the hydronium ion, H_3O^+, the hydrated aluminum ion, $Al(H_2O)_6{}^{3+}$, the hydrated chromic ion, $Cr(H_2O)_6{}^{3+}$, and the hydrated beryllium ion, $Be(H_2O)_4{}^{++}$.

Ammoniates. Many cations form coordination compounds with ammonia. The ammonium ion, $NH_4{}^+$, results from the union of an ammonia molecule with a proton:

$$NH_3 + H_2O \rightleftharpoons NH_4{}^+ + OH^-$$

This equation indicates that a water solution of NH_3 will also contain hydroxide ions. In low concentrations of ammonia, the hydroxide ions may produce the first reaction with a cation:

$$Zn^{++} + 2OH^- \rightleftharpoons Zn(OH)_2$$
$$Cu^{++} + 2OH^- \rightleftharpoons Cu(OH)_2$$
$$Ni^{++} + 2OH^- \rightleftharpoons Ni(OH)_2$$

In the presence of excess ammonia, the hydroxide precipitates are dissolved because of the formation of complex ions:

$$Zn^{++} + 4NH_3 \rightleftharpoons Zn(NH_3)_4{}^{++}$$
$$Cu^{++} + 4NH_3 \rightleftharpoons Cu(NH_3)_4{}^{++}$$
$$Ni^{++} + 6NH_3 \rightleftharpoons Ni(NH_3)_6{}^{++}$$

Other frequently encountered ammonia complexes are $Ag(NH_3)_2{}^+$, $Cd(NH_3)_4{}^{++}$, and $Co(NH_3)_6{}^{3+}$.

The extent to which a hydroxide or an ammonia complex is formed with a cation depends not only upon the concentration of ammonia but also upon the stability of the complex that is produced. Certain cations, *e.g.*, aluminum and iron, always precipitate as hydroxides with ammonia because the stabilities of the ammonia complexes are insufficient to put the hydroxides into solution.

7·6 Complex Ions Formed by the Union of Cations with Inorganic Anions.

The majority of anions may enter into complex formation with certain cations. Usually these cations are low in the reactivity series, consequently showing a marked tendency to form coordinate bonds.

Halide Complexes. Insoluble chlorides are somewhat soluble in a high concentration of chloride ions. The composition of the soluble complex ion which is formed depends upon the concentration of the excess chloride ion. For example,

$$AgCl + Cl^- \rightleftharpoons AgCl_2{}^-$$

or

$$AgCl + 2Cl^- \rightleftharpoons AgCl_3^=$$

and

$$PbCl_2 + 2Cl^- \rightleftharpoons PbCl_4^=$$

Among the many other complex chloride ions which have been identified are $CuCl_2^-$, $CuCl_4^=$, $HgCl_4^=$, $AuCl_4^-$, $PtCl_6^=$, $SnCl_6^=$, $CdCl_4^=$, and $CoCl_6^{3-}$.

The bromide and iodide ions form complex ions similar to the complex chloro ions. One familiar complex iodide ion is formed by the solvent action of excess iodide ions upon mercuric iodide:

$$HgI_2 + 2I^- \rightleftharpoons HgI_4^=$$

Other bromide and iodide complexes most commonly encountered are $AgBr_2^-$, $PbBr_4^=$, $PbI_4^=$, BiI_4^-, and SbI_4^-.

The fluoride ion is the most effective complexing agent among the halides. As a consequence, the fluoro complexes are usually extremely stable. A few of the most common examples are $SiF_6^=$, FeF_6^{3-}, AlF_6^{3-}, and BF_4^-.

Cyanide Complexes. The cyanide, thiocyanate, and thiosulfate ions are sometimes referred to as pseudohalogens, since their chemical reactions resemble those of the halides. Many insoluble cyanides are soluble in excess cyanide ions due to the formation of complex cyanide ions. Three such cyanides are silver, cadmium, and ferric cyanides:

$$Ag^+ + 2CN^- \rightleftharpoons Ag(CN)_2^-$$
$$Cd^{++} + 4CN^- \rightleftharpoons Cd(CN)_4^=$$
$$Fe^{3+} + 6CN^- \rightleftharpoons Fe(CN)_6^{3-}$$

A few of these complexes, such as the ferrocyanide and ferricyanide ions, are so stable that they are not decomposed in strong-acid solutions.

Other cyanide complexes of interest in analytical chemistry are $Cu(CN)_3^=$, $Zn(CN)_4^=$, $Hg(CN)_4^=$, $Co(CN)_6^{3-}$, and $Ni(CN)_4^=$.

Thiocyanate Complexes. As may be expected, the thiocyanate complexes are somewhat analogous to complex halogen ions.

Insoluble silver thiocyanate and mercuric thiocyanate are soluble in excess thiocyanate ions:

$$AgCNS + CNS^- \rightleftharpoons Ag(CNS)_2^-$$
$$Hg(CNS)_2 + 2CNS^- \rightleftharpoons Hg(CNS)_4^=$$

The ferric ion and thiocyanate ion may combine to produce colored complex ions varying ion composition from $Fe(H_2O)_5CNS^{++}$ to $Fe(CNS)_6^{3-}$.

Thiosulfate Complexes. Silver chloride and silver bromide dissolve in sodium thiosulfate solution to form a stable complex silver thiosulfate anion. This reaction is important in photography. After the development of a photographic film, the sodium thiosulfate solution is used to dissolve away the silver halide not reduced by the developer. The equation for this dissolving action is

$$AgBr + 2S_2O_3^= \rightleftharpoons Ag(S_2O_3)_2{}^{3-} + Br^-$$

Other complex thiosulfate ions are $Hg(S_2O_3)_2^=$, $Bi(S_2O_3)_3{}^{3-}$, $Cu_2(S_2O_3)_2^=$, and $Pb(S_2O_3)_2^=$.

Sulfide Complexes. The sulfides of arsenic, antimony, and tin are soluble in excess sulfide ions due to the formation of stable complex ions. This complex formation may be utilized in separating these three sulfides from the other sulfides of Cation Group II of the qualitative scheme. The production of these soluble complex ions is represented by the following equations:

$$As_2S_3 + 3S^= \rightleftharpoons 2AsS_3{}^{3-}$$
$$Sb_2S_3 + 3S^= \rightleftharpoons 2SbS_3{}^{3-}$$
$$SnS_2 + S^= \rightleftharpoons SnS_3^=$$

A very high concentration of sulfide ions will dissolve mercuric sulfide to produce the mercuric sulfide complex, as follows:

$$HgS + S^= \rightleftharpoons HgS_2^=$$

Homoatomic Anions. These complexes result from the union of neutral atoms or molecules with their ions to form soluble complex anions. Two familiar examples of homoatomic anions are the tri-iodide ion and the sulfur-sulfide ion. Iodine molecules dissolve only slightly in water but are readily soluble in potassium iodide solution. The equation for the reaction which produces this increased solubility is

$$I_2 + I^- \rightleftharpoons I_3^-$$

Ammonium polysulfide is a reagent that will dissolve the sulfides of arsenic, antimony, and tin. Consequently, it is sometimes utilized to separate Cation Group II into subgroups in which these sulfides are dissolved from the other cations which make up the group. This reagent is prepared by dissolving sulfur in ammonium sulfide solution, according to the following equation:

$$S^0 + S^= \rightleftharpoons S_2^=$$

The reaction is not limited to the formation of the diatomic ion. There is considerable evidence that the ions $S_3^=$, $S_4^=$, and $S_5^=$ may also be formed.

Hydroxide Complexes (amphoteric hydroxides). Certain insoluble hydroxides combine with acids and bases to form salts. Such hydroxides are referred to as *amphoteric hydroxides* because of their dual nature in acid-base reactions. Equations representing some of the most familiar hydroxides of this type acting as acids are

$$Al(H_2O)_3(OH)_3 + 3H_3O^+ \rightleftharpoons Al(H_2O)_6{}^{3+} + 3H_2O$$
$$Zn(H_2O)_2(OH)_2 + 2H_3O^+ \rightleftharpoons Zn(H_2O)_4{}^{++} + 2H_2O$$
$$Sn(H_2O)_2(OH)_2 + 2H_3O^+ \rightleftharpoons Sn(H_2O)_4{}^{++} + 2H_2O$$
$$Pb(H_2O)_2(OH)_2 + 2H_3O^+ \rightleftharpoons Pb(H_2O)_4{}^{++} + 2H_2O$$
$$Cr(H_2O)_3(OH)_3 + 3H_3O^+ \rightleftharpoons Cr(H_2O)_6{}^{3+} + 3H_2O$$

Although the reactions of insoluble hydroxides with bases are also acid-base reactions, such reactions proceed because of the formation of stable hydroxide complex ions. These reactions may be represented as

$$Al(H_2O)_3(OH)_3 + OH^- \rightleftharpoons Al(H_2O)_2(OH)_4{}^- + H_2O$$
$$Cr(H_2O)_3(OH)_3 + OH^- \rightleftharpoons Cr(H_2O)_2(OH)_4{}^- + H_2O$$
$$Zn(H_2O)_2(OH)_2 + 2OH^- \rightleftharpoons Zn(OH)_4{}^= + 2H_2O$$
$$Sn(H_2O)_2(OH)_2 + OH^- \rightleftharpoons Sn(H_2O)(OH)_3{}^- + H_2O$$
$$Pb(H_2O)_2(OH)_2 + OH^- \rightleftharpoons Pb(H_2O)(OH)_3{}^- + H_2O$$

The reactions of the zinc ion to form a series of hydroxide complexes may be represented as either complex-ion formations or acid-base reactions. From the viewpoint of complex-ion formation, the following equations are illustrative:

$$Zn^{++} + OH^- \rightleftharpoons Zn(OH)^+$$
$$Zn(OH)^+ + OH^- \rightleftharpoons Zn(OH)_2(s)$$
$$Zn(OH)_2(s) + OH^- \rightleftharpoons Zn(OH)_3{}^-$$
$$Zn(OH)_3{}^- + OH^- \rightleftharpoons Zn(OH)_4{}^=$$

The reactions indicated by the preceding equations are reversible, and the stability of each complex is indicated by the size of its equilibrium constant. The expressions for the dissociation of the hydroxide complexes of the zinc ion are

$$\frac{[Zn^{++}][OH^-]}{[Zn(OH)^+]} = 4.1 \times 10^{-5}$$

$$\frac{[Zn(OH)^+][OH^-]}{[Zn(OH)_2](s)} = 1.1 \times 10^{-12}$$

$$\frac{[Zn(OH)_2](s)[OH^-]}{[Zn(OH)_3{}^-]} = 5 \times 10^{-1}$$

$$\frac{[Zn(OH)_3{}^-][OH^-]}{[Zn(OH)_4{}^=]} = 2 \times 10^{-1}$$

Another interpretation of the behavior of an amphoteric hydroxide is to consider such a hydroxide as an intermediate stage in the hydrolysis of a hydrated ion. The coordinated water molecules of the hydrated ion may be replaced by hydroxide ions. To illustrate this point of view, consider the hydrated zinc ion as an acid with four replaceable protons:

$$Zn(H_2O)_4^{++} + H_2O \rightleftharpoons Zn(H_2O)_3(OH)^+ + H_3O^+$$
$$Zn(H_2O)_3(OH)^+ + H_2O \rightleftharpoons Zn(H_2O)_2(OH)_2(s) + H_3O^+$$
$$Zn(H_2O)_2(OH)_2(s) + H_2O \rightleftharpoons Zn(H_2O)(OH)_3^- + H_3O^+$$
$$Zn(H_2O)(OH)_3^- + H_2O \rightleftharpoons Zn(OH)_4^= + H_3O^+$$

The acid constants and equilibrium expressions for the reactions represented by the foregoing equations are

$$\frac{[Zn(H_2O)_3(OH)^+][H_3O^+]}{[Zn(H_2O)_4^{++}]} = 2.45 \times 10^{-10}$$

$$\frac{[Zn(H_2O)_2(OH)_2](s)[H_3O^+]}{[Zn(H_2O)_3(OH)^+]} = 9 \times 10^{-3}$$

$$\frac{[Zn(H_2O)(OH)_3^-][H_3O^+]}{[Zn(H_2O)_2(OH)_2](s)} = 2 \times 10^{-16}$$

$$\frac{[Zn(OH)_4^=][H_3O^+]}{[Zn(H_2O)(OH)_3^-]} = 5 \times 10^{-14}$$

If the complete hydrolysis of the hydrated zinc ion is represented by one equation, as

$$Zn(H_2O)_4^{++} + 4H_2O \rightleftharpoons Zn(OH)_4^= + 4H_3O^+$$

then the over-all equilibrium expression, with its acid constant, is

$$\frac{[Zn(OH)_4^=][H_3O^+]^4}{[Zn(H_2O)_4^{++}]} = 2.2 \times 10^{-41}$$

7·7 Complex Ions Formed by the Union of Cations with Organic Anions or Molecules. Certain inorganic cations may form coordination compounds with specific organic ions or organic molecules. If the coordinated groups are organic ions, the complex produced is usually an anion and is soluble in water. Such an electrolyte is produced when the ferric ion reacts with oxalate ions. A simple equation for the formation of this complex is

$$Fe^{3+} + 3C_2O_4^= \rightleftharpoons Fe(C_2O_4)_3^{3-}$$

The structure of the complex ion may be represented as

If the coordinate ion or molecule is attached to the central group by two bonds in such a manner as to produce a closed ring, a chelate compound is produced. Complexes incorporating ring structures, particularly where there are five or six atoms in the ring, are generally quite stable. A ring structure could be indicated as

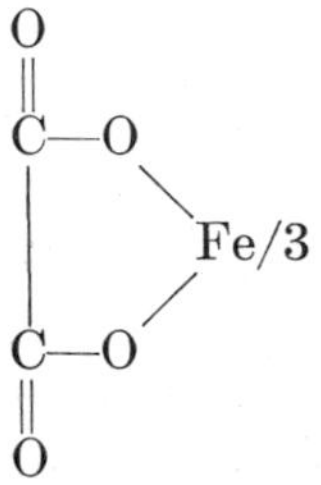

$$
\begin{array}{c}
O \\
\parallel \\
C\text{---}O \\
| \qquad\qquad\searrow \\
| \qquad\qquad\quad Fe/3 \\
| \qquad\qquad\nearrow \\
C\text{---}O \\
\parallel \\
O
\end{array}
$$

The appearance of the closed ring resembles the claw of a lobster, and for this reason compounds containing this structure are referred to as chelate compounds. *Chelate* is derived from the Greek word meaning claw.

Probably the most familiar chelate compound in qualitative analysis is produced when the nickel ion reacts with dimethylglyoxime. The structure of the complex produced by this reaction may be represented as

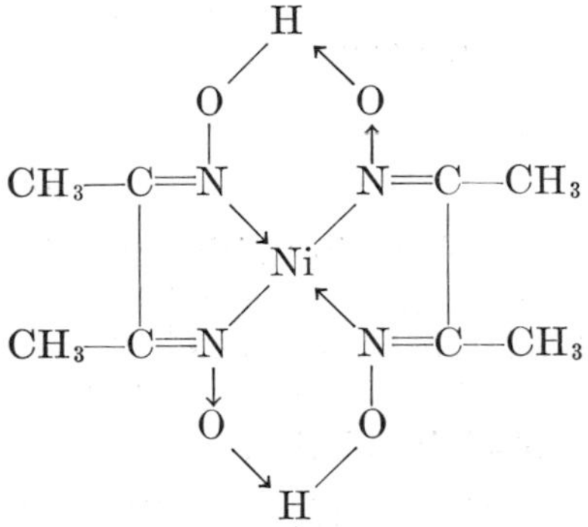

$$
\begin{array}{ccccc}
& & H & & \\
& \nearrow & & \nwarrow & \\
& O & & O & \\
& | & & \uparrow & \\
CH_3\text{---}C\!\!=\!\!N & & N\!\!=\!\!C\text{---}CH_3 \\
& | & \searrow \quad \nearrow & | \\
& & Ni & & \\
& | & \nearrow \quad \nwarrow & | \\
CH_3\text{---}C\!\!=\!\!N & & N\!\!=\!\!C\text{---}CH_3 \\
& \downarrow & & | & \\
& O & & O & \\
& \searrow & & \nearrow & \\
& & H & &
\end{array}
$$

In this compound, the nickel ion has a coordination number of 4, and is attached to two molecules of dimethylglyoxime by two covalent bonds and two coordinate bonds.

The hundreds of known chelate compounds have been classified in many ways. One simple method of classification, used by Sidgwick,[1] is by the nature of the links which close the ring, or rings, of the chelate compound. In respect to the nature of these links, he distinguishes three types:

Type A. Complexes in which the cation is combined through covalent bonds only. Rings of this type are formed by the replacement of two

[1] N. V. Sidgwick, "The Electronic Theory of Valency," pp. 239–243, Oxford University Press, New York, 1927.

hydrogen atoms by the metallic cation.   Usually the two hydrogen atoms split from hydroxyl or carboxyl groups, where the latter are so positioned as to produce five-membered rings.   A typical example is the complex formed between the beryllium and oxalate ions:

$$\left[\begin{array}{cc} O=C-O & O-C=O \\ | \quad \diagdown \diagup \quad | \\ \quad Be \quad \\ | \quad \diagup \diagdown \quad | \\ O=C-O & O-C=O \end{array} \right]^{=}$$

Type B.   Complexes in which the cation is combined through both covalent and coordinate bonds.   Complexes of this type are nonelectrolytes and are insoluble in water.   One such complex, nickel dimethylglyoxime, has already been given.   Another example is the chelate structure produced in an identification test for the aluminum ion with alizarin red S.   In this compound, three molecules of the dye combine with one aluminum ion to form a red precipitate whose partial structure may be indicated as

Type C.   These are complexes in which the cation forms only coordinate bonds in closing a ring.   The diamines which have two amine groups, each of which may donate electrons, tie up certain cations with only coordinate linkages.   Such a complex is formed by the union of ethylene diamine with platinic chloride.

$$\left[\begin{array}{c} NH_2-CH_2 \\ Pt \diagup \quad \quad | \\ \diagup \quad \quad \\ NH_2-CH_2 \end{array} \right]^{4+}$$

7·8   Dissociation Constants of Complex Ions.   The strength of the linkage between the constituent ions or molecules within a complex varies widely.   In a concentrated solution, cobaltous ions react with thiocyanate ions to give the blue complex ions, $Co(CNS)_4^=$, but this complex is broken down upon dilution with water because of the lesser activity of the thiocyanate ion.   On the other hand, the complex ferrocyanide, $Fe(CN)_6^{4-}$, in water solution will not give a test for the ferrous ion with the most sensitive reagents.   These two examples represent extremes in terms of binding forces within complex ions.   Between these two extremes are many complexes which dissociate in water solution to such a degree that the extent of dissociation may be expressed quantitatively.

From the equilibrium reaction of a complex dissociating into its components is obtained a constant which is similar to an ionization constant. However, this constant is usually referred to as a *dissociation constant*, or, less frequently, as an instability constant. A few examples of dissociation equilibria of this type are given here with their respective dissociation constants. A more complete listing of these constants is to be found in Table A·8.

The cadmium-ammonia complex dissociates to give

$$Cd(NH_3)_4{}^{++} \rightleftharpoons Cd^{++} + 4NH_3$$

and the equilibrium expression for this reaction is

$$\frac{[Cd^{++}][NH_3]^4}{[Cd(NH_3)_4{}^{++}]} = K = 2.5 \times 10^{-7}$$

The cuprous cyanide complex dissociates to give cuprous ions and cyanide ions:

$$Cu(CN)_3{}^= \rightleftharpoons Cu^+ + 3CN^-$$

The equilibrium expression for this reaction, with its dissociation constant, is

$$\frac{[Cu^+][CN^-]^3}{[Cu(CN)_3{}^=]} = 5 \times 10^{-28}$$

The dissociation of a complex ion into its components may be written in a stepwise fashion. For example, the silver-ammonia complex ion dissociates as follows:

$$Ag(NH_3)_2{}^+ \rightleftharpoons Ag(NH_3)^+ + NH_3$$

and

$$Ag(NH_3)^+ \rightleftharpoons Ag^+ + NH_3$$

The equilibrium expression for the first dissociation is

$$\frac{[Ag(NH_3)^+][NH_3]}{[Ag(NH_3)_2{}^+]} = 4 \times 10^{-4}$$

and for the second dissociation is

$$\frac{[Ag^+][NH_3]}{[Ag(NH_3)^+]} = 1.7 \times 10^{-4}$$

The over-all dissociation may be indicated as

$$Ag(NH_3)_2{}^+ \rightleftharpoons Ag^+ + 2NH_3$$

for which the equilibrium expression is

$$\frac{[Ag^+][NH_3]^2}{[Ag(NH_3)_2{}^+]} = 6.8 \times 10^{-8}$$

7·9 Use of Organic Reagents in Qualitative Analysis. Many metal ions form highly colored solutions or precipitates with certain organic reagents, and these colored substances are sometimes useful as identification tests for these ions. The use of organic reagents is usually avoided in elementary qualitative analysis because the students within such a course have had very little contact with organic chemistry. On the other hand, in the absence of a satisfactory inorganic reagent, it may be necessary to resort to the use of an organic reagent. Quite often the latter type of reagent is more specific in its action and more sensitive to small quantities of the ion under analysis.

All three types (Sec. 7·7) of chelate structures have been used for analytical tests, but Type B represents the most useful and common ones. In the cation scheme of analysis presented in this book, four ions are identified with the use of organic reagents. One of these tests, the identification of nickel, produces the chelate structure given in Sec. 7·7. The other cations identified in this manner are antimony, aluminum, and magnesium. The structural formulas which have been proposed for the compounds produced in these tests indicate that they are probably Type B complexes.

Rhodamine B, a pink dye, produces a finely divided violet precipitate in the presence of pentavalent antimony in a hydrochloric acid solution. The formula for the dyestuff in combination with the antimony ion has been proposed as

Aluminon, a trade name for the ammonium salt of aurintricarboxylic acid, gives a bright red lake with aluminum salts, when the latter are precipitated from ammoniacal solutions. The colored substance probably possesses a chelate structure, which has been indicated as follows:

The magnesium ion may be detected with a dyestuff called p-nitrobenzeneazoresorcinol in a strongly basic solution. The blue precipitate which is produced in this test may have the following structure:

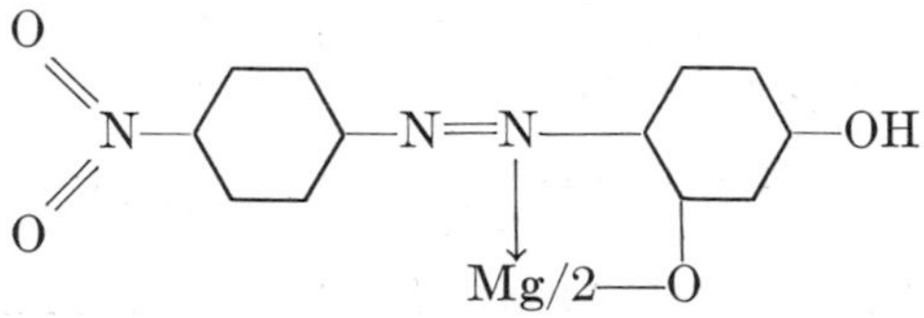

Types of Exercises Involving Complex Ions

Type 1. *An amphoteric hydroxide, which has a formula of* $X(OH)_3$, *has a dissociation constant of* 4×10^{-13} *for the reaction*

$$X(OH)_3 \rightleftharpoons H_3O^+ + XO_2^-$$

If all other dissociation reactions which may produce hydronium ions are considered negligible, calculate the solubility product constant for a saturated solution of $X(OH)_3$.

The ionization equilibrium expression is

$$\frac{[XO_2^-][H_3O^+]}{[X(OH)_3](s)} = 4 \times 10^{-13}$$

If $X = [XO_2^-] = [H_3O^+]$, and the concentration of $[X(OH)_3](s)$ is treated as a constant, then

$$X^2 = 4 \times 10^{-13}$$
$$X = 6.3 \times 10^{-7} \, F = [H_3O^+]$$

Therefore,

$$[OH^-] = \frac{1 \times 10^{-14}}{6.3 \times 10^{-7}} = 1.6 \times 10^{-8}$$

If the solution of the solid amphoteric substance is represented as

$$X(OH)_3(s) \rightleftharpoons X^{3+} + 3OH^-$$

the solubility product expression is

$$[X^{3+}][OH^-]^3 = K_{s.p.}$$

The concentration of $[X^{3+}]$ is one-third of the $[OH^-]$ concentration; therefore, the expression for obtaining the $K_{s.p.}$ is

$$(5.3 \times 10^{-9})(1.6 \times 10^{-8})^3 = K_{s.p.}$$
$$K_{s.p.} = 2.2 \times 10^{-32}$$

Type 2. *What is the formula-weight concentration of* Cr^{3+} *and* CrO_2^- *in a solution which is 0.1 F in respect to* OH^- *ions, and in equilibrium with solid* $Cr(OH)_3$? *The dissociation constant for* $Cr(OH)_3$ *as an acid is* 1×10^{-16}, *and the solubility product expression is*

$$[Cr^{3+}][OH^-]^3 = 1 \times 10^{-30}$$

Since the $[OH^-]$ concentration is 0.1 F, the Cr^{3+} may be obtained as

$$[Cr^{3+}] = \frac{1 \times 10^{-30}}{1 \times 10^{-3}} = 1 \times 10^{-27} \, F$$

The ionization reaction of $Cr(OH)_3$, as an acid, may be expressed by the equation

$$Cr(OH)_3 \rightleftharpoons CrO_2^- + H_3O^+$$

Since the $[OH^-]$ is $0.1\ F$, the $[H_3O^+]$ must be 1×10^{-13} as calculated from K_w. Substituting the value for $[H_3O^+]$ into the ionization equilibrium expression permits the calculation of the value for $[CrO_2^-]$.

$$[CrO_2^-](1 \times 10^{-13}) = 1 \times 10^{-16}$$
$$[CrO_2^-] = 1 \times 10^{-3}\ F$$

Type 3. *What is the formula-weight concentration of cyanide ions in a $0.1\ F$ solution of $Hg(CN)_4^-$?* The dissociation reaction is

$$Hg(CN)_4^- \rightleftharpoons Hg^{++} + 4CN^-$$

The dissociation constant for this reaction is 4×10^{-42}, and the equilibrium expression is

$$\frac{[Hg^{++}][CN^-]^4}{[Hg(CN)_4^-]} = 4 \times 10^{-42}$$

If X is the concentration of Hg^{++}, then $4X$ is the concentration of the CN^-.

$$\frac{X \times (4X)^4}{0.1} = 4 \times 10^{-42}$$
$$256X^5 = 4 \times 10^{-43}$$
$$X^5 = 1.5 \times 10^{-45}$$
$$X = 1.1 \times 10^{-9}$$
$$4X = 4.4 \times 10^{-9}\ F = \text{concentration of } CN^- \text{ ion}$$

Type 4. *How many grams of $AgCl$ will dissolve in a liter of $3\ F$ NH_3 solution?* The $K_{s.p.}$ of $AgCl$ is 1.56×10^{-10}, and the dissociation constant of $Ag(NH_3)_2^+$ is 6.8×10^{-8}. The reaction between ammonia and solid silver chloride is

$$AgCl(s) + 2NH_3 \rightleftharpoons Ag(NH_3)_2^+ + Cl^-$$

The extent of the reaction depends not only upon the concentration of the ammonia, but also upon the solubility product constant of $AgCl$ and the dissociation constant of $Ag(NH_3)_2^+$. Dividing the dissociation constant expression of $Ag(NH_3)_2^+$ by the solubility product expression of $AgCl$ produces the following setup:

$$\frac{\dfrac{[Ag^+][NH_3]^2}{[Ag(NH_3)_2^+]}}{[Ag^+][Cl^-]} = \frac{6.8 \times 10^{-8}}{1.56 \times 10^{-10}}$$

Upon simplifying,

$$\frac{[NH_3]^2}{[Ag(NH_3)_2^+][Cl^-]} = 4.36 \times 10^2$$

If X = concentration of $[Ag(NH_3)_2^+]$, the $[Cl^-]$ concentration also equals X, and

$$\frac{(3)^2}{X^2} = 4.36 \times 10^2$$
$$X = 1.44 \times 10^{-1}\ F = \text{concentration of } Ag^+ \text{ ion}$$

Multiplying the formula-weight concentration by the formula weight of $AgCl$ gives the solubility of silver chloride in grams per liter.

$$1.44 \times 10^{-1}\ F \times 143.34 = 20.6\ g/liter$$

Type 5. *If the* Hg^{++} *concentration in* 0.1 *F* $HgCl_4^-$ *is* 1.3×10^{-4} *F, calculate the dissociation constant of* $HgCl_4^-$. *Assume the dissociation reaction to be*

$$HgCl_4^- \rightleftharpoons Hg^{++} + 4Cl^-$$

It can be seen from the above dissociation reaction that the concentration of the chloride ion must be four times as great as the mercuric-ion concentration. The equilibrium expression for this dissociation is

$$\frac{[Hg^{++}][Cl^-]^4}{[HgCl_4^-]} = K$$

Upon substituting known values into this expression, it becomes

$$\frac{(1.3 \times 10^{-4})(5.2 \times 10^{-4})^4}{0.1} = K$$
$$K = 9.5 \times 10^{-17}$$

Type 6. *Calculate the concentration of* NH_3 *necessary to prevent the precipitation of silver chloride when a* 0.01 *F solution of silver nitrate is made* 0.01 *F with sodium chloride. The* $K_{s.p.}$ *for* AgCl *is* 1.56×10^{-10}, *and the dissociation constant for* $Ag(NH_3)_2^+$ *is* 6.8×10^{-8}.

The two expressions for the solubility product constant and the dissociation constant may be combined as follows:

$$\frac{[Ag^+][Cl^-]}{\frac{[Ag^+][NH_3]^2}{[Ag(NH_3)_2^+]}} = \frac{1.56 \times 10^{-10}}{6.8 \times 10^{-8}}$$

The combined expressions may be simplified into

$$\frac{[Ag(NH_3)_2^+][Cl^-]}{[NH_3]^2} = 2.3 \times 10^{-3}$$

If the original concentration of Ag^+ is 0.01 *F*, then to keep it in solution the concentration of $[Ag(NH_3)_2^+]$ must be 0.01 *F*. The concentration of Cl^- is given as 0.01 *F*· If these values are substituted into the above expression,

$$\frac{(0.01)(0.01)}{[NH_3]^2} = 2.3 \times 10^{-3}$$

and

$$[NH_3]^2 = 4.35 \times 10^{-2}$$
$$[NH_3] = 0.21 \ F$$

which is the concentration of ammonia necessary to prevent the precipitation of silver chloride under the stipulated conditions.

Exercises

(Consult the Appendix for physical constants needed.)

1. How many gram-formula weights of KOH must be added to a liter of water to dissolve 0.05 gfw of lead hydroxide?

2. What is the concentration of the Pb^{++} ion and the $HPbO_2^-$ ion in a solution which is 0.01 *F* with respect to OH^-, and which contains undissolved $Pb(OH)_2$?

3. How many gram-formula weights of $Al(OH)_3$ will dissolve in a liter of 0.05 *F* NaOH solution?

4. A saturated solution of $Cr(OH)_3$ contains CrO_2^-, Cr^{3+}, H_3O^+, and OH^- ions. Calculate the concentration of each ion in the solution.

5. A solution is $0.2\ F$ with respect to OH^- ion, and is in equilibrium with saturated $Zn(OH)_2$. What is the concentration of the Zn^{++} ion and the ZnO_2^- ion in the solution?

6. How many gram-formula weights of silver iodide will dissolve in a liter of $15\ F$ NH_3 solution?

7. What concentration of NH_3 is necessary to prevent the precipitation of AgBr when a $0.01\ F$ solution of $AgNO_3$ is made $0.01\ F$ with NaBr?

8. Calculate the solubility of CuS in $15\ F$ NH_3 solution.

9. What is the concentration of Ag^+ in a solution which is $0.1\ F$ with respect to $Ag(NH_3)_2^+$, and $3\ F$ with respect to NH_3?

10. Calculate the solubility of Ag_2S in a solution which is $0.5\ F$ in respect to CN^- ions.

11. What is the concentration of cuprous ions in a solution which is $0.1\ F$ with respect to cuprocyanide ions, and $0.1\ F$ in cyanide ions?

12. Calculate the solubility of ZnS in $6\ F$ NH_3 solution in terms of gram-formula weights per liter.

13. What is the concentration of Cd^{++} ions in a solution that is $0.1\ F$ in respect to $Cd(NH_3)_4^{++}$, and $3\ F$ in NH_3?

14. The mercuric-ion concentration in a $0.1\ F$ solution of HgI_4^- is $1.8 \times 10^{-7}\ F$. Calculate the dissociation constant of the complex ion.

15. Calculate the Hg^{++} ion concentration in a solution which is $0.01\ F$ in respect to $Hg(CNS)_4^-$, and $0.01\ F$ in CNS^- ions.

16. What concentration of CN^- is necessary to dissolve 2 g of AgCl in a liter of solution?

17. Calculate the solubility of NiS in $3\ F$ KCN solution in terms of gram-formula weights per liter.

18. How many gram-formula weights of CdS will dissolve in a liter of $1\ F$ NaCN solution?

19. Solid KCN is added to a solution containing $0.1\ F$ Cu^{++} ions, until the final concentration of CN^- is $0.6\ F$. If this solution is saturated with H_2S, will Cu_2S precipitate?

CHAPTER 8

COLLOIDS

The word *colloid* is derived from the Greek word for glue. It was first used by Thomas Graham in 1861 to distinguish noncrystalline from crystalline material. The original meaning has little significance at present, and the term colloids now embraces a branch of physical chemistry which is concerned with most of the materials of man's ordinary experience. Strictly speaking, colloids are not a class of materials but are more aptly described as materials in a state of restricted subdivision. The colloidal state is intermediate between a true solution and a coarse suspension.

8·1 Dispersions. Upon the basis of particle size, dispersions may be divided into three classes:

1. *Coarse dispersions* consist of particles with diameters greater than 10^{-5} cm, which may be visible to the eye, and which settle fairly rapidly to the bottom of the container.

2. *Colloidal dispersions* consist of particles with diameters between 10^{-5} and 10^{-7} cm, which are invisible to the eye, even with a microscope, but which appear in the field of an ultramicroscope.

3. *Molecular dispersions* contain particles with diameters less than 10^{-7} cm. These particles are not visible in the field of an ultramicroscope and are considered as true solutions, in which the dispersed particles will not settle to the bottom of the container.

These divisions are quite approximate, since it is impossible to restrict colloidal dispersions within exact limitations as to particle size.

It is difficult to give a clear-cut definition of what constitutes a colloidal dispersion. McBain[1] describes colloidal material as consisting of three coordinating factors: (1) particles, (2) a continuous medium, and (3) a stabilizing agent. Inasmuch as the particles within a colloidal dispersion are larger than molecular size, a dispersion of this class may be considered as a heterogeneous mixture, in which the dispersed phase is scattered through the dispersing medium. Actually, the distinction between homogeneous and heterogeneous systems offers no sharp line of demarcation. Such a distinction is based on the presence of particles

---

[1] J. W. McBain, "Colloid Science," p. 4, D. C. Heath and Company, Boston, 1950.

with definite phase boundaries, and boundaries of this kind, in colloidal systems, are sometimes more imaginary than real.

In colloidal systems the dispersed medium is so finely subdivided that surface effects are of primary importance. Consequently, the scope of colloid science includes not only the different types of dispersed materials and dispersing mediums, but also the broad field of surface chemistry. Any attempt to discuss this branch of science within the confines of a short chapter must be necessarily inadequate and incomplete. Only a few general principles as applied to a few simple colloidal systems can be considered.

8·2 Types of Dispersions. There are three states of matter, and from these three all types of colloidal dispersions are possible except a gas-gas dispersion. Table 8·1 lists these possibilities with a few familiar examples.

TABLE 8·1   TYPES OF COLLOIDAL DISPERSIONS

Dispersed phase	Dispersing medium	Example
Solid	Solid	Ruby glass
Liquid	Solid	Jellies
Gas	Solid	Floating soaps
Liquid	Liquid	Emulsions
Liquid	Gas	Fog
Gas	Liquid	Foams
Solid	Liquid	Suspensions
Solid	Gas	Smoke

This table, listing the types of colloids, indicates the broad scope covered by this field. In the present elementary discussion only one type of colloid will be considered, and that is the one of a solid dispersed within a liquid. Such a colloid is usually called a *sol*. Colloids of this type are of common occurrence in qualitative analysis, and they have certain properties which must be recognized and dealt with during the course of an analytical procedure.

8·3 Sols. A sol is defined as a dispersion of finely divided solid particles within a liquid medium. If the medium is restricted to water, sols may be classified according to their affinity for the dispersing phase. Where there is a decided affinity between the two phases, the system is termed a *hydrophilic sol*. Where the attraction is negligible or very small, the dispersed phase is said to be *hydrophobic*.

Hydrophilic (water-loving) colloids are reversible, since they may be separated from the dispersion medium and then under suitable conditions be made to return to the colloidal state. Wheat gluten, glue, gelatin, and tissues of plants and animals are examples. Colloids of this type have indefinite or variable electrical charges and are, consequently, little affected by the addition of electrolytes. Because of their remarkable affinity for water, hydrophilic colloids are, in general, viscous and may form a gel or jelly on cooling.

Hydrophobic (water-fearing) colloids are irreversible, because if they are coagulated and dried, they cannot be dispersed again. Hydrophobic colloids do not greatly alter the viscosity of water and are readily precipitated by the addition of electrolytes. Ferric hydroxide and arsenic sulfide in water are examples.

Hydrophobic colloidal particles carry electrical charges, usually due to adsorbed ions from incompletely removed electrolytes. Hydrophilic colloidal particles may carry electrical charges resulting from the self-dissociation of chemically active or polar groups on the particle. Thus, the protein-type colloids behave like amphoteric electrolytes which can dissociate to give either hydronium ions or hydroxide ions. Proteins carry carboxylic groups, —COOH, which may furnish hydronium ions, and amino groups, —NH₂, which may produce hydroxide ions. The dual acid-base nature of a protein particle permits it to become positively charged in acid solution and negatively charged in alkaline solution. The electrical charge of a hydrophilic protein molecule is predicted from the following chemical equations:

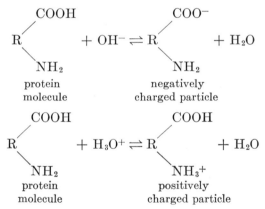

8·4 **Methods of Preparing Sols.** Since colloidal particles are intermediate in size between those in a molecular dispersion and those in a suspension of coarse particles, it is obvious that a colloidal dispersion may be prepared from either of these two extremes. By the "dispersion method" coarse particles may be reduced to colloidal size, and by the "condensation method" molecules of a true solution may be made to agglomerate into larger aggregates.

At least three processes are available for producing colloids by the dispersion method. These processes are: (1) mechanical grinding, (2) the dispersion action of an electric arc under water, and (3) the dispersion action of certain chemicals. Of these processes only the last one is of interest in qualitative analysis. To illustrate the dispersion action of a chemical, precipitated cadmium sulfide, thoroughly washed and then suspended in water, may be dispersed by passing hydrogen sulfide through the suspension. In this process the H_2S not only reduces the cadmium sulfide into smaller particles, but also stabilizes the sol through the adsorption of sulfide ions by the particles.

The method of greatest interest and importance in analytical chemistry by which a sol may be produced is the condensation of ions or molecules in a true solution to form larger aggregates which remain within the size limitations of colloidal particles. The process by which ions condense to produce larger particles is, as yet, somewhat of a mystery. When the solubility product of a relatively insoluble substance is exceeded, a supersaturated solution results. This condition is usually temporary because of the instability of such a solution, and is succeeded by a process of crystallization. The first crystals formed by condensation of ions are very small and are usually called *micelles*. What causes the first micelles to form is not known. There is some speculation as to the possibility of dust particles within the solution serving as the first nuclei for ion condensation. There is also the possibility of a multiple collision of ions, following the laws of chance, to produce the first micelles. The microcrystals, or micelles, may continue to grow by the further condensation of ions from the solution. This is certainly true for microcrystals which are fairly soluble. However, if a large number of micelles of approximately the same size are formed at the same time and if the particles are only slightly soluble, they may not grow, or if so, the growth will be slow. Whenever precipitation and crystal growth do not follow rapidly, the particles may acquire an electrical charge by preferential adsorption of ions from the solution. The presence of such a charge tends to stabilize particle size because of the electrical repulsive forces which prevent further agglomeration.

8·5 Some Properties of Sols. *Colligative Properties.* In an earlier chapter it was pointed out that certain physical properties of a solution, such as freezing point, boiling point, vapor pressure, and osmotic pressure, are changed by the presence of dissolved particles. Furthermore, it is recognized that the extent to which these colligative properties are altered is due to the number of particles rather than the kind of particles. A sol resembles a true solution inasmuch as the colligative properties of the dispersing medium are altered by the presence of the dispersed particles. The total effect of the colloidal particles upon the dispersing medium is quite small, since the size of sol particles is large and their number small, as compared with particles in true solution.

Tyndall Effect. A colloidal dispersion may appear as clear as a true solution under diffused light. However, if a beam of light is passed through a dispersion, its path becomes visible by the light reflected from the dispersed particles. Under similar conditions, a true solution shows only a faint beam, which is produced by dust particles that are present everywhere. This test for a colloidal dispersion is known as the Tyndall effect. When an intense, narrow beam of light is passed through a colloidal dispersion and viewed through a microscope set at right angles to the beam, the colloidal particles become visible as a multitude of moving points of light. Such an optical system is known as an *ultramicroscope.*

Brownian Movement. The molecules of a liquid are in rapid and constant motion due to their kinetic energies. Consequently, colloidal particles within a liquid are under constant bombardment on all sides by the molecules of the liquid. Despite the much larger diameters of the colloidal particles, the molecular bombardment produces a random movement of the particles. This unordered movement of dispersed particles is called the Brownian movement, and can best be observed by means of an ultramicroscope. The rapid, disordered movement of the points of light in the field of this instrument corresponds to the kinetic motion assumed for molecules, as predicted by the molecular theory.

Dialysis. Colloidal particles will not pass through animal or vegetable membranes. On the other hand, substances in a true solution do pass through such membranes. Separation of dispersions from solutes by means of membranes is called *dialysis.* This process is quite slow and depends upon the area of the membrane as well as the difference in concentrations between the liquids on either side of the membrane.

Electrophoresis. The electrical charge of a colloidal particle is many times larger than that of an ion, but the mass of the particle is also much greater than that of an ion. However, the number of particles in a sol is relatively small as compared with the number of ions in a dilute solution. Consequently, the electrical conductivity of a sol is quite low. The application of an external voltage causes charged sol particles to move toward one of the electrodes. A negative sol moves to the positive electrode, and a positive sol moves to the negative. The phenomenon of the migration of colloidal particles between two electrodes is called *electrophoresis.* This movement may be observed with an ultramicroscope. There are many practical applications of electrophoresis. For example, rubber plating is a process somewhat similar to the electroplating of metals. In the commercial process, a negative sol of rubber latex is deposited upon a suitably shaped anode to produce the rubber article.

8·6 Adsorption. The distinguishing properties of colloids, as compared with larger dispersed particles, are due almost entirely to the larger surface area per unit mass for the colloidal particles. If a given particle of matter with a known surface area is subdivided progressively, in steps, the total area increases with each subdivision. As a definite illustration, assume that a cube, with a volume of 1 cu cm and an area of 6 sq cm, is subdivided in consecutive steps so that each subdivision reduces the particle size by one-tenth in volume, until the final particles are of colloidal dimension. The successive increases in area are given in Table 8·2. The total of the subdivisions represents an increase in area from 6 sq cm to 60 million sq cm, or from approximately 1 sq in. to an area greater than that of a football gridiron.

TABLE 8·2   INCREASE OF SURFACE AREA WITH SUBDIVISION

Volume of cube, cu cm	Total surface produced, sq cm
1	6
1×10^{-1}	6×10^{1}
1×10^{-2}	6×10^{2}
1×10^{-3}	6×10^{3}
1×10^{-4}	6×10^{4}
1×10^{-5}	6×10^{5}
1×10^{-6}	6×10^{6}
1×10^{-7}	6×10^{7}

Adsorption is a surface phenomenon which is dependent upon surface area.   One theory of adsorption postulates that the electrostatic forces which bind ions into a crystal lattice extend in all directions, and that ions at the surface of the crystal present unsatisfied electrostatic bonds extending outwardly, which may hold atoms, molecules, or ions upon the surface of the crystal.   Such a surface arrangement might be visualized as resembling a checkerboard on which adsorbed particles are arranged in an orderly fashion; the number of particles which are adsorbed being dependent upon the volume of the adsorbed particle and the lattice structure of the crystalloid.   The layer of adsorbed particles is usually considered to be only one molecule deep, but experimental evidence of monomolecular layers is conflicting and difficult to interpret.

A surface composed of ions will adsorb ions of opposite charge.   As a general rule, electrovalent sols tend to adsorb ions which are common to them; thus colloidal silver chloride tends to adsorb either silver or chloride ions.   This tendency is to be expected, since it simply illustrates the way an electrovalent crystal may extend its space lattice.   In the building up of a crystal only ions of the proper size will fit into the lattice.   It is probable that the same is true when an ion is adsorbed at the surface of the crystal.   If the ion is of the proper diameter to fit into the crystal lattice, it should be held more tightly upon the surface.   The presence of the adsorbed ions imparts a charge to the colloidal particle.   Since all the particles have the same charge, they repel each other and tend to prevent combination and coagulation of the colloidal material.

The adsorption of a monomolecular layer of ions upon the surface of a particle results in an electrical unbalance in the solution. This unbalance is corrected by the formation of another layer of ions, of opposite charges, extending into the solution which surrounds the colloidal particle. The resulting electrical double layer resembles a parallel-plate condenser, except for the fact that the primary layer of charges on the particle is monomolecular in depth and immovable, whereas the secondary layer is diffuse and mobile. The difference in potential between the immovable liquid layer of ions attached to the surface of the particle and

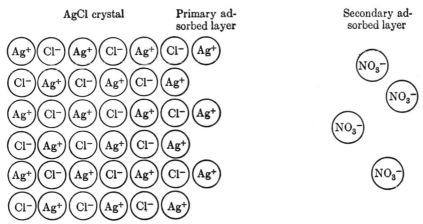

FIG. 8·1   Diagrammatic representation of a colloidal silver chloride particle in the presence of excess silver nitrate solution.

the movable liquid layer of ions immediately surrounding the particle is called the *zeta potential*. The presence of the electrical double layer accounts for the stability and electrical properties of electrovalent sols.

The formation of the electrical double layer at the surface of a colloidal particle may be illustrated by consideration of a silver chloride sol. When a solution of sodium chloride is added dropwise to a solution of silver nitrate, colloidal particles of silver chloride result. Since electrovalent sols tend to adsorb their own ions, the particles of silver chloride are positively charged in the presence of an excess of silver ions. The primary layer of ions adsorbed on the surface of the particle is composed of silver ions, and the secondary layer extending into the solution is composed of nitrate ions. These conditions are indicated diagrammatically in Fig. 8·1. On the other hand, if a solution of silver nitrate is added dropwise to a solution of sodium chloride, the first silver chloride particles will be formed in the presence of an excess of chloride ions. Consequently, the sol particles will adsorb chloride ions and have a negative charge. The secondary layer of ions contains the positively charged sodium ions to counterbalance the negatively charged $AgCl \cdot Cl^-$ particles. The diagrammatic representation of these conditions is given in Fig. 8·2.

8·7 Coagulation of Colloids. To precipitate a colloid, the colloidal particles must coalesce into large aggregates. In a stable sol, coalescence is prevented by the mutual repulsion of the micelles, all of which carry a similar electric charge. It is obvious that to coagulate a colloid it is necessary to neutralize the charges carried by the dispersed particles. Although low concentrations of ions are essential for the stabilization of

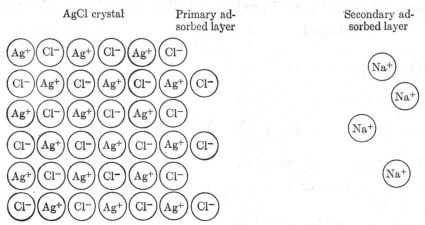

AgCl crystal   Primary adsorbed layer   Secondary adsorbed layer

FIG. 8·2 Diagrammatic representation of a colloidal silver chloride particle in the presence of excess sodium chloride solution.

hydrophobic sols, higher concentrations cause the micelles to aggregate until precipitation is accomplished. The ions which effect the precipitation, or coagulation, of sols are of opposite charge to the ions which impart the charge to the particles. As a general rule, ions with multiple charges are more effective in producing coagulation than ions with single charges.

The increase in precipitating effect with increasing valence of an ion is not a quantitative increment. Trivalent ions are more effective in precipitating colloids of opposite charge than are divalent ions, and divalent ions are more effective than univalent ions. This is not to indicate that a divalent ion has twice the coagulating power of a monovalent ion. Svedberg found that the efficiency of the ions K^+, Ba^{++}, and Al^{3+} as coagulants of an arsenious sulfide sol are in a ratio of approximately 1 : 20 : 1,000.

Table 8·3 shows the minimum concentrations, in millimoles per liter, of various electrolytes required to cause the precipitation of a negatively charged arsenious sulfide sol. It can be seen from this table that ions of the same valence vary as to the concentrations required for the precipitation of the same sol.   Another general rule indicates that the ions which are the most effective as coagulants are those which form the most insoluble substance with the oppositely charged ion of the colloid particles. Consequently, the silver ion is a more effective coagulant of a $AgCl \cdot Cl^-$ particle than is the sodium ion.   It is also true that when the amount of electrolyte added to a sol greatly exceeds the quantity required for coagulation, the excess may actually stabilize the sol by reversing its charge.   This may happen when an excess of silver ions is added to a sol of $AgCl \cdot Cl^-$ particles, in which the resulting sol contains $AgCl \cdot Ag^+$ particles.

TABLE 8·3   MINIMUM ELECTROLYTE CONCENTRATIONS FOR THE PRECIPITATION OF AN ARSENIOUS SULFIDE SOL*

Electrolyte	Cation valence	Minimum concentrations, millimoles/liter
LiCl	1	58
NaCl	1	51
KCl	1	50
NH_4Cl	1	42
HCl	1	31
$MgCl_2$	2	0.72
$CaCl_2$	2	0.65
$SrCl_2$	2	0.64
$AlCl_3$	3	0.093

* H. B. Weiser, "Colloid Chemistry," p. 224, John Wiley & Sons, Inc., New York, 1939.

8·8   Analytical Applications.   Analytical chemistry is concerned with the separation of various substances from one another for either quantitative determination or for the purpose of identification.   Up until the present, precipitations have been treated as if the products were pure, but this assumption is far from true.   Since the colloidal state is intermediate between true solution and coarse suspension, it is apparent that all precipitates must pass, at least temporarily, through a colloidal condition.   As a result, the particles of any precipitate will adsorb, more or less, some ions in the process of precipitation.   In analytical separations it is desirable to reduce adsorption of ions to a minimum.

Adsorption is reduced when the micelles are relatively few in number, and under conditions which favor rapid growth of micelles into large crystals.   The slow addition of a precipitating agent decreases the number of micelles and favors crystal growth.   Likewise, precipitations are commonly made from hot solutions to take advantage of the increased solubilities of most salts, and as a result, the formation of fewer micelles.

Under optimum conditions, where no colloid formation is apparent, some adsorption accompanies any precipitation. Electrically charged micelles exist, for an interval of time, in all precipitations, but after precipitation the resulting precipitate is neutral. As a result, the process of precipitation must involve the carrying down of sufficient oppositely charged ions to be equivalent to those ions upon the charged micelles. Thus all precipitates are contaminated with two types of ions: those which produced the electrically charged micelles, and those which neutralized the charged particles. To illustrate, if an excess of silver nitrate is added to a sodium chloride solution, positively charged $AgCl \cdot Ag^+$ particles are produced. These micelles may be coagulated by the addition of excess nitric acid. The nitrate ion, from nitric acid, causes coagulation, and this ion is carried down with the precipitate in an amount equivalent to the adsorbed silver ion.

In qualitative analysis electrolytes are usually present in sufficient concentrations to minimize the formation of colloidal dispersions. But in washing processes, if the electrolytes are removed, precipitates may be dispersed (peptized) into a colloidal state. For this reason, some noninterfering electrolyte, usually an ammonium salt, is added to the wash water.

Colloidal dispersions are not always undesirable in qualitative analysis. There are some sensitive tests for ions which utilize the formation of colloidal dispersions. Identification tests for aluminum and magnesium ions illustrate this use. The micelles of aluminum hydroxide are positively charged because of the adsorption of cations from the solution in which they are formed. These micelles attract negatively charged colloidal particles which are added to the solution. Thus, aluminum may be identified by the red lake produced when its hydroxide adsorbs the negatively charged particles of the dye, aluminon. Likewise, magnesium may be identified by a blue lake produced by the adsorption of p-nitrobenzeneazoresorcinol by magnesium hydroxide.

Exercises

1. What is the difference between a heterogeneous dispersion and a homogeneous dispersion?

2. What is the minimum diameter of dispersed particles in a liquid, in order for them to be visible to the naked eye?

3. Name two general classes of colloids.

4. What is the Tyndall effect?

5. Describe the principle of the ultramicroscope.

6. Differentiate between a solution of sodium sulfide and a cadmium sulfide sol with respect to (a) charge on the particles, (b) effect of adding ammonium nitrate.

7. What is the origin of the electrical charges on the micelles of a sol?

8. State the characteristics of hydrophilic and hydrophobic colloids.

9. How would you expect the Brownian movement to be affected by the size of the dispersed particles?

10. Explain why two colloids containing particles of opposite charges will precipitate upon being mixed.

11. How can the sign of the charge on a colloid be determined?

12. How is it possible to hasten the coagulation of a colloidal dispersion in water?

13. What is the relation between the charge of an ion and its ability to coagulate a colloid?

14. What conditions are necessary to produce colloidal dispersions?

15. What conditions are most suitable for preventing the formation of colloids during the process of precipitation?

16. How may the addition of an electrolyte to wash water prevent peptization of a precipitate?

17. Make a sketch to illustrate how dialysis is accomplished.

18. List and illustrate seven different types of dispersions.

CHAPTER 9

OXIDATION AND REDUCTION THEORY

All chemical reactions involve changes in energy relationships. In 1879, Berthelot arrived at the false conclusion that the evolution of heat in a chemical reaction was a measure of the driving force of the reaction. However, the fact that many reactions proceed with the adsorption of heat proves that Berthelot's idea could not be correct. A true measure of the driving force of a chemical reaction is the maximum work that can be obtained from the reaction under specified conditions. Substances combine chemically when their total energy contents change from a higher level of availability to a lower level. In other words, if the free energy of the reactants is greater than that of the products, the reaction will proceed. Also, the size of the free-energy decrease is a quantitative measure of the driving force of the reaction.

9·1 Some Free-energy Relationships. *Free energy* is defined as the capacity of a reaction for doing work. It is a measure of the maximum available work which can be obtained from a reaction regardless of whether work is done or not. In any chemical reaction there is a change in free energy, and this free-energy change is the sum of the free energies of formation for the products minus the sum of the free energies of formation for the reacting substances. Free energy, likewise, measures the tendency of a reaction to proceed; consequently, there are three possibilities for any given chemical reaction:

1. If the free-energy change is a negative value, the reaction is spontaneous, and will proceed in the direction as the equation is written.

2. If the free-energy change is a positive value, the reaction is not spontaneous, but will proceed in the reverse direction.

3. If the free-energy change is equal to zero, the system is in equilibrium, and the reaction will not proceed in either direction.

Therefore, in mathematical terms, the change in free energy is equal to the negative of the maximum work, or

$$\text{Change in free energy} = -W_{\max}$$

To every substance may be assigned a relative energy quantity called its free energy. Since absolute values for free energies are not known, they are not measurable; on the other hand, changes in free energy are

152

measurable. To illustrate these statements consider the reaction between zinc atoms and copper ions to produce zinc ions and copper atoms:

$$Zn + Cu^{++} \rightleftharpoons Zn^{++} + Cu$$

The absolute free energies of the substances involved in the reaction are not known, but, from their many known reactions, relative values, called *standard free energies*, have been assigned to them. The standard free energies of the Cu^{++} and Zn^{++} ions are 15,910 and $-35,110$ cal/gram atom, respectively; the free energies of the metals are taken as zero.

$$Zn + Cu^{++} \rightleftharpoons Zn^{++} + Cu$$
$$(0 + 15,910) \qquad (-35,100 + 0)$$
$$F_1 \text{(reactants)} \qquad F_2 \text{(products)}$$

Change in free energy $= F_2 - F_1$
$$= -35,110 - 15,910 = -51,020 \text{ cal}$$

The reaction proceeds from left to right, as written, because there is a driving force, produced by a change in free energy from a higher to a lower energy level, equal to $-51,020$ cal.

Since the free-energy change of a chemical reaction is a quantitative measure of chemical affinity, such measurements are used by industrial as well as theoretical chemists to predict which chemical reactions can be expected to take place, and which ones will not. Earlier discussions of equilibrium constants indicated that the course and extent of chemical reactions could also be predicted by the values of the equilibrium constants for the reactions. Consequently, it is to be expected that there is a direct relationship between free-energy changes and equilibrium constants. This relationship is expressed by the equation

Change in free energy $= -RT \ln K$

where R is a constant equal to 1.988 cal. Thus, at 25°C, the equilibrium constant for the reaction of zinc and copper ions is

$$-51,020 \text{ cal} = -1.988 \times 298 \times \ln K$$

Or
$$\log K = \frac{51,020}{1.988 \times 298 \times 2.3} = 37$$
$$K = 10^{37}$$

This relationship is extremely convenient as a means of recording equilibrium constants with a small number of entries. A table of standard free energies of a large number of substances can be recorded on a few pages, whereas a tabulation of the equilibrium constants involving these same substances would require hundreds of pages.

Another method of evaluating the free-energy change, or driving force

of a redox reaction, is in terms of volts.   The standard redox potential is
related to the free-energy change by the expression

$$\text{Change in free energy} = -nFE^{\circ}$$

where change in free energy is expressed in joules (1 cal = 4.183 j), n is
the number of electrons, per atom or ion, exchanged in the reaction,
$F = 1$ faraday (96,494 coulombs), and $E^{\circ} = $ volts (standard redox
potential).

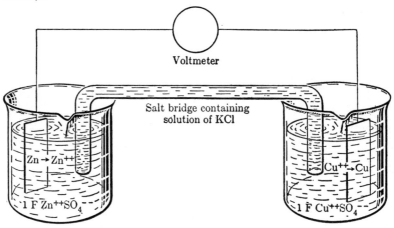

Fig. 9·1   Diagrammatic representation of a galvanic cell.

Using this expression to determine the voltage produced by the reaction of zinc with a 1 F solution of cupric ions at 25°C, the equation
becomes

$$4.183 \times 51{,}020 = 2 \times 96{,}494 \times E^{\circ}$$
$$E^{\circ} = \frac{51{,}020 \times 4.183}{2 \times 96{,}494} = 1.10 \text{ volts}$$

9·2   Galvanic Cells.   The driving force of a reaction may be evaluated
if the reaction can be arranged in the form of a galvanic cell from which
the maximum electromotive force can be determined.   Since electromotive force results from a flow of electrons, such a reaction must necessarily be one involving oxidation and reduction.   A galvanic cell is composed of electrodes dipping into solutions of electrolytes with electrical
contact between electrodes, and electrolytic contact between the solutions.   The electrodes and solutions are so selected that a spontaneous
chemical reaction takes place, resulting in an exchange of electrons.

The arrangement in a galvanic cell is shown in Fig. 9·1.   A solution of
an oxidizing agent is placed in one beaker and a solution of a reducing
agent in the other beaker.   A conducting electrode is immersed in each
solution, and electrolytic contact between the two solutions is established

by means of a salt bridge.   The latter is an inverted U tube containing
a solution of an electrolyte.   No current flow is produced until the external circuit is closed.   When the current does flow, in this particular cell,
electrons move along the wire from the zinc electrode to the copper electrode, since zinc holds its electrons more loosely than does copper.   The
two half-reactions are

$$\text{Zn} \rightleftharpoons \text{Zn}^{++} + 2e \qquad \text{and} \qquad \text{Cu}^{++} + 2e \rightleftharpoons \text{Cu}$$

and the over-all reaction for the cell is expressed in the equation,

$$\text{Zn} + \text{Cu}^{++} \rightleftharpoons \text{Zn}^{++} + \text{Cu}$$

If a sensitive voltmeter is inserted in the external circuit, the voltage of
this particular cell is found to be 1.10 volts.

The cell cannot operate without a transfer of ions.   As zinc enters
solution the concentration of Zn^{++} becomes greater, whereas the deposition of copper at the other electrode decreases the concentration of Cu^{++}
ions.   Consequently, an excess of sulfate ions accumulates around the
copper electrode, and an excess of zinc ions around the zinc electrode.
In any ionic solution, the sum of the negative charges must equal the
positive charges.   Hence, if no provision is made for the migration of
ions from one beaker to the other, the current will cease to flow.   The
salt bridge provides a pathway for the transfer of ions between the two
solutions so that the ionic charges within the solutions remain balanced.

It was stated that the potential difference between the zinc and copper
electrodes is measured as 1.10 volts, but this potential is obtained only
under certain specified conditions.   Actually, the magnitude of the potential difference between the two electrodes depends upon many factors.

Most important of the factors which determine the potential difference
developed by a galvanic cell is the nature of the two half-cells.   The
tendency of a metal to go into solution as ions (loss of electrons) is called
its *electrolytic solution pressure*.   The tendency for ions to lose their charge
(gain electrons) and form the free metal is called their *osmotic pressure*.
If nickel were used in the reducing half-cell, replacing zinc, the potential
of the cell would be lowered because nickel has a lower electrolytic solution pressure than zinc.   On the other hand, if the copper-cupric ion
half-cell were replaced by the silver-silver ion half-cell, the potential of
the cell would be increased.   This increase is due to the greater osmotic
pressure of the silver ions as compared with the cupric ions.

The concentration or activity of the ions of the metal in solution
affects the potential of the electrode.   When the cell in Fig. 9·1 is not
in operation, zinc exists in equilibrium with its ions and the charge upon
the electrode:

$$\text{Zn} \rightleftharpoons \text{Zn}^{++} + 2e$$

If the concentration of zinc ions is increased, the equilibrium is shifted to the left; from the principle of Le Chatelier, it can be predicted that the charge on the electrode will be decreased.   When the cell is in operation, the zinc metal is entering solution and cupric ions are plating out as copper metal.   Since the cell reaction and voltage are produced by the two half-reactions

$$Zn \rightleftharpoons Zn^{++} + 2e \qquad and \qquad Cu^{++} + 2e \rightleftharpoons Cu$$

the increase in zinc ions and decrease in cupric ions will each cause a decrease in the potential produced.   Consequently, as the cell reaction proceeds the cell "runs down" until, at equilibrium, the potential is zero.

Other factors of lesser importance which may affect the potential difference between two half-cells are temperature and the emf arising at the liquid-liquid junction of the two half-cells, the latter being known as the *liquid junction potential*.   This discussion will be confined to electrode reactions occurring at constant temperature, arbitrarily selected as 25°C, and the salt bridge usually contains a suitable electrolyte such that the liquid junction potential is reduced to a negligible amount.

9·3   Single Electrode Potential.   When a strip of metal, *e.g.*, zinc, is placed in a 1 F solution of its ions, an equilibrium reaction develops between the metal and its ions, as

$$Zn \rightleftharpoons Zn^{++} + 2e$$

The equilibrium expression may be written as

$$K_e = \frac{[Zn^{++}][e]^2}{[Zn]}$$

The term [Zn] may be omitted since the concentration, or activity, of a solid is constant at a given temperature; therefore,

$$K_e = [Zn^{++}][e]^2$$

No method is known for determining the absolute value of the equilibrium constant of a half-cell reaction.   Furthermore, it is impossible to measure directly the electrode potential between a metal and a solution of its ions.   Only the potential of a cell, resulting from a combination of two electrodes, may be measured.

To measure and evaluate potential differences between various electrodes (half-cells), it is necessary arbitrarily to designate a particular electrode as a standard.   The electrode which has been chosen for this purpose is the standard hydrogen electrode.   This electrode is so constructed (see Fig. 9·2) that hydrogen atoms are in contact with a 1 F (or activity equal to 1) solution of hydronium ions.   Hydrogen gas, at 1

atm pressure and at a temperature of 25°C, is bubbled over a plati-
nized platinum electrode which is immersed in a solution of hydronium
ions.   The finely divided platinum adsorbs hydrogen gas which exists in
equilibrium with hydronium ions, resulting in a definite electrode potential.   The equation for the half-cell reaction is

$$\tfrac{1}{2}H_2(g) + H_2O \rightleftharpoons H_3O^+(\text{soln}) + e$$

This potential is arbitrarily assigned a value of zero.

Figure 9·2 shows how the potential of the zinc electrode may be measured against that of the hydrogen electrode.

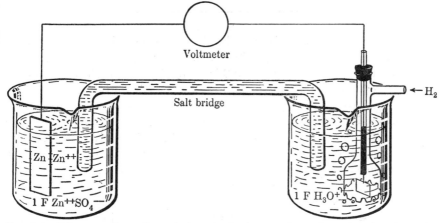

Fig. 9·2   Diagram of a cell consisting of a hydrogen electrode and a zinc electrode.

9·4   Electrochemical Conventions.   Certain conventions and nota-
tions have become fairly well standardized in connection with electrochemical cells.   A half-cell, such as a strip of zinc immersed in a solution
of 1 F Zn^{++}, is indicated as $Zn|Zn^{++}$ (1 F).   The vertical line denotes a
solid phase in contact with a liquid phase.   A galvanic cell, such as the
one in Fig. 9·1, is designated as

$$Zn|Zn^{++}(1\ F)||Cu^{++}(1\ F)|Cu$$

where the liquid junction is represented by two vertical lines.   The cell
in Fig. 9·2 may be indicated as

$$Zn|Zn^{++}(1\ F)||H_3O^+(1\ F)|H_2\ (1\ \text{atm})|Pt$$

Many different types of electrodes, or half-cells, are possible.   Some
of these possibilities are given in Table 9·1, along with the symbols
designating examples of such electrodes.

Standard electrode potentials are listed in this book (see Table 9·2) as oxidation potentials. Therefore, a half-cell reaction is written with the electron, or electrons, on the right-hand side of the equation, *e.g.*,

$$Li \rightleftharpoons Li^+ + e \qquad E = 3.02 \text{ volts}$$

TABLE 9·1   TYPES OF ELECTRODES

Metal, metal ion	$Zn|Zn^{++}$
Inert electrode, nonmetal, nonmetal ion	$Pt|Br_2(l)|Br^-$
Inert electrode, metal ions in different valences	$Pt|Sn^{++}, Sn^{4+}$
Inert electrode, gas, ion	$Pt|H_2|H_3O^+$
Metal, insoluble salt, ion	$Ag|AgCl|Ag^+$

For purposes of comparison and reference, electrode potentials must be evaluated at a fixed temperature and under standardized conditions of concentrations. Thus, Table 9·2 is a list of standard electrode potentials at 25°C, in which the reactants are at unit activity. The term *activity* refers to effective concentration, and in order to express activities numerically, it is customary to choose for each component of an electrode a reference state, known as the *standard state*. The activity is taken as unity in the standard state of a substance, and the actual standard state for a component is arbitrarily chosen as a matter of convenience.

The following standard states are generally accepted:

1. A gas is at standard state and unit activity at a pressure of 1 atm. When it is not at unit activity, the partial pressure, in atmospheres, is the effective concentration.

2. The standard state and unit activity of a liquid or solid are taken as the pure substance under atmospheric pressure.

3. The standard state of a solute in aqueous solutions is approximately 1 F (strictly, when $a = 1$).

4. The standard state and unit activity of a difficultly soluble salt are those of a saturated solution.

Potentials of half-cells, in which the reactants are at standard state, are represented as E^o. The potential difference developed by two half-cells, at standard state, is indicated as $E^o_{1-2} = E^o_1 - E^o_2$. Potentials of half-cells, in which the reactants are not at standard state, are denoted by the symbol E.

The voltage of a cell is the algebraic difference of the potentials of the two half-cells. For example, consider the cell

$$Pt|Sn^{4+}(1 \ F), \ Sn^{++}(1 \ F)||Ag^+(1 \ F)|Ag$$

By convention, the half-cell reaction of the right-hand electrode is sub-

TABLE 9·2 STANDARD OXIDATION-REDUCTION POTENTIALS

Half-cell reaction	E^o, volts
$Li \rightleftharpoons Li^+ + e$	3.02
$K \rightleftharpoons K^+ + e$	2.92
$Ba \rightleftharpoons Ba^{++} + 2e$	2.90
$Ca \rightleftharpoons Ca^{++} + 2e$	2.87
$Na \rightleftharpoons Na^+ + e$	2.71
$Mg \rightleftharpoons Mg^{++} + 2e$	2.34
$Al \rightleftharpoons Al^{3+} + 3e$	1.67
$Mn \rightleftharpoons Mn^{++} + 2e$	1.05
$Zn \rightleftharpoons Zn^{++} + 2e$	0.76
$Cr \rightleftharpoons Cr^{3+} + 3e$	0.71
$S^= \rightleftharpoons S + 2e$	0.51
$H_2C_2O_4(aq) + 2H_2O \rightleftharpoons 2CO_2(g) + 2H_3O^+ + 2e$	0.49
$Fe \rightleftharpoons Fe^{++} + 2e$	0.44
$H_2 + 2H_2O \rightleftharpoons 2H_3O^+(10^{-7}) + 2e$	0.41
$Cr^{++} \rightleftharpoons Cr^{3+} + e$	0.41
$Cd \rightleftharpoons Cd^{++} + 2e$	0.40
$Co \rightleftharpoons Co^{++} + 2e$	0.28
$Ni \rightleftharpoons Ni^{++} + 2e$	0.25
$Sn \rightleftharpoons Sn^{++} + 2e$	0.14
$Pb \rightleftharpoons Pb^{++} + 2e$	0.13
$H_2 + 2H_2O \rightleftharpoons 2H_3O^+ + 2e$	0.00
$H_2S + 2H_2O \rightleftharpoons S + 2H_3O^+ + 2e$	−0.14
$Sn^{++} \rightleftharpoons Sn^{4+} + 2e$	−0.15
$Cu^+ \rightleftharpoons Cu^{++} + e$	−0.17
$Cl^- + Ag \rightleftharpoons AgCl + e$	−0.22
$2Cl^- + 2Hg \rightleftharpoons Hg_2Cl_2 + 2e$	−0.27
$Cu \rightleftharpoons Cu^{++} + 2e$	−0.34
$2I^- \rightleftharpoons I_2 + 2e$	−0.54
$3I^- \rightleftharpoons I_3^- + 2e$	−0.54
$4H_2O + HAsO_2 \rightleftharpoons H_3AsO_4 + 2H_3O^+ + 2e$	−0.56
$H_2O_2 + 2H_2O \rightleftharpoons O_2 + 2H_3O^+ + 2e$	−0.68
$Fe^{++} \rightleftharpoons Fe^{3+} + e$	−0.77
$2Hg \rightleftharpoons Hg_2^{++} + 2e$	−0.80
$Ag \rightleftharpoons Ag^+ + e$	−0.80
$Hg \rightleftharpoons Hg^{++} + 2e$	−0.85
$CuI \rightleftharpoons Cu^{++} + I^- + e$	−0.88
$Hg_2^{++} \rightleftharpoons 2Hg^{++} + 2e$	−0.91
$HNO_2 + 4H_2O \rightleftharpoons NO_3^- + 3H_3O^+ + 2e$	−0.94
$NO + 6H_2O \rightleftharpoons NO_3^- + 4H_3O^+ + 3e$	−0.96
$2Br^- \rightleftharpoons Br_2(l) + 2e$	−1.07
$2Br^- \rightleftharpoons Br_2(aq) + 2e$	−1.09
$I_2 + 18H_2O \rightleftharpoons 2IO_3^- + 12H_3O^+ + 10e$	−1.20
$6H_2O \rightleftharpoons O_2 + 4H_3O^+ + 4e$	−1.23
$6H_2O + Mn^{++} \rightleftharpoons MnO_2 + 4H_3O^+ + 2e$	−1.28
$2Cl^- \rightleftharpoons Cl_2(g) + 2e$	−1.36
$21H_2O + 2Cr^{3+} \rightleftharpoons Cr_2O_7^- + 14H_3O^+ + 6e$	−1.36
$Au \rightleftharpoons Au^{3+} + 3e$	−1.42

TABLE 9·2   STANDARD OXIDATION-REDUCTION POTENTIALS (*Continued*)

Half-cell reaction	E^o, volts
$9H_2O + Br^- \rightleftharpoons BrO_3^- + 6H_3O^+ + 6e$	-1.44
$9H_2O + Cl^- \rightleftharpoons ClO_3^- + 6H_3O^+ + 6e$	-1.45
$12H_2O + Mn^{++} \rightleftharpoons MnO_4^- + 8H_3O^+ + 5e$	-1.52
$Ce^{3+} \rightleftharpoons Ce^{4+} + e$	-1.61
$6H_2O + MnO_2 \rightleftharpoons MnO_4^- + 4H_3O^+ + 3e$	-1.67
$4H_2O \rightleftharpoons H_2O_2 + 2H_3O^+ + 2e$	-1.77
$Co^{++} \rightleftharpoons Co^{3+} + e$	-1.84
$2SO_4^- \rightleftharpoons S_2O_8^- + 2e$	-2.05
$2F^- \rightleftharpoons F_2(g) + 2e$	-2.85

tracted from the left-hand electrode; the half-cell potentials are subtracted in like manner.   Thus,

$$
\begin{array}{ll}
Sn^{++} \rightleftharpoons Sn^{4+} + 2e & E_1^o = -0.14 \\
\underline{2Ag \rightleftharpoons 2Ag^+ + 2e} & \underline{E_2^o = -0.80} \\
Sn^{++} + 2Ag^+ \rightleftharpoons Sn^{4+} + 2Ag & E_{1-2}^o = -0.14 - (-0.80) \\
& E_{1-2}^o = +0.66 \text{ volt}
\end{array}
$$

The sign of the voltage developed by the cell indicates the polarity of the right-hand electrode.   If the sign is positive it indicates that the reaction will proceed from left to right as written.   On the other hand, if the sign is negative the reaction will take place from right to left.

The magnitude of the voltage produced by a cell indicates the driving force of the reaction, or the relative energy level of one half-cell as compared with the other half-cell.

9·5   Application of Standard Electrode Potentials.   Table 9·2 indicates the relative tendencies for substances at standard state to lose or gain electrons.   Those substances at the top of the table lose their electrons most easily and are, therefore, the strongest reducing agents.   The substances at the bottom gain electrons most readily and are the strongest oxidizing agents.   The table is sometimes called the *reactivity series*, since the reactivity of the metals decreases from top to bottom, while that of the nonmetals increases in the same direction.

Standard electrode potentials may be used to calculate the emf of any cell whose reactants are at standard state.   For example, given the cell

$$Cd|Cd^{++}(1\ F)||Br^-(1\ F)|Br_2(l)|Pt$$

calculate the voltage produced and write the cell reaction.

$$
\begin{array}{ll}
Cd \rightleftharpoons Cd^{++} + 2e & E_1^o = 0.40 \\
\underline{2Br^- \rightleftharpoons Br_2 + 2e} & \underline{E_2^o = -1.07} \\
Cd + Br_2 \rightleftharpoons Cd^{++} + 2Br^- & E_{1-2}^o = 0.40 - (-1.07) \\
& E_{1-2}^o = 1.47 \text{ volts}
\end{array}
$$

The table of standard electrode potentials permits the prediction as to whether a reaction (with reactants at standard state) will proceed as written.   For example, will the reaction

$$Sn^{4+} + 2Ce^{3+} \rightleftharpoons Sn^{++} + 2Ce^{4+}$$

take place from left to right as written?   If a cell were constructed from the above reaction it would be

$$Pt|Ce^{3+}(a = 1), Ce^{4+}(a = 1)||Sn^{4+}(a = 1), Sn^{++}(a = 1)|Pt$$

The half-cell reactions and standard electrode potentials are

$2Ce^{3+} \rightleftharpoons 2Ce^{4+} + 2e$	$E_1^o = -1.61$
$Sn^{++} \rightleftharpoons Sn^{4+} + 2e$	$E_2^o = -0.15$
The reducing agent	$E_{1-2}^o = -1.46$ volt
is arbitrarily placed	
on the left	

The negative value obtained for the emf of this cell indicates that the chemical reaction obtained by combination of the half-cell reactions does not proceed in the direction as written but is spontaneous from right to left.

The potentials listed in Table 9·2 are not absolute values.   They are relative half-cell potentials in terms of the standard hydrogen electrode, which is arbitrarily given a value of zero.   For many reasons, the construction and use of the hydrogen electrode are not always convenient. Consequently, other reference electrodes have been devised whose emfs are accurately known in relation to the standard hydrogen electrode.

9·6   Effect of Concentration on Electromotive Force.   Table 9·2 lists the standard electrode potentials of a number of half-cells at 25°C. These values are reproducible only when the substances which make up the half-cell are in their standard states of unit activity.   If the substances are not at standard state the electrode potentials are no longer standard electrode potentials.   Therefore, electrode potentials, at a fixed temperature, will vary with changing concentrations of the reactants which constitute the half-cells.

The relation of concentration to a single electrode potential is given by the Nernst equation:

$$E = E^o - \frac{RT}{nF} \ln \frac{a_{\text{oxidized state}}}{a_{\text{reduced state}}}$$

where E is the measured electrode potential, E^o is the standard electrode potential, n is the number of electrons involved in the half-cell reaction, R is in joules per degree (8.314), T is temperature in degrees Kelvin, F is the faraday constant (96,494 coulombs), and a_{ox}/a_{red} is the ratio of the product of the activities of the reaction products divided by the product of the activities of the reactants, each activity raised to a numerical power equal to the coefficient of the number of ions involved in the half-cell equation. If all the constants are substituted into the equation at 25°C, it may be simplified to

$$E = E^o - \frac{0.059}{n} \log \frac{a_{ox}}{a_{red}}$$

The emf of a cell in which the reactants of the half-cells are not at unit activity is expressed by the equation

$$E_{1-2} = E^o_{1-2} - \frac{0.059}{n} \log Q$$

where Q is the product of the activities of the reaction products divided by the product of the activities of the starting substances, each activity raised to a numerical power equal to the coefficient of the number of molecules or ions involved in the chemical equation. By way of illustration, this equation may be used for calculating the emf of a Daniel cell in which the concentration of the Cu^{++} is 0.001 F and that of the Zn^{++} is 1 F. The cell is set up as follows:

$$Zn|Zn^{++}(1\ F)||Cu^{++}(0.001\ F)|Cu$$

The half-cell reactions are

$$Zn \rightleftharpoons Zn^{++} + 2e \qquad E^o_1 = 0.76$$
$$Cu \rightleftharpoons Cu^{++} + 2e \qquad E^o_2 = -0.34$$
$$\overline{Zn + Cu^{++} \rightleftharpoons Zn^{++} + Cu \qquad E^o_{1-2} = 1.10 \text{ volts}}$$

Therefore,

$$E = 1.10 - \frac{0.059}{2} \log \frac{[Zn^{++}]}{[Cu^{++}]}$$

where the concentration, of the solid metals, zinc and copper, remain constant. Thus,

$$E = 1.10 - 0.0295 \log \frac{(1)}{(0.001)}$$
$$E = 1.10 - 0.0295 \log 10^3 = 1.10 - (0.0295 \times 3)$$
$$E = 1.10 - 0.09 = 1.01 \text{ volts}$$

Since the potential difference between a metal and its ions depends upon ionic concentration, a cell can be constructed consisting of two electrodes of the same metal dipping into solutions of different ionic concentrations. This is one type of a concentration cell, which may be illustrated by measuring the potential between two zinc electrodes whose ionic concentrations are 1 F and 0.001 F, respectively. This cell is indicated symbolically as

$$Zn|Zn^{++}(0.001\ F)||Zn^{++}(1\ F)|Zn$$

If the two half-cells are designated as E_1 and E_2, then

$$E_1 = E^o - \frac{0.059}{2} \log\ (0.001)$$

$$E_2 = E^o - \frac{0.059}{2} \log\ (1)$$

Combining the two equations produces

$$E_{1-2} = -\frac{0.059}{2} (\log 0.001 - \log 1)$$

$$E_{1-2} = \frac{0.059}{2} \log 1{,}000$$

$$E_{1-2} = 0.0295 \times 3 = 0.088\ volt$$

9·7 Calculation of Equilibrium Constants from Electrode Potentials.
Redox reactions are reversible and, therefore, subject to the law of chemical equilibrium. Consequently, when a cell is short-circuited until the voltage decreases to zero, the products and reactants of the half-cells reach a condition of concentrations in which they are in equilibrium with each other. At equilibrium, E_{1-2} is zero, and the Nernst equation for determining the emf of a cell is modified into the expression

$$0 = E^o_{1-2} - \frac{0.059}{n} \log K_e$$

where K_e is the equilibrium constant for the cell reaction. Further simplification reduces the equation to

$$\log K_e = \frac{nE^o_{1-2}}{0.059}$$

This expression permits the calculation of equilibrium constants from the electrode potentials of the half-cells involved in redox reactions. To illustrate, consider the reaction

$$Sn^{++} + 2Fe^{3+} \rightleftharpoons Sn^{4+} + 2Fe^{++}$$

from which the following cell may be set up:

$$Pt|Sn^{++},\ Sn^{4+}||Fe^{3+},\ Fe^{++}|Pt$$

The half-cell reactions and standard electrode potentials are

$$
\begin{array}{ll}
Sn^{++} \rightleftharpoons Sn^{4+} + 2e & E_1 = -0.15 \\
2Fe^{++} \rightleftharpoons 2Fe^{3+} + 2e & \underline{E^o_2 = -0.77} \\
& E^o_{1-2} = +0.62\ volt
\end{array}
$$

At equilibrium,

$$0 = 0.62 - \frac{0.059}{2} \log K_e$$

$$\log K_e = \frac{0.62}{0.0295} = 21$$

$$K_e = 10^{21}$$

The magnitude of the equilibrium constant of a reaction is an approximate indication of the completeness of the reaction under specified conditions. A large value for K_e indicates that the reaction goes, from left to right, a long way toward completion. The same general significance holds true for a very small equilibrium constant, except that such a value indicates that the reaction proceeds from right to left. When two standard potentials are not very different, the equilibrium constant which may be derived from the two half-cell reactions will not vary widely from unity. Such a value indicates that the over-all cell reaction will not be complete in either direction.

It should be pointed out that the evaluation of an equilibrium constant from two standard electrode potentials is not always a trustworthy indication of the completeness of the cell reaction. A wide difference in electrode potentials denotes that the reaction will proceed until the concentrations of the reactants are greatly altered, but this difference gives no information as to the rate at which equilibrium is approached. It is possible that the absence of a suitable catalyst may prevent such a reaction from reaching equilibrium within a reasonable time.

Types of Exercises Involving Oxidation Potentials

Type 1. *Calculate the potentials of the following half-cells at 25°C.*

(a) $Hg \rightleftharpoons Hg^{++}(0.01 \ F) + 2e$
(b) $Fe^{++}(0.0001 \ F) \rightleftharpoons Fe^{3+}(0.1 \ F) + e$

Solution (a): The standard electrode potential for $Hg \rightleftharpoons Hg^{++} + 2e$ is -0.85 volt, and from the Nernst equation

$$E = E^o - \frac{0.059}{n} \log \frac{[Hg^{++}]}{[Hg]}$$

Therefore,

$$E = -0.85 - \frac{0.059}{2} \log 10^{-2}$$

$$E = -0.85 + 0.059 = -0.79 \text{ volt}$$

Solution (b): The standard electrode potential for $Fe^{++} \rightleftharpoons Fe^{3+} + e$ is -0.77 volt; therefore,

$$E = -0.77 - \frac{0.059}{1} \log \frac{0.1}{0.0001}$$

and

$$E = -0.77 - 0.059 \log 10^3$$
$$E = -0.77 - 0.059 \times 3 = -0.95 \text{ volt}$$

Type 2. *Construct the cell which corresponds to the reaction*

$$Pb + 2Ag^+ \rightleftharpoons Pb^{++} + 2Ag$$

If all the substances are at standard state, calculate the voltage of the reaction at 25°C.
Solution: The cell which corresponds to this reaction is

$$Pb|Pb^{++}(1\ F)||Ag^+(1\ F)|Ag$$

The half-cell reactions and single electrode potentials are

$$Pb \rightleftharpoons Pb^{++} + 2e \qquad\qquad E_1^o = \quad 0.13$$
$$2Ag \rightleftharpoons 2Ag^+ + 2e \qquad\qquad E_2^o = -0.80$$

The potential difference is $\qquad E_{1-2}^o = 0.13 - (-0.80) = 0.93 \text{ volt}$

Type 3. *Give the cell reaction and calculate the emf of the following cell:*

$$Pt|Br_2(l)|Br^-(1\ F)||Cl^-(1\ F)|Cl_2(1 \text{ atm})|Pt$$

Solution:

$$2Br^- \rightleftharpoons Br_2(l) + 2e \qquad E_1^o = -1.07$$
$$2Cl^- \rightleftharpoons Cl_2 + 2e \qquad E_2^o = -1.36$$

$$2Br^- + Cl_2 \rightleftharpoons Br_2 + 2Cl^- \qquad E_{1-2}^o = +0.29 \text{ volt}$$

Type 4. *Set up the cell and calculate the potential at 25°C for the following reaction.*
(Indicated concentrations are those at the beginning of the reaction.)

$$Sn + Cu^{++}(0.1\ F) \rightleftharpoons Cu + Sn^{++}(0.5\ F)$$

Solution:

$$Sn|Sn^{++}(0.5\ F)||Cu^{++}(0.1\ F)|Cu$$
$$Sn \rightleftharpoons Sn^{++} + 2e \qquad E_1^o = \quad 0.14$$
$$Cu \rightleftharpoons Cu^{++} + 2e \qquad E_2^o = -0.34$$
$$E_{1-2}^o = +0.48 \text{ volt}$$

$$E_{1-2} = E_{1-2}^o - \frac{0.059}{n} \log \frac{[Cu][Sn^{++}]}{[Sn][Cu^{++}]}$$

$$E_{1-2} = 0.48 - \frac{0.059}{2} \log \frac{0.5}{0.1}$$

$$E_{1-2} = 0.46$$

Type 5. *Write the cell reaction and calculate the voltage which can be obtained from the following cell:*

$$Pt|Cl_2(1 \text{ atm})|Cl^-(1\ F)||Br^-(10^{-4}\ F)|Br_2(l)|Pt$$

Solution:

$$2Cl^- \rightleftharpoons Cl_2 + 2e \qquad E_1^o = -1.36$$
$$2Br^- \rightleftharpoons Br_2 + 2e \qquad E_2^o = -1.07$$

$$Br_2 + 2Cl^- \rightleftharpoons Cl_2 + 2Br^- \qquad E_{1-2}^o = -0.29 \text{ volt}$$

$$E_{1-2} = -0.29 - \frac{0.059}{2} \log \frac{[Br^-]^2}{[Cl^-]^2}$$

$$E_{1-2} = -0.29 - \frac{0.059}{2} \log (10^{-4})^2 = -0.29 + 0.0295 \times 8$$

$$E_{1-2} = -0.05 \text{ volt}$$

Type 6. *Compute the equilibrium constant for the reaction*

$$2Ce^{3+} + I_2 \rightleftharpoons 2Ce^{4+} + 2I^-$$

Solution:

$$2Ce^{3+} \rightleftharpoons 2Ce^{4+} + 2e \qquad E_1^o = -1.61$$
$$2I^- \rightleftharpoons I_2 + 2e \qquad \underline{E_2^o = -0.54}$$
$$E_{1-2}^o = -1.07$$

$$\log K_e = \frac{nE_{1-2}^o}{0.059} = \frac{2 \times (-1.07)}{0.059} = -36.3$$

$$K_e = 10^{-36.3} = 10^{.7} \times 10^{-37} = 5 \times 10^{-37}$$

Type 7. *From the following two half-cell reactions, calculate the solubility product constant of* CuI:

$$CuI(s) \rightleftharpoons Cu^{++} + I^- + e \qquad E^o = -0.877$$
$$Cu^+ \rightleftharpoons Cu^{++} + e \qquad E^o = -0.167$$

Solution: Subtracting the second equation from the first gives the following expression:

$$CuI(s) \rightleftharpoons Cu^+ + I^- \qquad E_{1-2}^o = -0.71$$

$$\log K_{s.p.} = \frac{nE_{1-2}^o}{0.059} = \frac{1 \times (-0.71)}{0.059} = -12$$

$$K_{s.p.} = 10^{-12}$$

Exercises

1. From the standard oxidation potentials given in Table 9·2, calculate the potentials of the following half-cells at 25°C:

(a) $Al|Al^{3+}(0.01\ F)$
(b) $Zn|Zn^{++}(0.001\ F)$
(c) $S|S^-(0.1\ F)$
(d) $Cr^{++}(0.001\ F),\ Cr^{3+}(0.1\ F)$
(e) $Br_2(l)|Br^-(0.01\ F)$
(f) $Co^{++}(0.1\ F),\ Co^{3+}(0.001\ F)$
(g) $SO_4^-(1\ F),\ S_2O_8^-(0.0001\ F)$
(h) $Cr^{3+}(0.1\ F),\ Cr_2O_7^-(0.001\ F),\ H_3O^+(0.001\ F)$

2. Calculate the voltage at 25°C, and write the cell reaction for each of the following cells:

(a) $Pb|Pb^{++}(1\ F)\|Ag^+(1\ F)|Ag$
(b) $Pt|I_2|I^-(1\ F)\|Ce^{4+}(1\ F),\ Ce^{3+}(1\ F)|Pt$

3. The following equations represent cell reactions in which all reactants and products are at standard state. Construct the cell and determine the voltage for each reaction.

(a) $Mg + 2Ag^+ \rightleftharpoons Mg^{++} + 2Ag$
(b) $2I^- + Cl_2 \rightleftharpoons I_2 + 2Cl^-$
(c) $2Fe^{3+} + 2Br^- \rightleftharpoons 2Fe^{++} + Br_2$
(d) $5Fe^{++} + MnO_4^- + 8H_3O^+ \rightleftharpoons 5Fe^{3+} + Mn^{++} + 12H_2O$
(e) $5Cl_2 + I_2 + 18H_2O \rightleftharpoons 2IO_3^- + 10Cl^- + 12H_3O^+$

4. What is the emf of each of the following concentration cells at 25°C?

(a) $Ag|Ag^+(0.01\ F)\|Ag^+(0.1\ F)|Ag$

(b) $Cu|Cu^{++}(0.01\ F)\|Cu^{++}(10^{-4}\ F)|Cu$

5. Calculate the emf of each of the following cells at 25°C, and write the chemical reaction for each cell.

(a) $Zn|Zn^{++}(10^{-4}F)\|Cd^{++}(0.2\ F)|Cd$

(b) $Pt|Fe^{++}(0.1\ F),\ Fe^{3+}(0.01\ F)\|Sn^{4+}(0.01\ F),\ Sn^{++}(0.1\ F)|Pt$

(c) $Pt|Mn^{++}(0.1\ F),\ MnO_4^-(0.05\ F),\ H_3O^+(0.2\ F)\|Sn^{4+}(0.01\ F),\ Sn^{++}(0.05\ F)|Pt$

(d) $Cd|Cd^{++}(0.01\ F)\|Cl^-(0.1\ F)|Cl_2(1\ atm)|Pt$

(e) $Pt|Sn^{++}(10^{-2}\ F),\ Sn^{4+}(10^{-6}\ F)\|Cl^-(10^{-2}\ F)|Cl_2(10^{-2}\ atm)|Pt$

6. Calculate the equilibrium constant for each of the following reactions:

(a) $Sn^{4+} + Pb \rightleftharpoons Pb^{++} + Sn^{++}$

(b) $2Fe^{3+} + 2I^- \rightleftharpoons 2Fe^{++} + I_2$

(c) $2I^- + H_3AsO_4 + 2H_3O^+ \rightleftharpoons I_2 + HAsO_2 + 4H_2O$

(d) $2MnO_4^- + 16H_3O^+ + 5Sn^{++} \rightleftharpoons 2Mn^{++} + 24H_2O + 5Sn^{4+}$

(e) $6Br^- + Cr_2O_7^- + 14H_3O^+ \rightleftharpoons 3Br_2 + 2Cr^{3+} + 21H_2O$

7. From the following two half-cell reactions, calculate the solubility product constant for AgCl:

$$Ag \rightleftharpoons Ag^+ + e \qquad E° = -0.80\ volt$$
$$Cl^- + Ag \rightleftharpoons AgCl + e \qquad E° = -0.22\ volt$$

8. Compute the solubility product constant for mercurous chloride from the following two half-cell reactions and potentials:

$$2Hg = Hg_2^{++} + 2e \qquad E° = -0.80\ volt$$
$$2Cl^- + 2Hg \rightleftharpoons Hg_2Cl_2 + 2e \qquad E° = -0.27\ volt$$

CHAPTER 10

BALANCING OF OXIDATION-REDUCTION EQUATIONS

(A Review from General Chemistry)

A chemical equation is a shorthand method of expressing what happens qualitatively and quantitatively when atoms, ions, or molecules undergo chemical change. In order to write a correct equation for a chemical reaction, one must know the chemical symbols for the elements, ions, or molecules which enter into the reaction, and the products which are formed. This involves a knowledge of the electrical charges upon the reacting particles and the change of charge, if any, as a result of the chemical reaction.

10·1 Chemical Equations in General. Chemical reactions may be divided into two general types: those which involve a change in the electrical charges on the reacting particles, and those in which there is no such change. The latter type is the simpler of the two and includes exchanges or combinations of ions and molecules, such as

$$H_3O^+ + OH^- \rightleftharpoons 2H_2O$$
$$H_3O^+ + C_2H_3O_2^- \rightleftharpoons HC_2H_3O_2 + H_2O$$
$$AgCl + 2NH_3 \rightleftharpoons Ag(NH_3)_2^+ + Cl^-$$
$$CaCO_3 + 2H_3O^+ \rightleftharpoons Ca^{++} + 3H_2O + CO_2$$
$$Ba^{++} + SO_4^= \rightleftharpoons BaSO_4$$

The balancing of equations of this type consists in maintaining the same number of atoms on either side of the equation.

10·2 Oxidation-Reduction Reactions. A chemical reaction which results in a change in the electrical charges on the reacting particles is called a *reduction-oxidation reaction*, or *redox* for short. In this type of reaction, an atom, ion, or molecule gains or loses negative charges of electricity. Unit negative charges are known as electrons, and the gain or loss of electrons produces a change in the total charge on the reacting particle. The substance which furnishes the electrons is oxidized, and the substance receiving the electrons is reduced. Consequently, those substances which donate electrons easily are called *reducing agents*, and those substances which accept electrons readily are termed *oxidizing agents*. The two processes, oxidation and reduction, cannot take place separately but must occur simultaneously.

In some redox reactions it is difficult to determine which atoms lose and which gain electrons. To aid in the identification of those atoms which change valence within an oxidation-reduction reaction, it is convenient to introduce the concept of *oxidation number*. Atoms in an elementary state have an oxidation number of zero. Accordingly, elementary atoms of Zn, Fe, Mg, S, etc., have a zero charge. Atoms, ions, or molecules may enter into certain chemical reactions in which electrons are lost or gained. In such reactions, the oxidation number designates the number of electrons which have been lost or gained by an atom in arriving at a particular oxidation state. Balanced equations for partial reactions indicate how oxidation numbers may be evaluated. Reactions of this type are illustrated as follows:

$$S \rightleftharpoons S^= - 2e$$

The oxidation number of the sulfur atom in the sulfide ion, $S^=$, is -2 since two electrons were gained in producing this ion from elementary sulfur. On the other hand, if electrons are lost in a reaction involving sulfur, as

$$S + 9H_2O \rightleftharpoons SO_3^= + 6H_3O^+ + 4e$$

the oxidation number of the sulfur atom in the sulfite ion is $+4$ since four electrons were released in forming the ion. In the formation of the sulfate ion from sulfur, six electrons are produced as is indicated by the equation,

$$S + 12H_2O \rightleftharpoons SO_4^= + 8H_3O^+ + 6e$$

consequently, the oxidation number of the sulfur atom in the sulfate ion is $+6$.

10·3   Redox Reactions between Ions Which Do Not Contain Oxygen.
Metals display a difference in electron affinities. No two metals hold their valence electrons with the same amount of energy. A list of the common metals in the order of the ease with which they lose electrons is called the *electromotive series* (see Table 9·2). If a strip of an active metal—one which loses electrons easily—is placed in a solution of metallic ions of a less active metal, the more active metal will go into solution as ions, and the ions of the less active metal will gain electrons and be plated out of solution as the elementary metal. This may be illustrated by magnesium metal displacing antimony ions from solution, and the equation for this reaction is

$$3Mg + 2Sb^{3+} \rightleftharpoons 3Mg^{++} + 2Sb$$

Ions of the same metal in different states of valency vary in their degree of reactivity. For example, stannous ions in a hydrochloric acid solution of stannous chloride reduce mercuric chloride to mercurous chloride.

$$2Hg^{++} + Sn^{++} \rightleftharpoons Hg_2^{++} + Sn^{4+}$$

A more correct equation for this reaction, in the presence of excess chloride ions, is

$$2HgCl_4^= + Sn^{++} \rightleftharpoons Hg_2Cl_2 + SnCl_6^=$$

Nonmetals also form a reactivity series analogous to the electromotive series of metals, in which the nonmetals are listed in the order of their affinity for electrons. Since the chlorine atom has a greater affinity for its valence electrons than the bromine atom, chlorine will replace bromine from an aqueous solution of a bromide.

$$Cl_2 + 2Br^- \rightleftharpoons 2Cl^- + Br_2$$

10·4 Redox Reactions Involving Ions Containing Oxygen. Ions containing oxygen constitute the most important class of oxidizing agents, and redox reactions involving such ions are of frequent occurrence in qualitative analysis. Some oxidizing ions containing oxygen are NO_3^-, MnO_4^-, ClO_3^-, $Cr_2O_7^=$, and IO_3^-. Two illustrations of reactions involving oxygen-bearing ions are the oxidation of hydrogen sulfide by the nitrate ion in an acid solution, and the oxidation of chromite ions by hydrogen peroxide in an alkaline solution. The balanced equations for these two reactions are

$$3H_2S + 2NO_3^- + 2H_3O^+ \rightleftharpoons 3S + 2NO + 6H_2O$$

and

$$2Cr(OH)_4^- + 3H_2O_2 + 2OH^- \rightleftharpoons 2CrO_4^= + 8H_2O$$

The latter equation may be more correctly written as

$$2Cr(H_2O)_2(OH)_4^- + 3H_2O_2 + 2OH^- \rightleftharpoons 2CrO_4^= + 12H_2O$$

The process of balancing equations containing oxygen-bearing ions is sometimes difficult for the student to grasp. Part of this difficulty arises from indecision as to which side of the equation to insert hydronium ions, hydroxide ions, and water molecules. The following rules, with examples, will serve to simplify the manipulations of these particular ions and molecules:

In an Acid Solution. Oxygen lost by an ion combines with hydronium ions to form water.

$$5e + MnO_4^- + 8H_3O^+ \rightleftharpoons Mn^{++} + 12H_2O$$

Oxygen acquired by an ion is removed from water to form hydronium ions.

$$SO_3^= + 3H_2O \rightleftharpoons 2H_3O^+ + SO_4^= + 2e$$

In an Alkaline Solution.   Oxygen lost by an ion combines with water to form hydroxide ions.

$$2e + ClO^- + H_2O \rightleftharpoons 2OH^- + Cl^-$$

Oxygen acquired by an ion is removed from the hydroxide ion to form water.

$$CN^- + 2OH^- \rightleftharpoons H_2O + CNO^- + 2e$$

10·5   Methods for Balancing Redox Equations.   Simple redox equations, such as those between ions which do not contain oxygen, often may be balanced by inspection.   The redox reactions involving ions containing oxygen are more complex; they are more easily balanced in a series of steps in which an accounting is kept of electrons lost and electrons gained, as well as the rearrangement of atoms and ions from the reacting substances to form the reaction products.   The two most widely used methods for balancing ionic redox equations are the *ion-electron method* and the *valence-change method*.   An explanation is given for both methods, but the ion-electron method is the better of the two, since it is unambiguous in all its steps and may be applied successfully to any ionic redox reaction.

Ion-electron Method.   Five successive steps may be recognized in balancing an equation by this method.   These steps are illustrated by applying this method to the balancing of the equation for the reaction in which the sulfite ion is oxidized by the permanganate ion in an acid solution.   A knowledge of the formulas for the reacting substances and of the products formed is necessary in writing the unbalanced equation:

$$SO_3^= + MnO_4^- \rightleftharpoons SO_4^= + Mn^{++} \qquad \text{(skeletal equation)}$$

1. First, separate the reaction into two half-reactions, the oxidizing half-reaction and the reducing half-reaction.   Write skeletal equations for these two half-reactions, as

Oxidizing half-reaction	Reducing half-reaction
$MnO_4^- + H_3O^+ \rightleftharpoons Mn^{++} + H_2O$	$SO_3^= + H_2O \rightleftharpoons SO_4^= + H_3O^+$

2. Balance the two equations for the half-reactions as to the number of atoms on either side of each equation by inserting the proper coefficients for the ions or atoms involved.

$$MnO_4^- + 8H_3O^+ \rightleftharpoons Mn^{++} + 12H_2O \qquad SO_3^= + 3H_2O \rightleftharpoons SO_4^= + 2H_3O^+$$

3. Balance the two equations for the half-reactions electrically by add-

ing that number of electrons to one side of the equation which will make the number of electrical charges equal on both sides of each equation.

$$MnO_4^- + 8H_3O^+ \rightleftharpoons Mn^{++} + 12H_2O \qquad SO_3^= + 3H_2O \rightleftharpoons SO_4^= + 2H_3O^+$$
$$(-1) \; + (+8) \; = (+2) \qquad\qquad (-2) \qquad\quad = (-2) + (+2)$$
$$(+7) \; = (+2) \qquad\qquad\qquad\quad (-2) = (0)$$

Five electrons must be added to the left side of the equation to balance it electrically.

Two electrons must be added to the right side of the equation to balance it electrically.

$$5e + MnO_4^- + 8H_3O^+ \rightleftharpoons Mn^{++} + 12H_2O$$
$$SO_3^= + 3H_2O \rightleftharpoons SO_4^= + 2H_3O^+ + 2e$$

4. Multiply the two equations of the half-reactions by such numbers as will make the total electron change the same for both half-reactions.

$$2(5e + MnO_4^- + 8H_3O^+ \rightleftharpoons Mn^{++} + 12H_2O)$$
$$5(SO_3^= + 3H_2O \rightleftharpoons SO_4^= + 2H_3O^+ + 2e)$$

$$10e + 2MnO_4^- + 16H_3O^+ \rightleftharpoons 2Mn^{++} + 24H_2O$$
$$5SO_3^= + 15H_2O \rightleftharpoons 5SO_4^= + 10H_3O^+ + 10e$$

5. Add the two equations from the half-reactions, canceling any common ions or molecules which appear on both sides of the equations.

$$\overset{6H_3O^+}{} \qquad\qquad \overset{9H_2O}{}$$
$$\cancel{10e} + 2MnO_4^- + \cancel{16H_3O^+} \rightleftharpoons 2Mn^{++} + \cancel{24H_2O}$$
$$5SO_3^= + \cancel{15H_2O} \rightleftharpoons 5SO_4^= + \cancel{10H_3O^+} + \cancel{10e}$$

$$2MnO_4^- + 5SO_3^= + 6H_3O^+ \rightleftharpoons 2Mn^{++} + 5SO_4^= + 9H_2O$$

Valence-change Method. This method is more rapid, but its use offers difficulties in those equations where the oxidation numbers of atoms within ions are not clearly indicated. The valence-change method of balancing equations is illustrated by using the same equation that was used as an example in the ion-electron method.

$$SO_3^= + MnO_4^- \rightleftharpoons SO_4^= + Mn^{++} \qquad \text{(skeletal equation)}$$

Again, a series of steps is used to explain the development of the balanced equation.

1. Select the atom of that element in the oxidizing agent whose oxidation number is changed within the reaction, and indicate in the equation the number of electrons gained in this change.

$$\text{(Mn gains 5 electrons)}$$
$$\overset{+7}{} \qquad\qquad\quad \overset{+2}{}$$
$$SO_3^= + MnO_4^- \rightleftharpoons SO_4^= + Mn^{++}$$

2. Select the atom of that element in the reducing agent whose oxidation number is changed within the reaction, and indicate in the equation the number of electrons lost in this change.

(Mn gains 5 electrons)

$$\overset{+7}{SO_3^=} + \overset{}{MnO_4^-} \rightleftharpoons SO_4^= + \overset{+2}{Mn^{++}}$$

$$\underset{+4}{} \qquad\qquad \underset{+6}{}$$

(S loses 2 electrons)

3. Determine the smallest common denominator for electrons lost and electrons gained, and multiply the oxidizing and reducing agents by suitable small numbers such that the total electrons gained and lost are equal to each other.

(2 Mn atoms gain 10 electrons)

$$5SO_3^= + 2MnO_4^- \rightleftharpoons 5SO_4^= + 2Mn^{++}$$

(5 S atoms lose 10 electrons)

4. Balance the equation electrically by inserting the proper number of hydronium ions and water molecules.

$$5SO_3^= + 2MnO_4^- \rightleftharpoons 5SO_4^= + 2Mn^{++}$$
$$(-10) + (-2) \quad = (-10) + (+4)$$
$$(-12) \quad = (-6)$$

The left side of the equation contains an excess of six negative charges. It is necessary, therefore, to add six hydronium ions to counterbalance these negative charges.   The hydronium ions account for the formation of nine water molecules, which are inserted on the right side of the equation.   The balanced equation becomes

$$5SO_3^= + 2MnO_4^- + 6H_3O^+ \rightleftharpoons 5SO_4^= + 2Mn^{++} + 9H_2O$$

The valence-change method is not entirely satisfactory for balancing equations involving ions in which the oxidation number of one or more atoms is debatable.   For example, the oxidation of the oxalate ion by the permanganate ion takes place in an acid solution according to the following equation:

$$2MnO_4^- + 5H_2C_2O_4 + 6H_3O^+ \rightleftharpoons 2Mn^{++} + 10CO_2 + 14H_2O$$

In this equation the manganese atom of the permanganate ion has a valence of $+7$ and is reduced in the reaction to $+2$ in the manganous ion, but the change in the oxidation number of the carbon atom, or atoms, in the oxalate ion to carbon dioxide is not entirely clear.

10·6   Redox Equations for Reactions Taking Place in Alkaline Solution.   The oxidation of the sulfite ion by the permanganate ion, used to illustrate the methods of balancing redox equations, takes place in an acid solution. In writing the equation for this reaction, it is necessary to use hydronium ions to combine with the oxygen atoms lost by the oxidizing agent to give water molecules as a product. Redox reactions also take place in an alkaline solution, but in this medium there is a balancing of hydroxide ions against water molecules. An illustration of a redox reaction in alkaline solution is the oxidation of the chromite ion by hydrogen peroxide. The equations for this reaction are

Oxidizing half-reaction

$$2e + H_2O_2 \rightleftharpoons 2OH^-$$

$$3(2e + H_2O_2 \rightleftharpoons 2OH^-)$$

or

Reducing half-reaction

$$Cr(H_2O)_2(OH)_4^- + 4OH^- \rightleftharpoons$$
$$CrO_4^= + 6H_2O + 3e$$

$$2(Cr(H_2O)_2(OH)_4^- + 4OH^- \rightleftharpoons$$
$$CrO_4^= + 6H_2O + 3e)$$

Upon adding the two equations and canceling common ions,

$$\cancel{6e} + 3H_2O_2 \rightleftharpoons \cancel{6OH^-}$$

$$2Cr(H_2O)_2(OH)_4^- + \cancel{8OH^-} \rightleftharpoons 2CrO_4^= + 12H_2O + \cancel{6e}$$

$$\underline{\hspace{3cm} 2OH^- \hspace{3cm}}$$

$$2Cr(H_2O)_2(OH)_4^- + 3H_2O_2 + 2OH^- \rightleftharpoons 2CrO_4^= + 12H_2O$$

10·7 Use of Hydrated Ions in Writing Equations. The majority of cations are hydrated in aqueous solution, but the exact degree of hydration has been established for only a few ions. It should be understood that the use of the symbol Mn^{++} for the manganous ion does not imply that the existence of the bare ion in a water solution is possible. Undoubtedly, a number of water molecules are held by the manganous ion, either by electrostatic attraction, by coordinate bonding, or by both of these binding forces. Therefore, the formula, $Mn(H_2O)_x^{++}$, is a more exact symbol for the hydrated ion. But since the degree of hydration for this ion and for most of the other cations is not known, it is customary to write such ions in the unhydrated form unless the addition of water molecules adds to the clarification of what is taking place in the reaction.

With the possible exception of the hydronium ion, the representation of hydrated ions in strongly acid solutions serves no useful purpose, since no theoretical relationship is involved to warrant the use of the hydrated form. But there is a definite advantage in writing the hydrated forms for weakly acid or basic solutions, since there is much experimental evidence indicating that cations exhibit acidic properties due to hydration. The reactions of amphiprotic substances with water (hydrolysis) and with strong bases (complex-ion formation—sometimes designated as amphoterism) cannot be satisfactorily interpreted without the use of hydrated ions.

Exercises

The following unbalanced equations represent redox reactions taking place in acid solutions. Convert them to balanced ionic equations, introducing hydronium ions and water molecules wherever necessary.

1. $Fe^{++} + ClO_3^- \rightleftharpoons Fe^{3+} + Cl^-$
2. $Cr_2O_7^- + NO_2^- \rightleftharpoons Cr^{3+} + NO_3^-$
3. $MnO_4^- + Fe^{++} \rightleftharpoons Mn^{++} + Fe^{3+}$
4. $Cr^{3+} + S_2O_8^- \rightleftharpoons Cr_2O_7^- + SO_4^-$
5. $MnO_4^- + Cl^- \rightleftharpoons Mn^{++} + Cl_2$
6. $Cr_2O_7^- + Fe^{++} \rightleftharpoons Cr^{3+} + Fe^{3+}$
7. $MnO_4^- + H_2O_2 \rightleftharpoons Mn^{++} + O_2$
8. $Cr^{3+} + MnO(OH)_2 \rightleftharpoons Mn^{++} + CrO_4^-$
9. $Mn^{++} + BiO_2 \rightleftharpoons MnO_4^- + Bi^{3+}$
10. $I_2 + H_2S \rightleftharpoons S + I^-$
11. $MnO_4^- + H_2S \rightleftharpoons Mn^{++} + S$
12. $NO_3^- + Cu \rightleftharpoons Cu^{++} + NO$
13. $Cu + SO_4^- \rightleftharpoons Cu^{++} + SO_2$
14. $VO^{++} + MnO_4^- \rightleftharpoons VO_3^- + Mn^{++}$
15. $MnO_4^- + S_2O_3^- \rightleftharpoons Mn^{++} + S_4O_6^-$
16. $Zn + NO_3^- \rightleftharpoons Zn^{++} + NH_4^+$
17. $PbO_2 + Pb + SO_4^- \rightleftharpoons PbSO_4$
18. $BrO_3^- + I^- \rightleftharpoons Br^- + I_2$
19. $NO_3^- + Fe \rightleftharpoons Fe^{3+} + NO$
20. $NO_3^- + Cu \rightleftharpoons Cu^{++} + NO_2$
21. $NO_3^- + Cl^- \rightleftharpoons NOCl + Cl_2$
22. $H_2AsO_4^- + Zn \rightleftharpoons AsH_3 + Zn^{++}$
23. $SO_4^- + I^- \rightleftharpoons I_2 + H_2S$
24. $MnO_4^- + I^- \rightleftharpoons Mn^{++} + I_2$
25. $Fe^{3+} + H_2S \rightleftharpoons Fe^{++} + S$
26. $IO_3^- + I^- \rightleftharpoons I_2$
27. $MnO_4^- + H_2C_2O_4 \rightleftharpoons CO_2 + Mn^{++}$
28. $NO_3^- + Zn \rightleftharpoons Zn^{++} + N_2$
29. $H_2SO_3 + I_2 \rightleftharpoons SO_4^- + I^-$
30. $MnO_4^- + NO_2^- \rightleftharpoons Mn^{++} + NO_3^-$
31. $Co_2O_3 + H_2O_2 \rightleftharpoons Co^{++} + O_2$

The following unbalanced equations represent redox reactions which take place in alkaline solutions. Convert them to balanced ionic equations, introducing hydroxide ions and water molecules wherever necessary.

32. $Cr(H_2O)_2(OH)_4^- + Na_2O_2 \rightleftharpoons CrO_4^- + Na^+$
33. $NO_2^- + Al \rightleftharpoons NH_3 + Al(H_2O)_2(OH)_4^-$
34. $Cu^{++} + CN^- \rightleftharpoons Cu(CN)_3^- + CNO^-$
35. $CH_2O + Ag_2O \rightleftharpoons Ag + HCO_2^-$
36. $Al \rightleftharpoons Al(H_2O)_2(OH)_4^- + H_2$
37. $ClO_3^- + Zn \rightleftharpoons Zn(H_2O)(OH)_3^- + Cl^-$
38. $CN^- + Fe(CN)_6^{3-} \rightleftharpoons CNO^- + Fe(CN)_6^{4-}$
39. $CN^- + MnO_4^- \rightleftharpoons CNO^- + MnO(OH)_2$
40. $Cr(H_2O)_2(OH)_4^- + ClO^- \rightleftharpoons Cl^- + CrO_4^-$
41. $CrO_4^- + Sn(H_2O)(OH)_3^- \rightleftharpoons Cr(H_2O)_2(OH)_4^- + Sn(H_2O)(OH)_5^-$
42. $Bi(H_2O)_3(OH)_3 + Sn(H_2O)(OH)_3^- \rightleftharpoons Bi + Sn(H_2O)(OH)_5^-$

PART II
EXPERIMENTAL PROCEDURES

CHAPTER 11

GENERAL LABORATORY DIRECTIONS—INTRODUCTION TO CATION ANALYSIS

The laboratory work of qualitative analysis, as the term implies, consists in the identification of the constituents of materials by systematic methods. The materials are restricted to ordinary inorganic substances, the components of which may be detected by means of cation and anion analysis.

11·1 Scale of Operations. Semimicro analysis differs from macro analysis in the amounts of materials used. Ordinary, or macro, analysis utilizes volumes of solutions ranging from 5 to 100 ml or more, whereas in semimicro procedures the volumes used range from 1 drop to approximately 1 ml. Therefore, it may be said that semimicro analysis deals with quantities of materials which are less than one-tenth of those amounts handled in ordinary analysis. As a result of this reduced scale in volumes and also weights of materials, the apparatus of semimicro analysis are designed to utilize the smaller quantities.

11·2 Apparatus to Be Constructed. In Table A·1 will be found a list of the apparatus issued to each student. In addition to these standard pieces of equipment, it will be necessary for the student to construct a few pieces of apparatus which have special uses in the laboratory procedures.

The liquid measurements of semimicro analysis are somewhat approximate, and are based largely upon the volume of a drop. We shall define a drop as being equal to 0.05 ml, although the actual volume varies with the diameter of the tip of the dropper. The ordinary medicine dropper is too short to reach to the bottom of a 10-ml test tube; therefore, it will be necessary for the student to construct three or more **micropipettes** from 7-mm glass tubing. These pipettes should be at least 12 cm in length with a tip of the diameter of a standard medicine dropper (1.5-mm inside diameter).

The four glass **stirring rods** (125 × 3 mm) should be fire-polished to prevent scratching of test tubes and beakers.

The H_2S generator is constructed from a 200 × 25 mm test tube, attached to a connecting (drying) tube from which a piece of rubber tubing (30 cm) leads to a delivery tip. A sketch of the generator is shown in Fig. 11·1.   The H₂S gas is obtained by gently heating a mixture of paraffin, sulfur, and asbestos.   (This mixture is sold commercially under the trade name *Aitch-Tu-Ess.*)   The generator should not be more than one-fourth filled with the material.   Several delivery tips should be prepared, since a tip becomes contaminated with use.

11·3   Reagents.   The reagents used in the experimental procedures of this book are listed in Table A·2.   Solutions frequently used (acids,

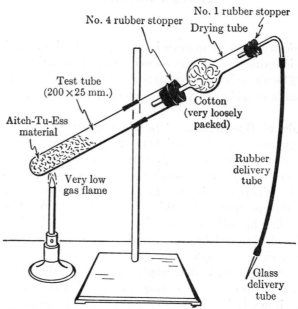

No. 4 rubber stopper

No. 1 rubber stopper

Drying tube

Test tube
(200 × 25 mm.)

Aitch-Tu-Ess
material

Cotton
(very loosely
packed)

Very low
gas flame

Rubber
delivery
tube

Glass
delivery
tube

FIG. 11·1   Sketch of the assembly of the H₂S generator.

bases, and reagent solutions) should be available to individual students. Solutions for individual kits should be contained in 30-ml bottles fitted with dropper assemblies.   A few solutions which attack rubber assemblies rapidly may be issued in small glass-stoppered bottles.   Those solutions which are less frequently used, such as test solutions (Table A·2), may be available in larger bottles on a side shelf.   The latter solutions are more conveniently utilized from 250-ml bottles fitted with dropper assemblies.

MANIPULATIONS OF SEMIMICRO ANALYSIS

11·4   Precipitations.   As a general rule precipitations of semimicro analysis are carried out in test tubes.   Two types of test tubes are available for this purpose: tapered test tubes with a capacity of approximately 5 ml, and the ordinary 10-ml test tubes.   The only advantage of the tapered test tube is that by its structure it tends to magnify the size of the precipitate which it contains. The tapered test tube has the decided disadvantage of being very difficult to clean. It is generally good technique to carry out all precipitations in ordinary test tubes except in those cases where the precipitates serve as confirmatory tests.

The precipitating agent should be added dropwise with stirring until precipitation is complete. Stirring is accomplished by means of a glass rod, care being exercised not to scratch the walls of the test tube.

11·5 Heating a Solution. A solution in a small test tube cannot be safely heated over a direct flame, since bumping would cause the loss of part or all of the liquid. The most satisfactory method for heating solutions contained in small test tubes is in a water bath. An aluminum bath rack, designed to fit a 250-ml beaker, provides a support for suspending test tubes in boiling water. The beaker should be kept three-fourths filled with water and heated to simmering during the entire time of an analysis.

11·6 Evaporation. It is frequently necessary to reduce the volume of a solution by evaporation. To accomplish an appreciable reduction in volume by heating a solution contained in a test tube within a water bath is a time-consuming process. If care is exercised, evaporation may be carried out satisfactorily by heating the solution in a small porcelain casserole over an open flame. When evaporating to dryness the casserole should be removed from the flame while a few drops of liquid remain. The heat of the dish is sufficient to complete the evaporation.

11·7 The Centrifuge. In semimicro procedures, the process of filtration is replaced by the use of a centrifuge. The success of semimicro methods in qualitative analysis can be attributed largely to the elimination of arduous filtrations. Filter paper loses its original purpose and is useful only as a medium upon which certain spot tests may be carried out. The centrifuge is a device by which a centrifugal force produced by an electric motor speeds up the rate of settling of a precipitate. Precipitates will usually settle, in a good centrifuge, in less than a minute's time. The test tube containing the solution to be centrifuged should always be balanced by placing another test tube, containing an equal volume of water, in the centrifuge opposite the solution.

11·8 Removal of Supernatant Liquid. When a solution containing a precipitate is centrifuged, the latter is thrown to the bottom of the test tube in a compact form. The supernatant liquid, which is referred to as the *centrifugate*, may be removed by means of a micropipette, using proper precautions not to disturb the precipitate. The clear centrifugate is usually transferred to another test tube.

11·9 Washing of Precipitates. After removal of the centrifugate, the precipitate remaining in the test tube is wet with the solution containing ions of the centrifugate.   These ions may cause interference in the analysis of the precipitate and are usually removed by washing.   The act of washing is accomplished by adding the required amount of distilled water (about 5 drops), and mixing the precipitate and wash water thoroughly with a stirring rod.   The mixture is then centrifuged, and the wash water removed by means of a micropipette.   Usually one or two washings suffice.

11·10   Transferring of Precipitates.   Occasionally it is necessary to transfer a precipitate from a test tube to another receptacle.   This is often a difficult operation, especially if the precipitate is gelatinous in nature.   Customarily such a transfer is accomplished with the use of a nickel microspatula.   However, this instrument cannot be used on a precipitate which is wet with a solution that reacts with nickel.

DIRECTIONS FOR LABORATORY WORK

The total time and number of operations allotted to laboratory work in qualitative analysis vary widely among different colleges and instructors.   Complete directions for the analyses of four known solutions and ten unknown samples are given in the Appendix (Secs. A·1 to A·9) under the heading Special Laboratory Directions.   A suggested schedule of laboratory work is also given in Sec. A·11.

11·11   The Known.   A student should be familiar with the procedures of an analytical scheme and be able to recognize the identifying tests for the ions within the scheme before he tackles the analyses of unknown mixtures.   This practice is obtained by analyzing solutions containing known mixtures of ions.   Known solutions are prepared from test solutions according to the directions given in Secs. A·1 to A·4.

One of the objectives of a laboratory course should be to train the student to keep a neat, accurate record of his laboratory observations.   A satisfactory form for recording the analysis of known and unknown solutions is given in Sec. A·11.[1]

11·12   The Unknown.   Samples for analysis are issued to the student as solutions and solids.   Specific directions for beginning the analysis of unknowns are given in Secs. A·1 to A·9.   The analyses of these unknowns increase in complexity from No. 1 through No. 9.   In addition to these special directions, Chap. 22 gives a detailed explanation of the generally accepted methods for the examination and complete analysis of an unknown sample.   A record of the analysis of the unknown should be kept, using the same form as was used in the analysis of a known.

---

[1] This general form was first suggested by William A. Noyes in "Elements of Qualitative Analysis," Henry Holt and Company, Inc., New York.

INTRODUCTION TO THE SYSTEMATIC ANALYSIS OF THE CATIONS

The first edition of the Fresenius "Qualitative Analysis" was published in 1840. This scheme, although modified and improved by subsequent investigators, has remained the standard procedure for the analysis of the cations until the present time. An analysis of a mixture containing all the known cations would be quite an involved process and certainly beyond the scope of an elementary course in qualitative analysis. The Fresenius scheme and those schemes modified from it attempt to identify only those cations of common occurrence. These cations, some 23 in number, are systematically separated into groups by the use of group reagents which precipitate chemically related ions. Thus the cations are divided into five major groups, four of which are precipitated by group reagents, whereas the fifth constitutes a soluble group. After group separation has been effected, it is necessary to separate, whenever feasible, the individual ions within a group for purposes of identification.

In the Fresenius scheme, two groups of cations are precipitated with hydrogen sulfide, one in an acid solution and the other in an ammoniacal solution. The greatest objection to the use of hydrogen sulfide is the poisonous nature of the gas when improperly used. The production and use of hydrogen sulfide, by any method, also limit the rapidity of the analysis. In spite of this undesirable feature of the Fresenius separation of the cations, the proponents of nonhydrogen sulfide schemes have not produced a satisfactory substitute during a period of more than a hundred years. An examination of solubility tables for possible precipitating anions other than the sulfide ion leads to the conclusion that the difference in the solubility products of any other anion is not sufficient to give complete and clear-cut separations.

Although the Fresenius scheme of analysis for the cations has survived for more than a hundred years, its usefulness in technical analysis has been fairly well outmoded. In the chemical industry, far more accurate and rapid methods are utilized for cation analyses. The value of this scheme of qualitative analysis is its pedagogical success in imparting to the student a considerable knowledge of fundamental and descriptive inorganic chemistry. Students are intrigued by the analyses of unknowns, and therefore willingly acquire skills and knowledge in matching wits against unknown mixtures.

No procedure of qualitative analysis is without faults. All texts vary to some extent in the separation of cations for identification. The scheme presented in this text is the result of constant revisions over years of laboratory instruction. Two objectives have ever been in mind: to present a scheme in which the student will have confidence in analyzing his unknowns, and to present useful and meaningful chemistry from a teaching standpoint. The use of organic reagents has been avoided as much as possible since such use adds very little practical chemistry to the sum of knowledge that may be assimilated by a student in elementary qualitative analysis.

SYSTEMATIC SEPARATION OF CATIONS INTO GROUPS

Test for NH_4^+ on a portion of the original solution.   Add 3 F HCl and centrifuge.

Residue contains chlorides of Group I: $PbCl_2$, AgCl, and Hg_2Cl_2.	**Centrifugate** contains cations of Groups II–V. Add HNO_3 to oxidize stannous ions, adjust acidity, and saturate with H_2S. Centrifuge.

Residue contains sulfides of Group II. Treat with 3 F KOH. Centrifuge. Undissolved **residue** contains sulfides of Group IIA, which are HgS, PbS, Bi_2S_3, CuS, and CdS. **Centrifugate** contains cations of Group IIB in the form of soluble anions, which are AsO_2^- and AsS_2^-, $Sb(OH)_4^-$ and SbS_2^-, $Sn(OH)_6^=$ and $SnS_3^=$.	**Centrifugate** contains cations of Groups III–V. Add saturated NH_4Cl solution, 3 F NH_3, and H_2S. Centrifuge.		
	Residue contains sulfides and hydroxides of Group III. Dissolve in aqua regia, and treat the solution with Na_2O_2 and 3 F KOH. Centrifuge. **Centrifugate** contains cations of Group IIIA as soluble anions. These are $CrO_4^=$, $Al(OH)_4^-$, and $Zn(OH)_3^-$. **Residue** contains hydroxides of Group IIIB. These are $MnO(OH)_2$, $Fe(OH)_3$, $Co(OH)_3$, and $Ni(OH)_2$.	**Centrifugate** contains cations of Groups IV and V. Add 0.5 $F(NH_4)_2HPO_4$ and concentrated NH_3. Centrifuge.	
		Residue contains phosphates of Group IV, which are $Ba_3(PO_4)_2$, $Sr_3(PO_4)_2$, $Ca_3(PO_4)_2$, and $MgNH_4PO_4$.	**Centrifugate** contains soluble cations, Na^+ and K^+, which did not precipitate in the first four groups.

CHAPTER 12

GROUP I CATIONS

The systematic analysis of the common cations is based upon the successive precipitation of groups of ions, so that the total number of ions can be broken down into a small number of groups, each containing a number of related cations. The first of these separations is the precipitation of Group I, which is composed of those common cations whose chlorides are relatively insoluble in dilute acids.

12·1 Theoretical Discussion. The successful separation of a group of cations is determined by the relative solubility products of the compounds formed by the cations with the precipitating anion. The insoluble chlorides of Group I are lead chloride, mercurous chloride, and silver chloride. The solubility products of these compounds are 1×10^{-4} for $PbCl_2$, 2×10^{-18} for Hg_2Cl_2, and 1.56×10^{-10} for $AgCl$. To the beginning student, the term solubility product may not be as significant as that of solubility. From the above figures the solubility of lead chloride is calculated to be approximately $0.04\,F$, that of mercurous chloride to be $7.5 \times 10^{-7}\,F$, and that of silver chloride as $1.3 \times 10^{-5}\,F$. A rough comparison of these solubilities indicates that lead chloride is one thousand times more soluble than silver chloride, and one hundred thousand times more soluble than mercurous chloride. Since the precipitating anion is in excess, the above solubilities are further decreased by common-ion effect.

The values for the solubilities of Group I chlorides indicate that silver chloride and mercurous chloride are almost completely precipitated, whereas lead chloride is always incompletely precipitated and in low concentrations may not be precipitated at all.

After the group separation is made, the ions within the group must be separated to the extent necessary for individual identification. Again, in the case of $PbCl_2$ there is a poor separation. Lead chloride is partially separated from mercurous chloride and silver chloride because of an increase in solubility of lead chloride in hot water. The solubility of $PbCl_2$ is 0.673 g/100 ml of water at 0°C and 3.34 g/100 ml at 100°C. In other words, the solubility of lead chloride increases approximately five times in going through this temperature range. Therefore, some $PbCl_2$ may be leached from the group precipitate by treating it with hot water,

185

provided that the water stays hot, but all the $PbCl_2$ is seldom removed. A portion of the undissolved $PbCl_2$ may remain as a white residue and cause some confusion in making the identification tests for silver and mercurous ions.

Silver chloride is separated from mercurous chloride by its solubility in ammonia, in which the soluble complex ion, $Ag(NH_3)_2{}^+$, is formed. The efficiency of this separation depends upon the concentration of the ammonia and the amount of AgCl. For most analytical concentrations this separation is clean, but the solubility of AgCl in ammonia water to form the soluble complex ion has a limiting value, and if the amount of AgCl is very large some of it may not be dissolved.

Ammonia water not only reacts with AgCl, but it also serves as a medium for the auto-redox action of Hg_2Cl_2 to produce mercury and mercuric aminochloride, both of which are insoluble. Metallic mercury, in a finely divided state, is black in color; therefore, a blackening at this point proves the presence of Hg_2Cl_2.

12·2   Analysis of Group I Cations. The analysis of this group is relatively simple. Three principal steps make up the procedures. First,

ANALYSIS OF GROUP I CATIONS

Procedure 1.   Precipitation of Group I Cations.   Place 10 drops of the solution to be analyzed (1) in a 10-ml test tube and add 4 drops of $3 F$ HCl.   (2) Mix thoroughly and centrifuge.   Test for completeness of precipitation by adding another drop of $3 F$ HCl to the supernatant liquid.   Centrifuge and remove centrifugate with a dropping tube. *This centrifuge is saved for analysis of Groups II–V.*   Precipitate remaining in the test tube is washed with 10 drops of cold water containing 1 drop of $3 F$ HCl.   (3) Discard wash water.

Procedure 2.   Separation of Lead Chloride.   White precipitate obtained in Procedure 1 may be $PbCl_2$, AgCl, and Hg_2Cl_2.   Add 6–7 drops of water and heat, with stirring, for 3 min in water bath.   Centrifuge quickly (4) and immediately remove centrifugate, while keeping mixture hot in a steam bath.

Centrifugate may contain Pb^{++}. Add 4 drops of $1 F$ K_2CrO_4. Yellow precipitate confirms presence of LEAD ION.	**Residue** may contain AgCl and Hg_2Cl_2. Treat with 10 drops of $3 F$ ammonia, stir thoroughly, and centrifuge. (5) A blackening of the residue indicates the presence of the mercurous ion.	
	Centrifugate may contain $Ag(NH_3)_2{}^+$. Acidify centrifugate with $3 F$ HNO_3. (6) Formation of a white precipitate confirms presence of SILVER ION.	**Residue** may contain mercury. (7) Wash with 10 drops of water and discard washings. Dissolve precipitate in 2 drops of concentrated HNO_3. Dilute with 5 drops of water. (If solution is not clear, centrifuge and retain centrifugate.) Add 1–2 drops of $SnCl_2$ solution. White or gray precipitate confirms presence of MERCUROUS ION.

the group is precipitated with dilute HCl as insoluble chlorides, and the resulting precipitate washed with cold water to remove other cation groups. Secondly, lead chloride is removed from the precipitate by leaching with hot water. The third step involves the separation of AgCl from Hg_2Cl_2 with ammonia water. Details of these procedures are given in the scheme of analysis for Group I cations.

Notes on the Analysis of Group I Cations

1. The solution to be analyzed may contain a white precipitate. Such a precipitate indicates either the presence of the chlorides of Group I cations, or the oxychlorides of antimony and bismuth. The oxychlorides of antimony and bismuth have precipitated due to hydrolysis and may be differentiated from the chlorides of Group I by their solubility in concentrated HCl. (Remove 2 drops of the solution containing some of the precipitate and add 1 drop of concentrated HCl. The oxychlorides of antimony and bismuth will dissolve, whereas the chlorides of Group I cations will not.) This reaction is reversible, and the presence of the oxychloride precipitate is dependent upon a low concentration of hydronium ions.

$$\underset{\substack{\text{white}\\\text{precipitate}}}{BiOCl} + 2H_3O^+ \rightleftharpoons Bi^{3+} + Cl^- + 3H_2O$$

2. A slight excess of HCl not only causes a more complete precipitation of the chlorides of Group I due to common-ion effect, but this excess also prevents the formation of BiOCl and SbOCl as indicated in the above equation. However, a large concentration of HCl or chloride ions is to be avoided, since the chloride ion in high concentration increases the solubilities of the precipitated chlorides through the formation of soluble complex ions.

$$AgCl + 2Cl^- \rightleftharpoons AgCl_3^-$$
$$PbCl_2 + 2Cl^- \rightleftharpoons PbCl_4^{--}$$

3. Lead chloride may dissolve appreciably during the washing process; consequently, the wash water should contain HCl so that the solubility of lead chloride may be reduced by common-ion effect.

4. Lead chloride is fairly soluble in hot water but reprecipitates if the solution is allowed to cool. The test for the lead ion is often missed because of failure to keep the solution hot during Procedure 2. If a micropipette (medicine dropper) is used for transferring the solution, it should be preheated by placing its tip in the hot water of the steam bath.

5. If the ammoniacal solution is left in contact with the precipitate of Hg and $HgNH_2Cl$ for an appreciable length of time, the soluble silver complex ion may react with metallic mercury.

$$2Hg + 2Ag(NH_3)_2^+ \rightleftharpoons Hg_2^{++} + 2Ag + 4NH_3$$

Therefore, a small concentration of Ag^+ may not give the usual test for the silver ion.

6. Test the acidity of the solution with litmus paper. The solution must be acid to convert the $Ag(NH_3)_2^+$ to AgCl; otherwise, even though silver ions be present, no precipitate will form.

7. If mercurous ions are present, the residue left from the ammonia treatment must be black or greatly discolored, because of the precipitation of colloidal mercury.

$$Hg_2Cl_2 + 2NH_3 \rightleftharpoons HgNH_2Cl + Hg + NH_4^+ + Cl^-$$

A white precipitate at this point may be either lead oxychloride formed by ammonia acting upon some undissolved lead chloride, or excess silver chloride undissolved by the ammonia.

12·3 Pertinent Chemical Reactions Involved in the Separation and Identification of Cations of Group I.

The purpose of this section is to give some explanation of the procedures followed in the analysis of Group I cations. As far as possible these explanations and equations for chemical reactions follow the same sequence as the successive steps in the analytical procedures.

Group Precipitation. Lead, silver, and mercurous ions give white precipitates with the chloride ion in an acid solution.

$$Pb^{++} + 2Cl^- \rightleftharpoons PbCl_2$$
$$Ag^+ + Cl^- \rightleftharpoons AgCl$$
$$Hg_2^{++} + 2Cl^- \rightleftharpoons Hg_2Cl_2$$

Separation and Identification of Lead Ion. An incomplete separation of $PbCl_2$ from the group precipitate is effected with hot water. $PbCl_2$ is soluble to the extent of approximately 1 g/100 ml at room temperature, and 3.34 g/100 ml at the temperature of boiling water. The threefold increase in solubility is small, but sufficient to give a lead-ion concentration that can be detected with chromate ions. $PbCrO_4$ is much less soluble than $PbCl_2$ (approximately 2×10^{-5} g/100 ml).

$$Pb^{++} + CrO_4^= \rightleftharpoons PbCrO_4$$

Treatment of Residue in Group I Analysis with Ammonia. When a mixture of AgCl and $HgCl_2$ is treated with ammonia, the AgCl dissolves, leaving a black residue composed of mercury and mercuric aminochloride.

$$AgCl + 2NH_3 \rightleftharpoons Ag(NH_3)_2^+ + Cl^-$$

Ammonia acts upon mercurous chloride to produce an internal redox reaction in which one mercurous ion is reduced to mercury and the other is oxidized to the mercuric state.

$$Hg_2Cl_2 + 2NH_3 \rightleftharpoons HgNH_2Cl + Hg + NH_4^+ + Cl^-$$

Mercuric aminochloride is white and the finely divided mercury is black; the resulting mixture is black. This blackening is an identification test for the mercurous ion.

Confirmation of Presence of Silver Ion. The centrifugate from the treatment of the Group I residue with ammonia contains $Ag(NH_3)_2^+$ and Cl^- ions. If this solution is made acid with nitric acid, the complex is destroyed and AgCl is reprecipitated.

$$Ag(NH_3)_2^+ + Cl^- + 2H_3O^+ \rightleftharpoons AgCl + 2NH_4^+ + 2H_2O$$

Identification of Mercurous Ion. The residue from the treatment of mercurous chloride with ammonia is a mixture of Hg and $HgNH_2Cl$. Although the production of this black mixture is sufficient to indicate the presence of the mercurous ion, additional confirmation is obtained by dissolving the mixture in nitric acid and testing with stannous chloride solution. Nitric acid dissolves Hg and $HgNH_2Cl$ with the following reactions:

$$3Hg + 2NO_3^- + 8H_3O^+ \rightleftharpoons 3Hg^{++} + 2NO + 12H_2O$$
$$2HgNH_2Cl + 2NO_3^- + 4H_3O^+ \rightleftharpoons 2Hg^{++} + N_2 + 2NO + 2Cl^- + 8H_2O$$

In the presence of chloride ions, the mercuric ions will tend to form the slightly dissociated mercuric chloride molecule, $HgCl_2$, or the complex ion, $HgCl_4^=$.

$$Hg^{++} + 2Cl^- \rightleftharpoons HgCl_2 \qquad \text{(low concentration of Cl}^- \text{ ions)}$$
$$HgCl_2 + 2Cl^- \rightleftharpoons HgCl_4^- \qquad \text{(high concentration of Cl}^- \text{ ions)}$$

Acid solutions containing $HgCl_2$ and $HgCl_4^=$ give precipitates with stannous ions. These precipitates may be white, gray, or black, depending upon the relative concentrations of the reactants.

$$2HgCl_2 + SnCl_4^= \rightleftharpoons Hg_2Cl_2 + SnCl_6^=$$
$$2HgCl_4^= + SnCl_4^= \rightleftharpoons Hg_2Cl_2 + SnCl_6^= + 4Cl^-$$

Further addition of stannous chloride reduces white Hg_2Cl_2 to black, finely divided mercury.

$$Hg_2Cl_2 + SnCl_4^= \rightleftharpoons 2Hg + SnCl_6^=$$

Usually a gray mixture of Hg_2Cl_2 and Hg is obtained.

CHAPTER 13

GROUP II CATIONS

This analytical group of cations is composed of eight cations which precipitate as sulfides from a solution which is 0.3 F in respect to hydronium ions. These are the sulfides of cupric, mercuric, lead, bismuth, cadmium, arsenic, antimony, and tin ions. The separation of this sulfide group from the sulfides of Group III is an arbitrary division based upon a careful control of the concentration of the sulfide ion, which is the precipitating agent for both groups.

13·1 Theoretical Discussion. In the Fresenius scheme of analysis, 13 cations of the heavy metals of common occurrence are precipitated as the sulfides. All these sulfides can be considered as fairly insoluble substances, but even so, their solubilities vary widely. This wide range in solubilities results in an equally wide scale for the values of their solubility products. An incomplete listing of these values is given in Table 13·1.

Use is made of the wide differences in the solubilities of these sulfides to effect a separation into two different groups: those sulfides which will precipitate in 0.3 F HCl solution, and those which will not. The sulfides which precipitate in an acid solution are classified as Group II sulfides, and those which are soluble in 0.3 F HCl are the Group III sulfides.

TABLE 13·1 SOLUBILITY PRODUCT CONSTANTS OF SOME SULFIDES WHICH PRECIPITATE IN CATION GROUPS II AND III
(The solubility products of those cations which comprise Group IIB are not given, since these values have not been accurately determined.)

Group IIA Sulfides		Group III Sulfides	
HgS	3×10^{-53}	ZnS	1.2×10^{-23}
CuS	8.5×10^{-45}	CoS	7×10^{-23}
Bi_2S_3	1.6×10^{-72}	NiS	1.4×10^{-24}
PbS	3.4×10^{-28}	FeS	3.7×10^{-19}
CdS	3.6×10^{-29}	MnS	1.4×10^{-15}

By means of this arbitrary division, the eight sulfides which will precipitate in 0.3 F HCl solution occur in Cation Group II. The real significance of the hydronium-ion concentration is as a control of the sulfide-ion concentration. The mechanism of this control can be seen by examining the expression for the over-all ionization of hydrogen sulfide. In this expression,

$$K_a = \frac{[H_3O^+]^2[S^=]}{[H_2S]} = 6.8 \times 10^{-23}$$

A saturated solution of hydrogen sulfide is approximately 0.1 F; therefore, for a saturated solution of hydrogen sulfide, the expression may be simplified to

$$K_a = \frac{[H_3O^+]^2[S^=]}{0.1} \quad \text{or} \quad [H_3O^+]^2[S^=] = 6.8 \times 10^{-24}$$

If the hydronium-ion concentration is arbitrarily controlled such that it is 0.3 F, the sulfide-ion concentration, which permits the precipitation of Group II cations, is decreased to 7.5×10^{-23} F. This value is obtained from the following calculation:

$$(0.3)^2[S^=] = 6.8 \times 10^{-24} \quad \text{or} \quad [S^=] = \frac{6.8 \times 10^{-24}}{0.09} = 7.5 \times 10^{-23}\ F$$

During the progress of an analysis the concentration of the cations before precipitation is approximately 0.01 F or less. For a divalent ion of this concentration to be precipitated by a sulfide-ion concentration of 7.5×10^{-23} F, the solubility product of the insoluble sulfide must be of the order of 7.5×10^{-25} or less. This fact is indicated by the following calculation:

$$[M^{++}][S^=] = K_{s.p.} \text{ for MS} \quad \text{(where } M^{++} \text{ is a divalent cation)}$$

or

$$(0.01)(7.5 \times 10^{-23}) = 7.5 \times 10^{-25}$$

To produce a fairly clean separation of two or more ions in solution by a common precipitating reagent requires that the equilibrium ratio between the two or more ions in the solid phase be quite large. The ratio for this separation process, usually referred to as *fractional precipitation*, should be of the order of one million to one. To illustrate with specific examples, the two divalent metallic sulfides CdS and ZnS have solubility products of 3.6×10^{-29} and 1.2×10^{-23}, respectively, indicating a relative solubility of three million to one. Therefore, it should be possible to separate the Cd^{++} ion from the Zn^{++} ion fairly completely by controlling the concentration of the sulfide ion.

An examination of the solubility product values listed in Table 13·1 indicates that the separation of the sulfides into two groups, by controlling the sulfide ion, may not be a clean separation. Not only is the control of the sulfide-ion concentration by means of the hydronium-ion concentration a critical one, but the formal concentration of the cations may be a determining factor as to whether a precipitate is formed in the presence of a sulfide-ion concentration of 7.5×10^{-23} F. Even under optimum conditions, those cations which have solubility products near the value of the arbitrary separation will be precipitated, to some extent, in the two different groups. As a result of this borderline separation, PbS and CdS do not precipitate completely in Group II and may appear in small concentrations in Group III. Likewise, ZnS, CoS, and NiS may precipitate in Group II, although they normally precipitate largely in Group III.

The precipitation of Group II sulfides is accomplished in two steps. Hydrogen sulfide is bubbled into a hot, fairly concentrated solution of hydronium ions to make certain of the precipitation of arsenious sulfide. In the presence of excess sulfide ions, arsenic tends to form the soluble complex anion, AsS_2^-, but in a hot, strongly acid solution, this complex is broken down to precipitate As_2S_3. In this concentration of hydronium ions, the sulfides of mercury and copper also may precipitate, but to precipitate the other sulfides of the group it is necessary to dilute the solution so that the hydronium-ion concentration will be 0.3 F.

The eight sulfides which make up Group II are HgS, CuS, Bi_2S_3, PbS, CdS, As_2S_3, SnS_2, and Sb_2S_3. The first five of these sulfides exhibit basic properties, whereas the latter three are acidic in nature. Therefore, if the Group II precipitate is treated with KOH solution, the sulfides of arsenic, antimony, and tin will dissolve, leaving the sulfides of mercury, copper, bismuth, lead, and cadmium as an insoluble residue. (In the presence of the sulfide ion, the KOH treatment will cause a partial solution of HgS to form the complex ion, $HgS_2^=$.) Group II contains more cations than any of the other groups, and this large number is too unwieldy to analyze satisfactorily without subgroup separation. It is customary to divide Group II into two subgroups, known as IIA and IIB, by the action of KOH solution. Consequently, Group IIA contains those cation sulfides which are insoluble in KOH, and Group IIB is composed of those cations whose sulfides dissolve in KOH solution.

The cations of the subgroups cannot be satisfactorily identified without further separation of the individual ions. An outline of these separations with the pertinent reactions involved in the separations is given in Sec. 13·3.

13·2 Analysis of Group II Cations. Three major steps are involved in the analysis of this group. First the group is precipitated as the sulfides, and then subdivided into subgroups by the action of potassium hydroxide solution. The second step is the analysis of Group IIA, and the final step is the analysis of Group IIB. Instructions for these operations are given in the following pages.

PRECIPITATION OF GROUP II CATIONS, AND SEPARATION INTO SUBGROUPS IIA AND IIB

Procedure 3.   Precipitation of Group II Cations.   Centrifugate from Group I may contain any or all of the cations of Groups II–V.   Add 2 drops of 3 F HNO$_3$ (1) to this centrifugate and heat in water bath for 3 min.   Make barely alkaline with 3 F NH$_3$ (2), then add 3 F HCl until it is just acid.   Concentrate (or dilute) to a volume of 2 ml, after which add 2 drops of concentrated HCl.   Heat to boiling and pass in H$_2$S slowly for 2 min.   (3) Cool, dilute to 4 ml, and pass H$_2$S into solution for 3 min. (4) (5) Centrifuge and test for complete precipitation by passing in H$_2$S again.   After precipitation is complete, centrifuge and remove centrifugate.

Centrifugate contains Groups III–V. Boil off H$_2$S (6) and reserve for Group III analysis (Procedure 7).	**Precipitate** consists of sulfides of cations of Group II. These sulfides may be As$_2$S$_3$ (yellow), As$_2$S$_5$ (yellow), Sb$_2$S$_3$ (orange-red), Sb$_2$S$_5$ (orange), SnS (brown), SnS$_2$ (yellow), HgS (black), PbS (black), CuS (black), Bi$_2$S$_3$ (brown-black), and CdS (yellow). This precipitate is treated according to Procedure 4.

Procedure 4.   Separation of Groups IIA and IIB.   Sulfide precipitate from Procedure 3 is washed with 10 drops of H$_2$S water containing 1 drop of saturated NH$_4$Cl.   (7) Discard wash water.   Add 8 drops of 3 F KOH.   Stir and heat in water bath for 3 min.   Centrifuge and separate centrifugate from residue.   Treat residue again with 8 drops of 3 F KOH.   Centrifuge, and combine two centrifugates.

Residue consists of sulfides of Group IIA: HgS, CuS, CdS, PbS, Bi$_2$S$_3$, and some free sulfur. This residue is analyzed according to Procedure 5.	**Centrifugate** is solution of soluble complex ions of Group IIB cations, which are arsenic, antimony, and tin. This centrifugate is analyzed according to Procedure 6.

NOTES ON THE PRECIPITATION OF GROUP II AND ITS SEPARATION INTO SUBGROUPS IIA AND IIB

1. It is necessary to oxidize any stannous ions which may be present to the stannic state, otherwise the subgroup separation with 3 F KOH will be incomplete with regard to tin.   SnS is not appreciably soluble in KOH, whereas SnS$_2$ is soluble.

2. A precipitate may result during the process of making the solution ammoniacal, but when HCl is added most of this precipitate will dissolve.   Regardless of whether the precipitate is dissolved or not, it will be converted into sulfides by the H$_2$S treatment which follows.

3. The precipitation of arsenic by means of H$_2$S is very slow except in a hot acid solution.

4. The directions for acidifying and diluting the solution, if properly carried out, produce a solution which is 0.3 F in respect to hydronium ions.   This is the correct acidity for the separation of Groups II and III; however, this separation is far from perfect.   If the solution is too acid, the precipitation of some of the cations may be incomplete or prevented entirely.   This is particularly true for the stannic, lead, and cadmium ions.   If the solution is not sufficiently acid, some of the cations of Group

III may be precipitated as sulfides along with the sulfides of the cations of Group II. This is especially true of zinc, nickel, and cobalt ions.

5. The color of the precipitate may give an indication of the cations present. If the precipitate is black, the presence of mercuric, bismuth, copper, or lead ions, or any combinations of these ions is indicated. A yellow precipitate shows the presence of arsenic, cadmium, or tin ions, or a combination of any of the three. An orange precipitate indicates the presence of antimony. A white precipitate which turns black indicates mercury. A white suspension formed after continued H_2S treatment is the result of the reaction of the sulfide ion with the nitrate ion, in acid solution, to produce free sulfur. This suspension may appear in the absence of Group II cations.

6. If the H_2S is not expelled from the centrifugate, atmospheric oxidation will convert $S^=$ to $SO_4^=$. The presence of the sulfate at this point will cause the partial precipitation of the Group IV cations as sulfates, particularly barium sulfate. These sulfate precipitates will occur in the Group III precipitate where they are not wanted, and the cations will be missed in the Group IV precipitation. If the Group III solution is to be analyzed immediately, the procedure of expelling H_2S may be omitted since the oxidation of the sulfide ion proceeds slowly.

7. The H_2S in the wash water retards oxidation of the precipitated sulfides to sulfates. The NH_4Cl is added to aid in breaking up any colloidal dispersion which may be present.

Notes on the Analysis of Group IIA Cations

1. Copper, bismuth, cadmium, and lead sulfides are dissolved due to the oxidation of the sulfide ion by the nitrate ion, in acid solution, to free sulfur.

2. Treatment of HgS with $3 F$ HNO_3 may result in the formation of white $Hg(NO_3)_2 \cdot 2HgS$. Therefore, the lack of a black precipitate of HgS at this point does not confirm the absence of the mercuric ion.

3. Aqua regia dissolves HgS by two different types of reactions: the oxidation of the sulfide ion to free sulfur by the nitrate ion, and the complexing action of the chloride ion to produce the $HgCl_4^=$ ion. Aqua regia is composed of three parts of concentrated HCl and one part of concentrated HNO_3. A small insoluble residue, after the aqua regia treatment, is free sulfur.

4. Aqua regia liberates chlorine which, if not removed, will oxidize stannous ions to stannic ions. Only stannous ions will give the characteristic test for the mercuric ion.

5. Lead ions are precipitated as $PbSO_4$. However, this precipitate is soluble in the presence or HNO_3 because of the formation of $Pb(HSO_4)_2$. The appearance of *dense* white fumes of SO_3 indicates that HNO_3 has been distilled from the solution.

6. Before precipitating lead as $PbCrO_4$, it is necessary that the solution be made acidic with HAc; otherwise, bismuth, which might be present, will also precipitate as the chromate.

7. To prepare potassium stannite solution, add $3 F$ KOH, drop by drop, to 2 drops of stannous chloride solution until the gelatinous precipitate of stannous hydroxide, which first forms, barely dissolves. The equations for these reactions are:

$$Sn^{++} + 2OH^- \rightleftharpoons Sn(OH)_2$$

or

$$Sn(H_2O)_4^{++} + 2OH^- \rightleftharpoons \underset{\text{precipitate}}{Sn(H_2O)_2(OH)_2} + 2H_2O$$

and

$$Sn(OH)_2 + OH^- \rightleftharpoons Sn(OH)_3^-$$

or

$$Sn(H_2O)_2(OH)_2 + OH^- \rightleftharpoons \underset{\text{soluble}}{Sn(H_2O)(OH)_3^-} + H_2O$$

ANALYSIS OF GROUP IIA CATIONS

Procedure 5. Separation and Identification of Group IIA Cations. Wash residue from subgroup separation with 10 drops of water to remove excess KOH, and discard washings. Add 10 drops of 3 F HNO$_3$, (1) heat in water bath for 3 min, and centrifuge. If much residue is left, repeat treatment, combining centrifugates.

Residue may be black HgS or white (2) Hg(NO$_3$)$_2$·2HgS and S. Dissolve in 4 drops of aqua regia. (3) Add 10 drops of water and boil (4) in water bath for 2 min. Cool and add 2 drops of SnCl$_2$ solution. White precipitate of Hg$_2$Cl$_2$ or gray precipitate of Hg and Hg$_2$Cl$_2$ confirms presence of MERCURIC ION.	**Centrifugate** contains lead, bismuth, copper, and cadmium ions. Transfer to a casserole and add 3 drops of concentrated H$_2$SO$_4$. Evaporate until *dense* white fumes appear (5) and only 2 or 3 drops of liquid remain. Cool thoroughly, and *cautiously* add 1 ml of water. Stir thoroughly and transfer to a centrifuge tube. Rinse casserole with 5 drops of water and add washings to the solution. Centrifuge.	
	Precipitate may be PbSO$_4$. Wash with 4 drops of water and discard washings. Add 10 drops of saturated NH$_4$Ac and heat, with stirring, in water bath for 3 min. If resulting solution is not clear, centrifuge and discard residue. Add 1 drop of concentrated HAc (6) and 2 drops of 1 F K$_2$CrO$_4$. Yellow precipitate confirms presence of LEAD ION.	**Centrifugate** contains bismuth, copper, and cadmium ions. Add concentrated NH$_3$ dropwise with stirring until solution is basic, and then 3 drops in excess. Centrifuge.
		Precipitate may be bismuth hydroxide. Wash with 5 drops of water and discard washings. To precipitate add 10 or more drops of freshly prepared potassium stannite solution. (7) Immediate blackening of precipitate indicates presence of BISMUTH ION. (8)	**Centrifugate** contains soluble copper-ammonia and cadmium-ammonia complex ions. Deep blue solution (9) confirms presence of COPPER ION. To test for cadmium ion, add sufficient 1 F KCN to decolorize solution. (10) Pass H$_2$S into solution for 1 min. Yellow precipitate indicates presence of CADMIUM ION. (11)

8. A brown stain is not a test for the bismuth ion. Bismuth hydroxide is reduced to metallic bismuth which is definitely black.

9. The blue color of the copper-ammonia complex is sufficient for ordinary concentrations of the cupric ion as a confirmatory test. If the cupric ion is in small concentration, make the solution acid with HAc and add a drop of potassium ferrocyanide solution. A reddish-brown precipitate of cupric ferrocyanide confirms the presence of the cupric ion.

10. The potassium cyanide solution is added to form the stable complex ion, Cu(CN)$_3^=$, by decomposing the cupric-ammonia complex, Cu(NH$_3$)$_4^{++}$, to prevent

interference with the cadmium test.   If the cupric ion is absent, the cyanide treatment is not necessary.

11. If a black precipitate is obtained here, the solution contained some cations whose sulfides are black.   To test for the cadmium ion in this black precipitate proceed as follows: Centrifuge the mixture and discard the centrifugate.   Wash the residue with 5 drops of water and discard the washing.   Add 10 drops of 1.5 F H_2SO_4, stir, and heat in water bath for 4 min.   Centrifuge and discard any residue.   Neutralize the centrifugate with concentrated NH_3.   Make slightly acid with 3 F HAc and saturate with H_2S.   The formation of a yellow precipitate confirms the presence of the cadmium ion.

ANALYSIS OF GROUP IIB CATIONS

Procedure 6.   Separation and Identification of Group IIB Cations.   To centrifugate from Procedure 4, add 3 F HCl until solution is barely acid.   (1) Centrifuge and discard centrifugate.   Add 10 drops of concentrated HCl, stir, heat in water bath for 1 min (2), and centrifuge.   Remove and save centrifugate.   Wash residue with a mixture of 8 drops of water and 4 drops of concentrated HCl; centrifuge, and add washing to centrifugate of concentrated HCl treatment.

Residue may be As_2S_3, As_2S_5, and S.   A small amount of HgS from Group IIA may also appear here.   (3) Wash residue with hot water three times.   (4) Add 4 drops of concentrated HNO_3 and heat for 5 min in water bath.   Add 5 drops of 0.5 F $AgNO_3$ and stir.   (If precipitation occurs, centrifuge and discard residue, which is AgCl from reaction of silver ions with unremoved chloride ions.)   To clear centrifugate add 15 drops of 2.5 F NaAc solution.   Formation of a reddish-brown precipitate of Ag_3AsO_4 confirms presence of ARSENIC.

Centrifugate contains antimony and stannous ions.   Divide into two unequal portions.

Small portion.   Make two tests for antimony as follows:
Test One.   Add 1 drop of the solution to the surface of a clean (5) silver coin.   Place a very small piece of tin on the coin so that the solution is in contact with the tin and coin.   Black deposit, (6) (7) insoluble in NaOCl solution, indicates presence of ANTIMONY.
Test Two.   Place a small crystal of $NaNO_2$ into each of two depressions of a white spot plate.   Place 2 drops of 3 F HCl upon each crystal and stir until oxides of nitrogen have been removed.   Add 2 drops of rhodamine B to each portion.   Now add 1 drop of distilled water to one depression and 1 drop of the unknown solution to the other.   Compare colors of the two solutions.   Conversion of red color of rhodamine B to a lavender shade indicates presence of ANTIMONY. (8)

Large portion.   Test for tin as follows: Add an equal volume of 3 F HCl to this portion.   Place a piece of Mg ribbon, 4 cm long, in the solution and allow to stand until completely dissolved.   (9) Add 4 drops of saturated $HgCl_2$ solution.   White or gray precipitate confirms presence of TIN.

NOTES ON THE ANALYSIS OF GROUP IIB CATIONS

1. The alkaline centrifugate from Procedure 4 contains the ions of Group IIB in the form of soluble complex thio or oxythio anions.   When this solution is acidified the complex ions are destroyed, and the cations of Group IIB precipitate as sulfides.

2. The solution is heated to expel H_2S; otherwise, the antimony and tin ions would

be reprecipitated as sulfides when the HCl solution is diluted.   Prolonged heating of the solution is avoided to prevent partial solution of As_2S_3 or As_2S_5.

3. In the subgroup separation with 3 F KOH, mercuric sulfide dissolves, to a small extent, to form the soluble complex ions, $HgS_2^{=}$.

4. The residue is washed to remove the chloride ion, which interferes with the confirmatory test for the arsenate ion.

5. If the coin is not bright, place it in 3 F HNO_3 for a few seconds, then pour off the acid and immediately wash with several portions of water.

6. If the arsenic ion is in the solution, it will be deposited as metallic arsenic. However, metallic arsenic is soluble in NaOCl solution and metallic antimony is not.

7. The presence of H_2S in the solution will cause the coin to darken.   Mercuric and cupric ions will also cause a black deposit on the coin.   Gentle rubbing with a soft cloth will cause black mercury to take on a silvery appearance, and the copper a copper-red color.

8. Sodium nitrite oxidizes antimony ions to the pentavalent state.   In the confirmatory test, pentavalent antimony apparently oxidizes rhodamine B to produce a color change.   The actual course of this reaction has not been determined.   *An excess of sodium nitrite will produce the same color change.*

9. The magnesium metal is added to reduce the antimony ions completely to the metal, and stannic ions to stannous ions.   The appearance of small black flakes in the solution indicates the presence of antimony.   All the magnesium ribbon must be dissolved before making the confirmatory test for tin.   If any magnesium ribbon is left undissolved, a positive test will be obtained, since metallic magnesium reduces mercuric chloride.

13·3   Pertinent Chemical Reactions Involved in Separation and Identification of Cations of Group II.

The purpose of this section is to give some explanation of the procedures followed in the analysis of Group II cations.   As far as possible these explanations and reactions follow the same sequence as the successive steps in the analytical procedures.

Oxidation of Stannous Ions to the Stannic State.   Under the conditions of precipitation for Group II, tin is precipitated as stannous sulfide, SnS. This sulfide is insoluble in KOH because of the basic nature of the compound.   For purposes of identification, it is preferable to have tin as a member of Group IIB, which is the KOH-soluble group.   Stannic sulfide, SnS_2, is soluble in KOH because it is more acidic in character than SnS.   The oxidation of stannous ions to stannic ions is accomplished by heating with nitric acid in the presence of chloride ions.

$$3Sn^{++} + 2NO_3^- + 8H_3O^+ + 18Cl^- \rightleftharpoons 3SnCl_6^{=} + 2NO + 12H_2O$$

Precipitation of Group II with H_2S.   The cations of Group II are precipitated as sulfides in a 0.3 F HCl solution with hydrogen sulfide.

Mercuric ions give a white, brown, or black-colored precipitate with hydrogen sulfide.

$$3HgCl_2 + 2H_2S + 4H_2O \rightleftharpoons HgCl_2 \cdot 2HgS + 4H_3O^+ + 4Cl^-$$
$$\text{white}$$
$$HgCl_2 \cdot 2HgS + H_2S + 2H_2O \rightleftharpoons 3HgS + 2H_3O^+ + 2Cl^-$$
$$\text{black}$$

Copper ions precipitate as black CuS with hydrogen sulfide.

$$Cu^{++} + H_2S + 2H_2O \rightleftharpoons CuS + 2H_3O^+$$

Bismuth ions precipitate as dark brown Bi_2S_3 with hydrogen sulfide.

$$2Bi^{3+} + 3H_2S + 6H_2O \rightleftharpoons Bi_2S_3 + 6H_3O^+$$

Lead ions give a black precipitate of PbS with hydrogen sulfide.

$$Pb^{++} + H_2S + 2H_2O \rightleftharpoons PbS + 2H_3O^+$$

Cadmium ions precipitate with hydrogen sulfide to give cadmium sulfide. The color and composition of the precipitate depend upon the acidity and temperature of the precipitating solution. In a cold, slightly acid solution the precipitate is yellow, but in a hot acid solution the color of the precipitate may be from orange to red.

$$Cd^{++} + H_2S + 2H_2O \rightleftharpoons CdS + 2H_3O^+$$

Arsenious acid and the arsenate ion give yellow precipitates with hydrogen sulfide.

$$\underset{\text{arsenious acid}}{2H_3AsO_3} + 3H_2S \rightleftharpoons As_2S_3 + 6H_2O$$

$$\underset{\text{arsenate}}{2H_2AsO_4^-} + 5H_2S + 2H_3O^+ \rightleftharpoons As_2S_5 + 10H_2O$$

(The second reaction takes place to only a limited extent, since H_2S tends to reduce pentavalent arsenic to the trivalent state.)

The antimonous and antimonic ions react with hydrogen sulfide to give orange-red precipitates of Sb_2S_3 and Sb_2S_5. The two antimony ions probably exist in hydrochloric acid solution as complex ions, $SbCl_4^-$ and $SbCl_6^-$, which hydrolyze upon dilution to give white precipitates of antimony oxychlorides.

$$SbCl_4^- + 3H_2O \rightleftharpoons SbOCl + 2H_3O^+ + 3Cl^-$$
$$SbCl_6^- + 6H_2O \rightleftharpoons SbO_2Cl + 4H_3O^+ + 5Cl^-$$

The reactions of $SbCl_4^-$ and $SbCl_6^-$ with hydrogen sulfide are as follows:

$$2SbCl_4^- + 3H_2S + 6H_2O \rightleftharpoons Sb_2S_3 + 6H_3O^+ + 8Cl^-$$
$$2SbCl_6^- + 5H_2S + 10H_2O \rightleftharpoons Sb_2S_5 + 10H_3O^+ + 12Cl^-$$

Stannous ions produce a brown precipitate of SnS with H_2S.

$$Sn^{++} + H_2S + 2H_2O \rightleftharpoons SnS + 2H_3O^+$$

The stannic ion can exist only as a complex chlorostannate ion, $SnCl_6^=$. This ion yields a light yellow precipitate of SnS_2 with hydrogen sulfide.

$$SnCl_6^= + 2H_2S + 4H_2O \rightleftharpoons SnS_2 + 4H_3O^+ + 6Cl^-$$

Separation of Group II *Cations into Subgroups* IIA *and* IIB. Dilute KOH solution dissolves the sulfides of arsenic, antimony, and tetravalent tin and incompletely dissolves mercuric sulfide. The first three sulfides dissolve because of their acidic character, and HgS dissolves to a small extent because of the formation of the complex ion, $HgS_2^=$. The equations for these reactions are

$$2As_2S_3 + 4OH^- \rightleftharpoons AsO_2^- + 3AsS_2^- + 2H_2O$$
$$2Sb_2S_3 + 4OH^- \rightleftharpoons Sb(OH)_4^- + 3SbS_2^-$$
$$3SnS_2 + 6OH^- \rightleftharpoons Sn(OH)_6^= + 2SnS_3^=$$
$$HgS + S^= \rightleftharpoons HgS_2^=$$

Separation and Identification of Mercuric Ion. All the sulfides of Group IIA, except HgS, are oxidized by dilute nitric acid. In these reactions the sulfides are oxidized to sulfur, and the cations are brought into solution.

$$3CuS + 2NO_3^- + 8H_3O^+ \rightleftharpoons 3Cu^{++} + 2NO + 3S + 12H_2O$$
$$Bi_2S_3 + 2NO_3^- + 8H_3O^+ \rightleftharpoons 2Bi^{3+} + 2NO + 3S + 12H_2O$$
$$3PbS + 2NO_3^- + 8H_3O^+ \rightleftharpoons 3Pb^{++} + 2NO + 3S + 12H_2O$$
$$3CdS + 2NO_3^- + 8H_3O^+ \rightleftharpoons 3Cd^{++} + 2NO + 3S + 12H_2O$$

Mercuric sulfide, HgS, is insoluble in dilute nitric acid but readily dissolves in aqua regia. The latter is a mixture of concentrated HCl and concentrated HNO_3. In dissolving HgS, aqua regia acts as an oxidizing agent and also a complexing agent. The nitrate ion, in the presence of hydronium ions, oxidizes the sulfide ion to free sulfur; the chloride ion combines with the mercuric ion to form the soluble complex ion, $HgCl_4^=$. These reactions are represented by the following equations:

$$3HgS + 2NO_3^- + 8H_3O^+ \rightleftharpoons 3S + 2NO + 12H_2O + 3Hg^{++}$$
$$\underline{3Hg^{++} + 12Cl^- \rightleftharpoons 3HgCl_4^=}$$
$$3HgS + 2NO_3^- + 8H_3O^+ + 12Cl^- = 3HgCl_4^= + 2NO + 3S + 12H_2O$$

The presence of the mercuric ion is confirmed by adding stannous chloride solution to the solution containing $HgCl_4^=$ ions. A white precipitate of Hg_2Cl_2 is obtained in this reaction.

$$2HgCl_4^= + SnCl_4^= \rightleftharpoons Hg_2Cl_2 + SnCl_6^= + 4Cl^-$$

Separation of Lead Ion in Group IIA. The lead ion is precipitated as $PbSO_4$ in the presence of bismuth, copper, and cadmium. A large excess of hydronium ions is avoided to prevent the formation of soluble $Pb[HSO_4]_2$.

$$Pb^{++} + SO_4^= \rightleftharpoons PbSO_4$$

Identification of Lead Ion in Group IIA. Lead sulfate dissolves in excess acetate ions to form slightly dissociated lead acetate.

$$PbSO_4 + 2C_2H_3O_2^- \rightleftharpoons Pb(C_2H_3O_2)_2 + SO_4^=$$

However, lead acetate is sufficiently dissociated to furnish lead ions in a concentration to exceed the solubility product of lead chromate. The formation of this yellow precipitate is the confirmatory test for the lead ion.

$$Pb(C_2H_3O_2)_2 + CrO_4^= \rightleftharpoons PbCrO_4 + 2C_2H_3O_2^-$$

Separation of Bismuth Ion. The bismuth ion is precipitated as the hydroxide by excess ammonia in the presence of cupric and cadmium ions. The latter two ions are converted into the tetrammine complex ions, $Cu(NH_3)_4^{++}$ and $Cd(NH_3)_4^{++}$, by the ammonia.

$$Bi^{3+} + 3NH_3 + 3H_2O \rightleftharpoons Bi(OH)_3 + 3NH_4^+$$

or

$$Bi(H_2O)_6^{3+} + 3NH_3 \rightleftharpoons Bi(H_2O)_3(OH)_3 + 3NH_4^+$$

and

$$Cu^{++} + 4NH_3 \rightleftharpoons Cu(NH_3)_4^{++}$$
$$Cd^{++} + 4NH_3 \rightleftharpoons Cd(NH_3)_4^{++}$$

Identification of Bismuth Ion. Bismuth hydroxide, $Bi(OH)_3$, also written as $Bi(H_2O)_3(OH)_3$, is readily reduced by the stannite ion to black metallic bismuth. This reaction serves as the confirmatory test for bismuth.

$$2Bi(OH)_3 + 3Sn(OH)_3^- + 3OH^- \rightleftharpoons 2Bi + 3Sn(OH)_6^=$$

or

$$2Bi(H_2O)_3(OH)_3 + 3Sn(H_2O)(OH)_3^- \rightleftharpoons 2Bi + 3Sn(H_2O)(OH)_5^-$$
$$+ 6H_2O$$

Detection of Cupric Ion. The deep blue color produced by the complex ion, $Cu(NH_3)_4^{++}$, formed upon the addition of ammonia to a solution of copper ions, is sufficient to identify the cupric ion in Group IIA analysis. When copper occurs in a very small concentration, a more sensitive test may be made by the addition of ferrocyanide ions. Cupric ferrocyanide is a reddish-brown precipitate which is insoluble in dilute acids but soluble in ammonia.

$$2Cu^{++} + Fe(CN)_6^{4-} \rightleftharpoons Cu_2[Fe(CN)_6]$$

Identification of Cadmium Ion in Presence of Copper Ion. The presence of either $Cu(H_2O)_4^{++}$ or $Cu(NH_3)_4^{++}$, both of which are colored, interferes with the identification test for the cadmium ion. This interference is overcome by the complexing action of the cyanide ion upon the two ions, copper and cadmium. The cyanide ion forms a stable, colorless complex with copper ions, $Cu(CN)_3^=$; the cyanide also complexes the cadmium ion to produce the ion, $Cd(CN)_4^=$, but the cadmium complex is less stable than the copper complex. When a mixture of $Cu(CN)_3^=$ and $Cd(CN)_4^=$ ions is treated with H_2S, the cadmium complex is destroyed and yellow cadmium sulfide precipitates, but the $Cu(CN)_3^=$ ion is unaffected by the H_2S. The stepwise equations for the reaction of excess cyanide with $Cu(NH_3)_4^{++}$ are

$$2Cu(NH_3)_4^{++} + 4CN^- \rightleftharpoons 2Cu(CN)_2 + 8NH_3$$

Cupric cyanide is unstable and decomposes into cuprous cyanide.

$$2Cu(CN)_2 \rightleftharpoons Cu_2(CN)_2 + (CN)_2$$

This is a redox equation in which cupric ions are reduced to the cuprous state. The cuprous cyanide is soluble in excess cyanide ions to form the soluble, colorless complex ion, $Cu(CN)_3^=$.

$$Cu_2(CN)_2 + 4CN^- \rightleftharpoons 2Cu(CN)_3^=$$

In an ammoniacal solution the cyanogen, $(CN)_2$, is hydrolyzed to CNO^- and CN^-.

$$(CN)_2 + 2OH^- \rightleftharpoons CNO^- + CN^- + H_2O$$

The sum of the foregoing equations may be written as

$$2Cu(NH_3)_4^{++} + 7CN^- + 2OH^-$$
$$\rightleftharpoons 2Cu(CN)_3^= + 8NH_3 + CNO^- + H_2O$$

Hydrogen sulfide produces no reaction with the copper cyanide complex.

$$Cu(CN)_3^= + H_2S \rightarrow \text{no reaction}$$

The equation for the reaction of excess cyanide ions with $Cd(NH_3)_4^{++}$ is

$$^\bullet Cd(NH_3)_4^{++} + 2CN^- \rightleftharpoons Cd(CN)_2 + 4NH_3$$

Cadmium cyanide is a white precipitate which dissolves in excess cyanide ions to form the soluble complex ion, $Cd(CN)_4^=$.

$$Cd(CN)_2 + 2CN^- \rightleftharpoons Cd(CN)_4^=$$

This complex is not sufficiently stable to prevent the precipitation of yellow CdS when a solution of the complex is treated with H_2S. This serves as a means of identifying the cadmium ion in the presence of the copper ion.

$$Cd(CN)_4^= + H_2S \rightleftharpoons CdS + 2HCN + 2CN^-$$

Precipitation of Group IIB Cations from KOH Solution. The alkaline centrifugate from the separation of Group II into subgroups contains the ions of Group IIB in the form of soluble complex anions. When this solution is acidified, the complex ions are destroyed and the ions of Group IIB precipitate as sulfides.

$$AsO_2^- + 3AsS_2^- + 4H_3O^+ \rightleftharpoons 2As_2S_3 + 6H_2O$$
$$Sb(OH)_4^- + 3SbS_2^- + 4H_3O^+ \rightleftharpoons 2Sb_2S_3 + 8H_2O$$
$$Sn(OH)_6^= + 2SnS_3^= + 6H_3O^+ \rightleftharpoons 3SnS_2 + 12H_2O$$

Reaction of Concentrated Hydrochloric Acid upon Sulfides of Group IIB. Concentrated hydrochloric acid dissolves antimonous sulfide and stannic sulfide. This serves as a method of separating antimony and tin ions from arsenic sulfide, the latter being unaffected by the concentrated hydrochloric acid.

$$SnS_2 + 4H_3O^+ + 6Cl^- \rightleftharpoons SnCl_6^= + 2H_2S + 4H_2O$$
$$Sb_2S_3 + 6H_3O^+ + 12Cl^- \rightleftharpoons 2SbCl_6^{3-} + 3H_2S + 6H_2O$$

Solution and Identification of Arsenic Ion. Although insoluble in concentrated HCl, arsenious trisulfide dissolves readily in concentrated nitric acid. This is a redox reaction in which trivalent arsenic is oxidized to the pentavalent arsenate ion.

$$As_2S_3 + 10NO_3^- + 8H_3O^+ \rightleftharpoons 2H_2AsO_4^- + 3S + 10NO_2 + 10H_2O$$

Sodium acetate is added to buffer the acidity of the nitric acid solution of the arsenate ion.

$$2C_2H_3O_2^- + H_3O^+ \rightleftharpoons 2HC_2H_3O_2 + OH^-$$

and

$$H_2AsO_4^- + 2OH^- \rightleftharpoons AsO_4^{3-} + 2H_2O$$

The addition of silver nitrate solution to a neutral solution of an arsenate precipitates reddish-brown silver arsenate, Ag_3AsO_4. This reaction is used to confirm the presence of arsenic in Group IIB of the cation scheme.

Identification of Antimony Ion. Metallic tin precipitates metallic antimony from solutions of antimony compounds. The action is accelerated by carrying out the test with a drop of solution upon the surface of a silver coin, with the tin in contact with the coin to form a Sn-Ag couple. Antimony is deposited from the solution upon the coin as a finely divided, black powder, insoluble in sodium hypochlorite. Any arsenic which may precipitate at this point is soluble in NaOCl.

$$2SbCl_6^{3-} + 3Sn \rightleftharpoons 2Sb + 3SnCl_4^=$$

Identification of Tin Ion in Presence of Antimony Ion. When the sulfides of tin and antimony are dissolved in concentrated HCl they are converted to the soluble anions, $SbCl_6^{3-}$ and $SnCl_6^=$. The addition of Mg metal to this solution converts the chloroantimonite ion to metallic Sb, and the chlorostannate ion to the stannous ion.

$$2SbCl_6{}^{3-} + 3Mg \rightleftharpoons 2Sb + 3Mg^{++} + 12Cl^-$$
$$SnCl_6{}^{=} + Mg \rightleftharpoons SnCl_4{}^{=} + Mg^{++} + 2Cl^-$$

The addition of mercuric chloride to a solution containing stannous ions produces a white or gray precipitate of Hg_2Cl_2 or Hg. (Mercuric chloride is written in the molecular form in the following equation because it is only slightly dissociated.)

$$SnCl_4{}^{=} + 2HgCl_2 \rightleftharpoons Hg_2Cl_2 + SnCl_6{}^{=}$$

and

$$Hg_2Cl_2 + SnCl_4{}^{=} \rightleftharpoons 2Hg + SnCl_6{}^{=}$$

CHAPTER 14

GROUP III CATIONS

The cations of Group III are precipitated in a solution containing ammonia, ammonium chloride, and ammonium sulfide; consequently, the group precipitate is a mixture of sulfides and hydroxides. This group contains five metallic sulfides whose solubility products are too large to permit them to precipitate in Group II, and two hydroxides whose solubility products are much smaller than the solubility products of their corresponding sulfides. The seven cations of this group are iron, cobalt, nickel, zinc, manganese, aluminum, and chromium.

14·1 Theoretical Discussion. The separation of the cations of Groups II and III is accomplished by a strict control of the sulfide-ion concentration. In a sulfide-ion concentration of $7.5 \times 10^{-23} F$, as used for the precipitation of Group II, only the solubility product constants of the sulfides of the cations of Groups I and II are exceeded. If the hydronium-ion concentration of the centrifugate from Group II is decreased, the sulfide-ion concentration will increase so as to permit the solubility products of the sulfides of Zn, Fe, Co, Ni, and Mn to be exceeded. This arbitrary separation by the control of the sulfide-ion concentration is not entirely clean, and small amounts of lead, cadmium, and stannous ions may be carried into Group III and precipitated as sulfides. A slight contamination of Group III by Group II sulfides does not interfere with the analysis of Group III except in the identification of the zinc ion. Zinc is identified by its separation and precipitation as the white sulfide. Lead ions from Group II, if present, tend to coprecipitate with zinc ions, and the formation of black lead sulfide will mask the confirmatory test for the zinc ion.

The high concentration of sulfide ion necessary for precipitation of Group III sulfides is obtained in an ammoniacal solution. This basic solution also produces the precipitation of chromium and aluminum as hydroxides in Group III. However, if the hydroxide-ion concentration of the precipitation solution for Group III is permitted to become large, it will cause the precipitation of magnesium, a member of Group IV cations, as magnesium hydroxide.

The conditions necessary to precipitate Group III cations, and to prevent the precipitation of magnesium hydroxide, are apparently contradictory. The hydroxide-ion concentration must be sufficiently high to increase the sulfide-ion concentration to a value that exceeds the solubility products of the members of Group III. Also, the hydroxide-ion concentration must be sufficiently large to permit the precipitation of the hydroxides of aluminum and chromium, but not large enough to permit the precipitation of magnesium hydroxide. Since magnesium hydroxide is more soluble than aluminum and chromium hydroxides, its precipitation is prevented by buffering the ammonia solution with a large excess of ammonium ions. The process by which the hydroxide-ion concentration is lowered by increasing the ammonium-ion concentration is indicated by the following equilibrium:

$$\frac{\overset{\text{excess}}{[NH_4^+]}[OH^-]}{[NH_3]} = K_b \qquad \text{or} \qquad [OH^-] = \frac{[NH_3]}{\underset{\text{excess}}{[NH_4^+]}} \times K_b$$

Thus, the addition of ammonium chloride to the Group III precipitation solution buffers the hydroxide-ion concentration to such a value that the two apparently contradictory conditions just mentioned are satisfied.

Group III is divided into two subgroups by the action of a strong base, in excess, upon a solution of the cations of this group. Chromium, zinc, and aluminum hydroxides dissolve in excess KOH solution to form a soluble group, whereas manganese, iron, nickel, and cobalt hydroxides precipitate to form an insoluble group. The separation of chromium by the action of a strong base alone is not always predictable. Under certain conditions, chromium hydroxide will not dissolve in excess base. This is true if the hydroxide is heated or permitted to age. To ensure uniform behavior of the chromium ion, it is better to oxidize it to the chromate. The soluble alkali chromate thus becomes a member of the soluble group which includes the zincate and aluminate ions.

The addition of sodium peroxide, for the purpose of oxidizing the chromic ion to the chromate, also oxidizes manganese to a valence of four, and iron and cobalt to a valence of three. Fortunately, the hydroxides of these elements in the higher valence states are more insoluble than the corresponding hydroxides in the lower valence states. Therefore, the peroxide treatment not only oxidizes the chromic ion but also permits a cleaner separation of the subgroups of Group III.

14·2 Analysis of Group III Cations. The size of this group makes it advisable to divide it into two subgroups. This is accomplished by the action of potassium hydroxide and sodium peroxide upon a solution of these cations. Subgroup IIIA contains the aluminate, chromate, and zincate ions, which must be separated from each other to be identified satisfactorily. The members of subgroup IIIB are the manganous, ferric, cobaltous, and nickel ions. These ions may be identified in the presence of each other. Details of the group analysis are given in the following pages:

ANALYSIS OF GROUP III CATIONS

Procedure 7. Precipitation of Group III Cations. To centrifugate from Group II (Procedure 3) add 4 drops of saturated NH_4Cl; then concentrated NH_3, drop by drop, until solution is distinctly alkaline. (1)(2) Pass in H_2S until precipitation is complete (3) and centrifuge. Precipitate contains sulfides and hydroxides of Group III and is analyzed according to Procedure 8.

    Centrifugate contains cations of Groups IV and V. Acidify at once with 3 F HCl and heat in water bath until volume has been reduced to one-half. (4) If a precipitate forms, centrifuge and discard precipitate. Save clear, colorless centrifugate for analysis of Group IV (Procedure 11).

Procedure 8. Separation of Group III into Subgroups. Treat precipitate with 5 drops of concentrated HCl and stir. If complete solution takes place, absence of Ni and Co is indicated. (5) Add 3 drops of concentrated HNO_3 and heat in water bath until solution is complete. Make solution basic with 3 F KOH, then add solid Na_2O_2 slowly with stirring until approximately 0.2 g (a heaping microspatulaful) has been added. (6) (7) Heat in water bath for 3 min and centrifuge. Wash residue with 10 drops of water by centrifuging, and add washings to centrifugate.

Centrifugate contains aluminate, chromate, and zincate ions. Analyze as directed in Procedure 9 under Group IIIA.	**Precipitate** consists of hydrated manganese dioxide and the hydroxides of iron, cobalt, and nickel. Analyze as directed in Procedure 10 under Group IIIB.

NOTES ON THE PRECIPITATION OF GROUP III CATIONS AND THE SEPARATION OF THE GROUP INTO SUBGROUPS

    1. The reaction of the cations of Group III with H_2S may produce a hydronium-ion concentration sufficient to prevent complete precipitation of the sulfides. Complete precipitation is assured by keeping the solution alkaline; on the other hand, the hydroxide-ion concentration must be maintained sufficiently low to prevent the precipitation of magnesium hydroxide—the magnesium ion rightly belonging in Group IV. The addition of ammonia, buffered with NH_4Cl, accomplishes both purposes. Ammonia neutralizes excess hydronium ions, and at the same time ammonium ions from NH_4Cl repress the hydroxide-ion concentration to the extent necessary to prevent the precipitation of $Mg(OH)_2$.

    2. If the centrifugate from Procedure 3 has been boiled to expel H_2S as previously directed, then the addition of ammonia may give useful information as to the cations present. A gelatinous reddish-brown precipitate, insoluble in excess NH_3, indicates the presence of ferric ions. An uncolored gelatinous precipitate indicates aluminum.

    3. To test for complete precipitation, centrifuge and pass H_2S into the supernatant liquid. If the addition of H_2S produces a white precipitate, the presence of zinc ions is indicated, and the absence of iron, cobalt, and nickel ions.

    4. If the sulfide ion is not removed by acidification and boiling, it will be oxidized slowly to the sulfate ion by atmospheric oxygen. This may cause the precipitation and consequent loss of some of the cations of Group IV as sulfates.

5. CoS and NiS dissolve quite slowly in HCl. A black precipitate at this point, which dissolves only when HNO_3 is added to the mixture, indicates the presence of nickel or cobalt or both.

6. A large excess of Na_2O_2 is to be avoided. The hydroxides of iron, cobalt, and nickel may be dispersed to some extent in a strongly basic solution, causing interference with the test for aluminum and zinc ions. Sufficient Na_2O_2 should be added to produce a bubbling action for 1 min.

7. The Na_2O_2 is added for the purpose of oxidizing the chromite ion to the chromate ion. At the same time, ferrous and cobaltous hydroxides are oxidized to ferric and cobaltic hydroxides. Manganous hydroxide is oxidized to hydrated manganese dioxide.

ANALYSIS OF GROUP IIIA CATIONS

Procedure 9. Separation and Identification of Group IIIA Cations. Centrifugate from Procedure 8 contains aluminate, chromate, and zincate ions. Add 10 drops of saturated NH_4Ac, then 3 F HAc until acid. Now add 3 F ammonia until solution is decidedly ammoniacal. (1) Centrifuge.

Residue may be aluminum hydroxide. Wash with 10 drops of water and discard washings. Add 3 F HCl, drop by drop, until residue dissolves. Add 3 drops of saturated NH_4Ac and 3 drops of aluminon; then make decidedly ammoniacal with 3 F NH_3. Allow mixture to stand 2 min, then centrifuge. Separation of a red precipitate confirms presence of ALUMINUM ION. (2)	**Centrifugate** may contain $CrO_4^=$ and $Zn(NH_3)_4^{++}$. (3) Add 1 F $Ba(Ac)_2$ until precipitation is complete. Centrifuge.

Residue may be $BaCrO_4$ and $BaSO_4$. (4) Add 10 drops of 3 F HCl, and warm 1 min in water bath. Centrifuge and discard white residue. Place 2 drops of centrifugate upon a piece of filter paper. Add 2 drops of H_2O_2. Formation of a blue color which fades rapidly confirms presence of CHROMIUM ION. (5)	**Centrifugate** may contain $Zn(NH_3)_4^{++}$ ion. Acidify solution with 3 F HAc and saturate with H_2S. Formation of a white precipitate confirms presence of ZINC ION. If precipitate is not white, consult Note (6).

NOTES ON THE ANALYSIS OF GROUP IIIA CATIONS

1. The precipitation of aluminum hydroxide is practically complete in the buffered ammonia–ammonium acetate solution. In this solution, zinc is not precipitated as the hydroxide but is held in solution as the soluble complex ion, $Zn(NH_3)_4^{++}$.

2. "Aluminon" is the coined name for the ammonium salt of aurintricarboxylic acid. The organic dye forms a red-colored lake with aluminum hydroxide. This test is specific for aluminum under the conditions described.

3. The solution must be yellow if chromium is present. The color can best be observed by looking down through the solution contained in a test tube.

4. Any sulfide ions in the solution are converted to sulfate ions by the action of sodium peroxide. The sulfate ions are precipitated by barium ions as acid-insoluble $BaSO_4$.

5. The addition of hydrogen peroxide to an acid solution of a chromate produces a blue coloration due to the formation of CrO_5. This compound is unstable, decomposing rapidly with an evolution of oxygen, accompanied by a fading of the blue color.

6. The formation of a milky precipitate within a few seconds indicates the presence of the zinc ion. The precipitate may darken because of the presence of small quantities of ferrous and cobaltous ions which precipitate as FeS and CoS, or lead ions which may have escaped from Group II and precipitated here as black PbS. Treatment of such a blackened precipitate with 3 F HCl causes ZnS, FeS, and PbS to dissolve, leaving CoS as a residue. Centrifuge, and add to the centrifugate 0.05 g of Na_2O_2 and 20 drops of 3 F KOH. Boil for 1 min, centrifuge, and discard any precipitate. Make the solution acid with 1.5 F H_2SO_4, centrifuge, and discard any precipitate which may have formed. Add 3 F NH_3 to the centrifugate until barely alkaline, and then acidify with 3 F HAc. Saturate with H_2S. A white precipitate is ZnS

ANALYSIS OF GROUP IIIB CATIONS

Procedure 10. Separation and Identification of Group IIIB Cations. Precipitate from Procedure 8 may contain the hydroxides of iron, cobalt, and nickel, and hydrated manganese dioxide. Wash with 10 drops of water and discard washings. Dissolve precipitate in concentrated HCl. Dilute resulting solution to approximately 2 ml and divide into four portions.

First portion. Add 0.2 g (a heaping microspatulaful) of solid sodium bismuthate. Stir well, then centrifuge. Reddish-purple color in supernatant liquid confirms presence of MANGANESE ION. (1)	Second portion. Test for ferric ion by adding 2 drops of 3 F NH_4CNS. Appearance of deep red coloration confirms presence of FERRIC ION. (2)	Third portion. Test for cobalt ion as follows: Add solid NaF (3), with stirring, until undissolved NaF remains. Let 10 drops of alcoholic NH_4CNS run down side of test tube containing this portion. Appearance of blue-green color at junction of the two liquids confirms presence of COBALT ION. (4)	Fourth portion. Test for nickel ion as follows: Add solid NaF (3), with stirring, until undissolved NaF remains. Make the solution basic with 3 F NH_3, then add 4 drops of dimethylglyoxime. Formation of a red precipitate confirms presence of NICKEL ION. (5)

NOTES ON THE ANALYSIS OF GROUP IIIB CATIONS

1. In an acid solution, sodium bismuthate ($NaBiO_3$) oxidizes manganous ions to the purple-colored permanganate ions.

2. The color of the solution must be *dark* reddish-brown. Traces of ferric ions from the reagents used in the analysis usually give a pale red color in response to this sensitive test.

3. The presence of the ferric ion will interfere with the tests for cobalt and nickel ions. If sodium fluoride is added to a solution containing a mixture of ferric, cobalt, and nickel ions, the interference from the ferric ion in the confirmatory tests for nickel and cobalt is eliminated. The fluoride ion reacts with the ferric ion to produce a stable, colorless ferrifluoride ion, which gives no reaction with either of the reagents used in the confirmatory tests for the cobalt and nickel ions.

4. The blue complex cobaltothiocyanate ion, $Co(CNS)_4^-$, is not stable in water solution. The alcoholic solution of NH_4CNS is added to the surface of the aqueous solution; if cobalt ions are present, the blue color appears at the junction of the two solvents. It may be necessary to add more than 10 drops of the reagent in making the test. If the solution is shaken or stirred during the addition of the alcoholic NH_4CNS, the characteristic color test may not appear.

5. Cobalt, if present, produces some interference in the nickel test by reacting with

dimethylglyoxime to form a dark-colored complex ion. An excess of the test reagent must be added to ensure precipitation of the red-colored nickel dimethylglyoxime.

14·3 Pertinent Chemical Reactions Involved in the Separation and Identification of Cations of Group III. The equations for the chemical reactions given in this section are listed in the same sequence as the steps in the analytical procedures for Group III.

Reaction of Ammonia with Group III *Cations.* If the centrifugate from Group II is made ammoniacal and buffered by the addition of ammonium chloride, the hydroxides of iron, chromium, and aluminum precipitate.

$$Al^{3+} + 3NH_3 + 3H_2O \rightleftharpoons Al(OH)_3 + 3NH_4^+$$
$$Fe^{3+} + 3NH_3 + 3H_2O \rightleftharpoons Fe(OH)_3 + 3NH_4^+$$
$$Cr^{3+} + 3NH_3 + 3H_2O \rightleftharpoons Cr(OH)_3 + 3NH_4^+$$

If the hydrated forms of these ions are used, the equations are written as

$$Al(H_2O)_6^{3+} + 3NH_3 \rightleftharpoons Al(H_2O)_3(OH)_3 + 3NH_4^+$$
white, gelatinous ppt

$$Fe(H_2O)_6^{3+} + 3NH_3 \rightleftharpoons Fe(H_2O)_3(OH)_3 + 3NH_4^+$$
brown, gelatinous ppt

$$Cr(H_2O)_6^{3+} + 3NH_3 \rightleftharpoons Cr(H_2O)_3(OH)_3 + 3NH_4^+$$
grayish-green, gelatinous ppt

Manganous ions are not precipitated by ammonia solutions buffered with ammonium salts. Ammonia converts the nickel, cobalt, and zinc ions into the ammonia complexes.

$$Ni^{++} + 6NH_3 \rightleftharpoons Ni(NH_3)_6^{++}$$
$$Co^{++} + 6NH_3 \rightleftharpoons Co(NH_3)_6^{++}$$
$$Zn^{++} + 4NH_3 \rightleftharpoons Zn(NH_3)_4^{++}$$

Reactions of Hydrogen Sulfide in an Ammoniacal Solution Containing a Mixture of Group III *Cations.* Except for manganese, these cations are in the form of hydroxides or ammonia complexes. Chromium and aluminum hydroxides are unaffected by ammonium sulfide. The sulfides of these two ions cannot exist in solution because of hydrolysis which produces the hydroxides. The ammoniacal mixture of hydroxides and complexes of the other cations of Group III is converted into the sulfides when treated with hydrogen sulfide.

$$2Fe(OH)_3 + 3S^= + 6NH_4^+ \rightleftharpoons Fe_2S_3 + 6NH_3 + 6H_2O$$
black

$$Mn^{++} + S^= \rightleftharpoons MnS$$
pink

$$Ni(NH_3)_6^{++} + S^= \rightleftharpoons NiS + 6NH_3$$
black

$$Co(NH_3)_6^{++} + S^= \rightleftharpoons CoS + 6NH_3$$
black

$$Zn(NH_3)_4^{++} + S^= \rightleftharpoons ZnS + 4NH_3$$
white

Solution of Group III *Precipitate.*   The Group III precipitate is composed of the hydroxides of aluminum and chromium, and the sulfides of iron, manganese, zinc, nickel, and cobalt.   All these compounds dissolve readily in HCl except NiS and CoS.

$$Al(OH)_3 + 3H_3O^+ \rightleftharpoons Al^{3+} + 6H_2O$$

or

$$Al(H_2O)_3(OH)_3 + 3H_3O^+ \rightleftharpoons Al(H_2O)_6{}^{3+} + 3H_2O$$
$$Cr(OH)_3 + 3H_3O^+ \rightleftharpoons Cr^{3+} + 6H_2O$$

or

$$Cr(H_2O)_3(OH)_3 + 3H_3O^+ \rightleftharpoons Cr(H_2O)_6{}^{3+} + 3H_2O$$
$$Fe_2S_3 + 6H_3O^+ \rightleftharpoons 2Fe^{3+} + 3H_2S + 6H_2O$$
$$MnS + 2H_3O^+ \rightleftharpoons Mn^{++} + H_2S + 2H_2O$$
$$ZnS + 2H_3O^+ \rightleftharpoons Zn^{++} + H_2S + 2H_2O$$

Nickel and cobalt sulfides dissolve slowly in hydrochloric acid, but readily in nitric acid.

$$NiS + 2NO_3{}^- + 4H_3O^+ \rightleftharpoons Ni^{++} + 2NO_2 + S + 6H_2O$$
$$CoS + 2NO_3{}^- + 4H_3O^+ \rightleftharpoons Co^{++} + 2NO_2 + S + 6H_2O$$

Separation of Group III *into Subgroups.*   If a solution containing the cations of Group III is treated with sodium peroxide and excess KOH, three of the cations are converted into water-soluble anions; the other four cations are precipitated as hydroxides or hydrated oxides.

(*a*) Group IIIA is composed of the water-soluble anions produced by sodium peroxide and excess KOH.   These anions are the aluminate, zincate, and chromate ions.

The aluminum ion reacts with KOH solution to precipitate as the hydroxide which is soluble in an excess of the hydroxide ions.

$$Al^{3+} + 3OH^- \rightleftharpoons Al(OH)_3$$
$$Al(OH)_3 + OH^- \rightleftharpoons Al(OH)_4{}^-$$

or

$$Al(H_2O)_6{}^{3+} + 3OH^- \rightleftharpoons Al(H_2O)_3(OH)_3 \; + 3H_2O$$
white gelatinous ppt

and

$$Al(H_2O)_3(OH)_3 + OH^- \rightleftharpoons Al(H_2O)_2(OH)_4{}^- + H_2O$$
soluble

The zinc ion behaves similarly to the aluminum ion in the presence of excess hydroxide ions.

$$Zn^{++} + 2OH^- \rightleftharpoons Zn(OH)_2$$
$$Zn(OH)_2 + OH^- \rightleftharpoons Zn(OH)_3{}^-$$

or

$$Zn(H_2O)_4{}^{++} + 2OH^- \rightleftharpoons Zn(H_2O)_2(OH)_2 \; + 2H_2O$$
white gelatinous ppt

and

$$Zn(H_2O)_2(OH)_2 + OH^- \rightleftharpoons Zn(H_2O)(OH)_3^- + H_2O$$
soluble

The chromium ion reacts similarly to the aluminum and zinc ions in the presence of excess hydroxide ions. But in the presence of sodium peroxide the chromic ion is oxidized to the chromate ion.

$$Cr^{3+} + 3OH^- \rightleftharpoons Cr(OH)_3$$
$$Cr(OH)_3 + OH^- \rightleftharpoons Cr(OH)_4^-$$
$$2Cr(OH)_4^- + 3O_2^= \rightleftharpoons 2CrO_4^= + 4OH^- + 2H_2O$$

or

$$Cr(H_2O)_6{}^{3+} + 3OH^- \rightleftharpoons \quad Cr(H_2O)_3(OH)_3 \quad + 3H_2O$$
grayish-green, gelatinous ppt

and

$$Cr(H_2O)_3(OH)_3 + OH^- \rightleftharpoons Cr(H_2O)_2(OH)_4^- + H_2O$$
soluble
$$2Cr(H_2O)_2(OH)_4^- + 3O_2^= \rightleftharpoons 2CrO_4^= + 4OH^- + 6H_2O$$

(b) Group IIIB is composed of the hydroxides of iron, cobalt, and nickel, and the hydrated oxide of manganese.

In the presence of sodium peroxide and excess hydroxide ions, manganese ions are oxidized from a valence of two to a valence of four. The soluble manganous ions are converted to the insoluble hydrated manganese dioxide in the redox process.

$$Mn^{++} + 2OH^- \rightleftharpoons Mn(OH)_2$$
$$Mn(OH)_2 + O_2^= + H_2O \rightleftharpoons MnO(OH)_2 + 2OH^-$$

or

$$Mn(H_2O)_4{}^{++} + 2OH^- \rightleftharpoons Mn(H_2O)_2(OH)_2 + 2H_2O$$
white precipitate

and

$$Mn(H_2O)_2(OH)_2 + O_2^= \rightleftharpoons \quad MnO(OH)_2 \quad + 2OH^- + H_2O$$
brown precipitate

The sum of these two equations is

$$Mn(H_2O)_4{}^{++} + O_2^= \text{ (basic solution)} \rightleftharpoons MnO(OH)_2 + 3H_2O$$

The most stable valence of iron is that of three, and iron probably exists in the ferric state throughout the analysis of Group III. Potassium hydroxide solution precipitates reddish-brown ferric hydroxide.

$$Fe^{3+} + 3OH^- \rightleftharpoons Fe(OH)_3$$

or

$$Fe(H_2O)_6{}^{3+} + 3OH^- \rightleftharpoons Fe(H_2O)_3(OH)_3 + 3H_2O$$

The cobaltous ion is converted to cobaltic hydroxide by the action of sodium peroxide in a high concentration of hydroxide ions. The stepwise equations are

$$Co^{++} + 2OH^- \rightleftharpoons Co(OH)_2$$

or

$$Co(H_2O)_6^{++} + 2OH^- \rightleftharpoons Co(H_2O)_4(OH)_2 + 2H_2O$$
$$\text{pink}$$

Sodium peroxide oxidizes cobaltous hydroxide to the trivalent hydroxide.

$$2Co(OH)_2 + O_2^= + 2H_2O \rightleftharpoons 2Co(OH)_3 + 2OH^-$$

or

$$2Co(H_2O)_4(OH)_2 + O_2^= \rightleftharpoons 2Co(H_2O)_3(OH)_3 + 2OH^-$$
$$\text{brown precipitate}$$

The nickel ion is precipitated as the green, gelatinous nickelous hydroxide by the action of a strong base. Nickelic hydroxide is unstable in solution and is not produced under these conditions.

$$Ni^{++} + 2OH^- \rightleftharpoons Ni(OH)_2$$

or

$$Ni(H_2O)_6^{++} + 2OH^- \rightleftharpoons Ni(H_2O)_4(OH)_2 + 2H_2O$$

Separation and Identification of Aluminum Ion. If a solution containing the aluminate ion is made acidic with acetic acid it is converted to the aluminum ion.

$$Al(OH)_4^- + HAc \rightleftharpoons Al^{3+} + 4Ac^- + 4H_2O$$

or

$$Al(H_2O)_2(OH)_4^- + 4HAc \rightleftharpoons Al(H_2O)_6^{3+} + 4Ac^-$$

The addition of ammonia buffered with ammonium acetate to a solution containing aluminum ions precipitates aluminum hydroxide.

$$Al^{3+} + 3NH_3 + 3H_2O \rightleftharpoons Al(OH)_3 + 3NH_4^+$$

or

$$Al(H_2O)_6^{3+} + 3NH_3 \rightleftharpoons Al(H_2O)_3(OH)_3 + 3NH_4^+$$

The colorless, gelatinous precipitate of aluminum hydroxide has the property of adsorbing certain organic dyes. One such dye is aluminon, the ammonium salt of aurintricarboxylic acid. The adsorption of this red dye by aluminum hydroxide is specific within this group and is used as the confirmatory test for the aluminum ion.

Separation and Identification of Chromium as Chromate Ion. Barium acetate precipitates the chromate ion as the yellow $BaCrO_4$.

$$Ba^{++} + CrO_4^= \rightleftharpoons BaCrO_4$$

This precipitate is soluble in 3 F HCl, which is used as a means of separating it from $BaSO_4$, the latter being insoluble in HCl.

$$BaCrO_4 + H_3O^+ \rightleftharpoons Ba^{++} + HCrO_4^- + H_2O$$

The acid solution of the chromate reacts with hydrogen peroxide to produce the blue-colored perchromate, CrO_5.

$$HCrO_4^- + 2H_2O_2 + H_3O^+ \rightleftharpoons CrO_5 + 4H_2O$$

The blue perchromate is unstable and breaks down rapidly in water solution, with the liberation of oxygen.

$$4CrO_5 + 12H_3O^+ \rightleftharpoons 4Cr^{3+} + 7O_2 + 18H_2O$$

Identification of Zinc Ion. The separation of $BaCrO_4$ in Group IIIA analysis leaves the zinc ion, in the ammoniacal solution, in the form of the ammonia complex ion, $Zn(NH_3)_4^{++}$. If this solution is acidified with acetic acid and saturated with hydrogen sulfide, a white precipitate of ZnS results.

$$Zn(NH_3)_4^{++} + 4HAc \rightleftharpoons Zn^{++} + 4NH_4^+ + 4Ac^-$$
$$Zn^{++} + H_2S + 2H_2O \rightleftharpoons ZnS + 2H_3O^+$$

Solution of Group IIIB *Cations.* Concentrated hydrochloric acid readily dissolves the hydroxides of iron, cobalt, and nickel, and hydrated manganese dioxide.

$$Ni(OH)_2 + 2H_3O^+ \rightleftharpoons Ni^{++} + 4H_2O$$
$$Fe(OH)_3 + 3H_3O^+ \rightleftharpoons Fe^{3+} + 6H_2O$$
$$2Co(OH)_3 + 6H_3O^+ + 2Cl^- \rightleftharpoons 2Co^{++} + Cl_2 + 12H_2O$$
$$MnO(OH)_2 + 4H_3O^+ + 2Cl^- \rightleftharpoons Mn^{++} + Cl_2 + 7H_2O$$

Identification of Manganese Ion. Sodium bismuthate, when added to a cold solution of manganous ions containing dilute hydrochloric acid, oxidizes the manganous ions to the purple-colored permanganate ions.

$$2Mn^{++} + 5BiO_3^- + 14H_3O^+ \rightleftharpoons 2MnO_4^- + 5Bi^{3+} + 21H_2O$$

Identification of Ferric Ion. Ferric ions react with excess thiocyanate ions to produce a dark reddish-brown complex ion, $Fe(CNS)_6^{3-}$.

$$Fe^{3+} + 6CNS^- \rightleftharpoons Fe(CNS)_6^{3-}$$

Ferric ions interfere with the confirmatory tests for cobalt and nickel. This interference is prevented by converting the ferric ion into the stable ferrifluoride ion by the addition of excess sodium fluoride.

$$Fe^{3+} + 6F^- \rightleftharpoons FeF_6^{3-}$$

Identification of Cobaltous Ion. If an alcoholic solution of ammonium thiocyanate is added, without mixing, to a slightly acid solution of cobaltous ions, an intense blue-colored complex, $Co(CNS)_4^=$, is formed at the interface of the two liquids. This complex is destroyed if the solutions are mixed or diluted with water.

$$Co^{++} + 4CNS^- \rightleftharpoons Co(CNS)_4^=$$

Identification of Nickelous Ion. When added to a slightly ammoniacal solution of nickel ions, an alcoholic solution of dimethylglyoxime produces a voluminous red precipitate of nickel dimethylglyoxime. The precipitate has an empirical formula of $(C_4H_7O_2N_2)_2Ni$.

$$Ni^{++} + 2NH_3 + 2C_4H_8O_2N_2 \rightleftharpoons (C_4H_7O_2N_2)_2Ni + 2NH_4^+$$

CHAPTER 15

GROUP IV CATIONS

Cation Group IV is composed of the ions of the alkaline earth metals and magnesium. Although these ions form a large number of slightly soluble salts with various anions, the only anion which will produce satisfactory precipitation of all four cations in aqueous solution is the phosphate. The centrifugate from Group III is made strongly ammoniacal and, upon addition of the phosphate ion, the alkaline earth ions are precipitated as the tertiary phosphates and the magnesium ion as magnesium ammonium phosphate.

15·1 Theoretical Discussion. The ions of this cation group, magnesium, calcium, strontium, and barium, occur within the same group of the periodic table. Therefore, the valence of these cations is the same, and they resemble each other closely in their chemical reactions. This is especially true of the ions of the alkaline earth metals—calcium, strontium, and barium. In fact, the close chemical relationship of these three cations prevents a clean separation from each other by precipitation methods. This scheme presents the most commonly used methods of separation in which the barium ion is precipitated as barium chromate, the strontium ion as strontium sulfate, and the calcium ion as calcium oxalate. However, the values of the solubility product constants of each of these cations with the three precipitating anions are too close to permit separation and identification by means of precipitates alone. For confirmation of these precipitates and their corresponding cations, it is necessary to employ flame tests, which are more specific. Again, in the case of calcium and strontium, there is difficulty in the identification of the two ions since the flame tests are sufficiently similar to cause indecision. Comparison with flame tests made upon known solutions of these two cations may restrict this obstacle.

15·2 Analysis of Group IV Cations. The confirmatory tests within this group are far from satisfactory. The flame tests are sometimes difficult to obtain from the precipitated ions, especially from the insoluble precipitates of $BaCrO_4$ and $SrSO_4$. The presence or absence of the alkaline earth ions should be judged not only by their flame tests but also by the amounts of precipitates obtained in the individual separations. The analysis of Group IV is contained in Procedures 11 and 12.

ANALYSIS OF GROUP IV CATIONS

Procedure 11. Precipitation of Group IV Cations. Centrifugate from Group III precipitation (Procedure 7) should be clear and have a volume of approximately 1 ml. If volume is greater than 1 ml, concentrate by evaporation in a casserole, then centrifuge and discard any precipitate that may occur. (1) To the clear solution, add 10 drops of $0.5 F$ $(NH_4)_2HPO_4$ and concentrated NH_3 until strongly ammoniacal. Centrifuge. (2) Test for complete precipitation by adding a few drops of $(NH_4)_2HPO_4$ to centrifugate. Combine any precipitate which may form with that originally obtained.

Precipitate contains phosphates of barium, calcium, strontium, and magnesium. Analyze as directed in Procedure 12.	**Centrifugate** may contain cations of Group V. Reserve for analysis as directed in Procedure 13.

ANALYSIS OF GROUP IV CATIONS (*Continued*)

Procedure 12. Separation and Identification of Group IV Cations. Precipitate may consist of phosphates of barium, calcium, strontium, and magnesium. Wash once with 5 drops of water and discard washings. Treat precipitate with 5 drops of concentrated HAc and stir thoroughly. (1) (Any undissolved precipitate will probably dissolve upon dilution.) Dilute the solution to 2 ml, add 5 drops of $1 F$ K_2CrO_4, and stir for 1 min. Centrifuge and test for complete precipitation.

Precipitate may be $BaCrO_4$. Add 6 drops of concentrated HCl and heat in water bath until volume is reduced to one-half. (2) Confirm presence of BARIUM ION by flame test. (3) (*yellow-green*)	**Centrifugate** may contain strontium, calcium, and magnesium ions, and excess chromate ions from above precipitation. Make solution strongly basic with NH_3 and centrifuge. (4)			
	Precipitate may be phosphates of strontium, calcium, and magnesium. Dissolve in 5 drops of concentrated HAc; after solution is effected, dilute with 5 drops of water. Add 5 drops of $1 F$ $(NH_4)_2SO_4$, heat to boiling in water bath, cool, and centrifuge. Test for complete precipitation by adding 1 drop of $(NH_4)_2SO_4$ to clear centrifugate.		**Centrifugate** contains chromate ions, etc. Discard.	
	Precipitate may be $SrSO_4$. (5) Wash three times with hot water and discard washings. Add 3 drops of concentrated HCl. (6) Confirm presence of STRONTIUM ION by flame test. (*crimson-red*)	**Centrifugate** may contain calcium and magnesium ions. Add 5 drops of $0.25 F$ $(NH_4)_2C_2O_4$ and heat to boiling in water bath. (7) White precipitate or clouding of solution indicates presence of calcium ion. Centrifuge.		
		Precipitate may be CaC_2O_4. (8) Add 2 drops of concentrated HCl, and confirm presence of CALCIUM ION by flame test. (*brick-red*)	**Centrifugate** may contain magnesium ion. Add 1 or 2 drops of *p*-nitrobenzeneazoresorcinol (9) and 3 ml of $3 F$ KOH. (10) Heat in water bath for 5 min, then centrifuge. Formation of a blue precipitate confirms presence of MAGNESIUM ION. (11) (12)	

Notes on the Precipitation of Group IV Cations

1. A precipitate occurring at this point is probably a trace of a sulfide from Group III.

2. The phosphates of barium, calcium, and strontium come down readily as gelatinous precipitates. These precipitates will also cause the coprecipitation of magnesium to take place rapidly. If, however, magnesium ions occur alone in the solution, precipitation may only take place after standing for some time. Rubbing the sides of the test tube with a glass rod hastens the formation of the magnesium precipitate. The chemical composition of this precipitate is $MgNH_4PO_4 \cdot 6H_2O$, which is definitely crystalline in appearance.

Notes on the Analysis of Group IV Cations

1. Barium chromate cannot be precipitated in the presence of an appreciable hydronium-ion concentration; therefore, acetic acid is used in place of a stronger acid.

2. Barium chromate is not sufficiently volatile to give a flame test; consequently, this compound must be converted to one which is volatile. By evaporation with concentrated hydrochloric acid, the chromate is reduced to chromic ions according to the following equation:

$$2BaCrO_4 + 16H_3O^+ + 6Cl^- \rightleftharpoons 2Ba^{++} + 2Cr^{3+} + 24H_2O + 3Cl_2$$

The solution of barium ions in excess hydrochloric acid gives an excellent flame test.

3. The platinum wire to be used for the flame test must be free from any adhering substances which will color the bunsen flame. Make a very small loop in the end of the wire and clean as follows: Dip the wire into clean, concentrated HCl, contained in a test tube, and then heat the wire in a flame until red-hot. If the flame is colored, dip the wire again into the acid and heat in the flame again. Repeat this procedure until the wire imparts no appreciable color to the flame. *To make a flame test* dip the loop of the clean platinum wire into the solution to be tested, and then insert the wire into the oxidizing portion of a colorless gas flame. Repeat this operation several times to make certain that the test is not missed.

4. The purpose of this step is to remove the highly colored chromate or dichromate ions. In the subsequent steps, $SrSO_4$ and CaC_2O_4 are precipitated as finely divided white precipitates which are not readily discerned in a colored solution.

5. The separation of strontium ions from calcium ions by precipitation of $SrSO_4$ is not complete. From concentrated solutions, $CaSO_4$ may coprecipitate with $SrSO_4$. It is also true that the solubility product of $SrSO_4$ is sufficiently large to permit some strontium ions to be carried into the subsequent step and there precipitated as SrC_2O_4 along with calcium oxalate.

6. Although $SrSO_4$ is not appreciably soluble in concentrated HCl, a sufficient amount of the chloride results to intensify the flame coloration.

7. Calcium oxalate tends to form supersaturated solutions and may not precipitate unless the solution is heated.

8. A white precipitate does not confirm the presence of the calcium ion. A slight precipitate of SrC_2O_4 may form here (see Note 5).

9. Since the precipitate can adsorb only a small amount of the dye, a minimum quantity of the reagent should be used. Any large excess may so color the solution as to obscure the confirmatory test.

10. Because of the presence of the phosphate ion, it is necessary to add a large concentration of hydroxide ions to ensure the precipitation of magnesium hydroxide. The formation of the latter precipitate is important, since a phosphate precipitate of magnesium will not adsorb the dye used as a confirmatory test for the magnesium ion

11. Heating the strongly alkaline solution drives off NH_3 gas, otherwise the presence of the NH_4^+ ion interferes with the formation of the blue lake.

12. The formation of a lavender-colored precipitate is not a test for the magnesium ion. Such a precipitate may be due to the other members of this group which were incompletely removed in the preceding steps.

15·3 Pertinent Chemical Reactions Involved in the Separation and Identification of the Cations of Group IV.

The equations for the chemical reactions produced in the analysis of Group IV cations are given in the order in which the reactions are encountered in the analytical scheme.

Precipitation of Group IV Cations. Dibasic ammonium phosphate precipitates barium, strontium, and calcium ions from ammoniacal solutions as white, gelatinous tertiary phosphates.

$$3Ba^{++} + 2HPO_4^= + 2NH_3 \rightleftharpoons Ba_3(PO_4)_2 + 2NH_4^+$$
$$3Sr^{++} + 2HPO_4^= + 2NH_3 \rightleftharpoons Sr_3(PO_4)_2 + 2NH_4^+$$
$$3Ca^{++} + 2HPO_4^= + 2NH_3 \rightleftharpoons Ca_3(PO_4)_2 + 2NH_4^+$$

Dibasic ammonium phosphate precipitates magnesium ions from an ammoniacal solution as white, crystalline magnesium ammonium phosphate.

$$Mg^{++} + HPO_4^= + NH_3 + 6H_2O \rightleftharpoons MgNH_4PO_4 \cdot 6H_2O$$

Solution of Group IV Precipitate. In the absence of a large excess of acetate ions, acetic acid dissolves the phosphates of barium, strontium, calcium, and magnesium.

$$Ba_3(PO_4)_2 + 4HAc \rightleftharpoons 3Ba^{++} + 2H_2PO_4^- + 4Ac^-$$
$$Ca_3(PO_4)_2 + 4HAc \rightleftharpoons 3Ca^{++} + 2H_2PO_4^- + 4Ac^-$$
$$Sr_3(PO_4)_2 + 4HAc \rightleftharpoons 3Sr^{++} + 2H_2PO_4^- + 4Ac^-$$
$$MgNH_4PO_4 \cdot 6H_2O + 2HAc \rightleftharpoons Mg^{++} + H_2PO_4^- + NH_4^+$$
$$+ 2Ac^- + 6H_2O$$

Separation and Identification of Barium Ion. Potassium chromate precipitates yellow barium chromate from an acetic acid solution of barium ions.

$$Ba^{++} + CrO_4^= \rightleftharpoons BaCrO_4$$

Barium chromate is not sufficiently volatile to give a satisfactory flame test for the barium ion. If $BaCrO_4$ is evaporated with concentrated HCl, the chromate ion is reduced to the chromic ion, and barium ions enter solution.

$$2BaCrO_4 + 16H_3O^+ + 6Cl^- \rightleftharpoons 2Ba^{++} + 2Cr^{3+} + 3Cl_2 + 24H_2O$$

When heated in the bunsen flame, barium salts, especially the chloride, impart a yellowish-green color to the flame.

Separation and Identification of Strontium Ion. Ammonium sulfate precipitates white $SrSO_4$ from an acetic acid solution of strontium ions.

$$Sr^{++} + SO_4^{=} \rightleftharpoons SrSO_4$$

Strontium sulfate is sufficiently soluble in concentrated HCl to give a flame test for the strontium ion. When heated in a bunsen flame, strontium salts, especially the chloride, impart a crimson color to the flame.

Separation and Identification of Calcium Ion. Ammonium oxalate precipitates white CaC_2O_4 from an acetic acid solution of calcium ions.

$$Ca^{++} + C_2O_4^{=} \rightleftharpoons CaC_2O_4$$

Calcium oxalate, although insoluble in acetic acid, dissolves readily in hydrochloric acid.

$$CaC_2O_4 + H_3O^+ \rightleftharpoons Ca^{++} + HC_2O_4^- + H_2O$$

When heated in a bunsen flame, calcium salts, especially the chloride, impart a brick-red color to the flame.

Precipitation and Identification of Magnesium Ion. Potassium hydroxide precipitates white, gelatinous magnesium hydroxide from a solution of magnesium ions.

$$Mg^{++} + 2OH^- \rightleftharpoons Mg(OH)_2$$

or

$$Mg(H_2O)_6^{++} + 2OH^- \rightleftharpoons Mg(H_2O)_4(OH)_2 + 2H_2O$$

This precipitate has the property of adsorbing certain organic dyes to form colored lakes. One such dye is *p*-nitrobenzeneazoresorcinol, which produces a blue lake with magnesium hydroxide. The formation of this lake is specific for the magnesium ion in the presence of other cations of Group IV and is used as a confirmatory test for the magnesium ion.

CHAPTER 16

GROUP V CATIONS

The centrifugate from Group IV contains the commonly occurring cations which are not precipitated by the chloride, sulfide, and phosphate ions under the conditions for precipitation of the first four groups of cations. This group is sometimes called the *soluble group* and includes sodium, potassium, and ammonium ions. The salts of these cations, with few exceptions, are quite soluble. This accounts for the fact that there is no precipitating agent for the group.

16·1 Theoretical Discussion. In systematic analysis the ammonium ion will always occur in Group V, since ammonium salts and ammonia solution are used as reagents throughout the cation scheme. Consequently, a test for this ion within Group V would be meaningless. It is necessary to test for the ammonium ion upon a portion of the original solution used in the beginning of the scheme of analysis. This test is quite simple and extremely sensitive. If a strong base such as KOH or NaOH is added to a solution containing ammonium ions and the solution is warmed, the escape of ammonia gas results. The increased concentration of hydroxide ions, resulting from the addition of the strong base, upsets the equilibrium existing in a water solution of ammonia.

$$NH_4^+ + OH^- \rightleftharpoons NH_3 + H_2O$$

The ammonia gas which escapes may be recognized by its odor or by its action upon moist red litmus paper.

A number of precipitation tests for the sodium and potassium ions are frequently used in qualitative analysis to identify these ions in the presence of each other. Probably the most widely used of these precipitating reagents are zinc uranyl acetate and sodium cobaltinitrite. The first of these will precipitate the sodium ion as a yellow precipitate of sodium zinc uranyl acetate. Potassium ions are precipitated by sodium cobaltinitrite as yellow potassium sodium cobaltinitrite. The NH_4^+ ion gives a similar precipitate; therefore, it is necessary to remove this ion before making this test for the potassium ion. In semimicro analysis the use of these reagents is not recommended. The low concentration of cations in the dilute solutions of systematic analysis gives disappointing confirmatory precipitates. Also, traces of other cations which escape into

Group V will cause precipitates with these reagents in the absence of the sodium and potassium ions.

The most reliable qualitative tests for sodium and potassium ions in low concentrations are their identifying flame spectra. An intense yellow flame persisting for several seconds confirms the presence of sodium ions. The presence of potassium ions is indicated by a pale violet flame which appears reddish-violet through cobalt glass. In making these flame tests, confirmation of the presence or absence of sodium or potassium is more easily determined by comparison with flame tests made upon known samples of these ions.

16·2 Analysis of Group V Cations. The most satisfactory confirmatory tests for the ions of Group V are contained in Procedures 13 and 14. These tests are relatively simple requiring little in the way of explanation.

ANALYSIS OF GROUP V CATIONS

Procedure 13. Identification of Sodium and Potassium Ions. Transfer centrifugate from Group IV (Procedure 11) to a casserole and evaporate to approximately 0.5 ml. Discard any precipitate that may form. Add 1 drop of concentrated HCl and make flame tests for sodium and potassium ions as follows:

Clean a platinum wire until it gives no color to a nonluminous flame (see Group IV, Note 3). Dip end of wire in above solution and return wire to flame. *Intense* yellow flame persisting for 5 sec confirms presence of SODIUM ION. (1)

In the absence of sodium ions, presence of potassium ions imparts a pale violet color to flame when viewed with the naked eye. If yellow flame of sodium is present, it will be necessary to view flame through a filter of cobalt glass. Repeat above test and examine flame through two thicknesses of blue cobalt glass. Reddish-violet flame persisting for about 2 sec confirms presence of POTASSIUM ION. (2)

Procedure 14. Identification of Ammonium Ion. Solutions of ammonia and ammonium salts have been added throughout the scheme of analysis; therefore, it is necessary to use some of original solution to make this test. Proceed as follows:

Place 5 drops of original solution in a small beaker and add 5 drops of water. Make solution alkaline with 3 F KOH. Immediately cover beaker with a watch glass to which adheres a strip of moistened red litmus paper on convex side. Warm solution gently for 1 min. Even shading of litmus paper from red to blue confirms presence of AMMONIUM ION. (3)

NOTES ON THE ANALYSIS OF GROUP V CATIONS

1. The test for the sodium ion is extremely sensitive. Traces of sodium ions occur in most reagents, and even glass bottles may contaminate solutions with sodium ions after long standing. It is essential that the flame test upon an unknown solution be compared with that of a known sample. The intensity and duration of the sodium flame are proportional to the concentration of the sodium ions present. An intense yellow flame of 5 sec or more duration should indicate the presence of sodium. A yellow flame which is not intense and is of short duration may be caused by traces of sodium and should be considered as a negative test.

2. Potassium compounds are more volatile than those of sodium; therefore, the flame spectrum produced by the presence of potassium ions is of shorter duration than

that of sodium. The reddish-violet color of the potassium flame is masked by the yellow flame produced by the presence of sodium ions. A blue filter will screen out this yellow color and at the same time permit the transmittance of the reddish-violet color of the potassium flame. Usually two thicknesses of cobalt glass are necessary for complete absorption of the yellow flame of sodium. As in the case of sodium, it is again necessary to compare the flame spectrum of the unknown solution with that of a known. It is also true that most solutions which have passed through the cation scheme will contain small traces of potassium ions due to contamination of reagents, but the distinction between a trace and a positive test is much sharper than in the case of the sodium-ion test.

3. A solution of ammonia gas represents an equilibrium between a physical solution of ammonia molecules and a chemical equilibrium producing ammonium ions and hydroxide ions. Conversely, a solution of ammonium ions in the presence of hydroxide ions will produce some ammonia molecules. A high concentration of hydroxide ions, following the law of mass action, will decrease the concentration of ammonium ions to produce a larger concentration of ammonia molecules. The ammonia molecules are less soluble in a warm solution than cold and escape from the solution to change the color of moist, red litmus paper. If the solution is heated sufficiently to cause spattering, droplets from the solution containing hydroxide ions from the KOH will cause a color change in the litmus paper. Such spattering is usually indicated by scattered spots of blue on the red litmus paper.

16·3 Pertinent Chemical Reactions Involved in Analysis of Cations of Group V. The present scheme of cation analysis offers no chemical tests for either the sodium or the potassium ions. Such tests do exist, but they are not sufficiently sensitive for semimicro qualitative analysis. This lack of sensitivity is due to the fact that most salts of sodium and potassium are too soluble to be adequate for precipitation tests. There are a few relatively insoluble compounds of sodium and potassium, such as $Na_2H_2Sb_2O_7$ and $K_3Co(NO_2)_6$, but the precipitating reagents for such compounds are not specific for these ions. The flame tests given in Procedure 13 are more satisfactory than any precipitation tests for sodium and potassium ions.

Identification of Sodium and Potassium Ions. The most widely used precipitation test for the sodium ion is the formation of sodium zinc uranyl acetate. The addition of zinc uranyl acetate to an acetic acid solution of sodium ions produces a yellow crystalline precipitate after about 5 min standing.

$$Na^+ + Zn^{++} + 3UO_2^{++} + 9Ac^- \rightleftharpoons NaZn(UO_2)_3(Ac)_9$$

Interfering ions which may produce a similar precipitate are aluminum, ammonium, barium, calcium, cadmium, cobalt, copper, magnesium, mercury, manganese, nickel, potassium, strontium, and zinc.

One of the most common precipitation tests for potassium ions is the formation of potassium-sodium cobaltinitrite. The addition of sodium cobaltinitrite to a solution of potassium ions, acidified with acetic acid, produces a yellow precipitate of potassium-sodium cobaltinitrite, after long standing.

$$2K^+ + Na^+ + Co(NO_2)_6{}^{3-} \rightleftharpoons NaK_2Co(NO_2)_6$$

The ammonium ion produces a similar precipitate with this reagent.

Identification of Ammonium Ion. Sodium hydroxide or potassium hydroxide liberates ammonia when added to a solution of ammonium ions. Ammonia gas is less soluble in hot than cold solution; therefore, heating drives the reaction in that direction to release ammonia.

$$NH_4{}^+ + OH^- \rightleftharpoons NH_3 + H_2O$$

The liberated ammonia may be identified by odor or by its action upon moistened red litmus paper.

CHAPTER 17

INTRODUCTION TO ANION ANALYSIS—GROUP I ANIONS

SYSTEMATIC ANALYSIS OF THE ANIONS

Early attempts toward systematic analysis of the anions date back, at least, to Bunsen, who in 1878 divided the "acid radicals" into related groups for the purpose of identification. The earlier schemes of analysis might best be described as groups of elimination tests, in which a sample could not be carried through a successive series of analytical separation groups. Only in recent years have anion schemes been developed which are truly systematic. The one employed here is taken from a system of qualitative analysis for the anions published by J. T. Dobbins and H. A. Ljung.[1] This scheme is quite flexible and covers all the most common anions. In this procedure, the solution being analyzed is kept slightly basic through most of the scheme to prevent or minimize the interaction of oxidizing and reducing anions.

The present scheme identifies 21 commonly occurring anions. These are as follows:

Arsenate	AsO_4^{3-}	Iodide	I^-
Arsenite	AsO_2^-	Nitrate	NO_3^-
Borate	BO_2^-	Nitrite	NO_2^-
Bromide	Br^-	Oxalate	$C_2O_4^=$
Carbonate	$CO_3^=$	Phosphate	PO_4^{3-}
Chlorate	ClO_3^-	Sulfate	$SO_4^=$
Chloride	Cl^-	Sulfide	$S^=$
Chromate	$CrO_4^=$	Sulfite	$SO_3^=$
Ferricyanide	$Fe(CN)_6^{3-}$	Thiocyanate	CNS^-
Ferrocyanide	$Fe(CN)_6^{4-}$	Thiosulfate	$S_2O_3^=$
Fluoride	F^-		

The anions are negatively charged ions produced by the ionization of acids and salts. With the exception of the fluoride, chloride, bromide, iodide, and sulfide ions, the anions are composed of two or more elements bound in chemical combination. Such combinations vary widely in sta-

[1] J. Chem. Educ., **12**, 586 (1935).

bility and reactivity. Oxidizing anions tend to react with reducing anions, and in the reactions, the ions lose their identities as a result of the oxidation-reduction reaction. For example, the sulfite ion will reduce the chlorate ion to produce the sulfate and chloride ions. Reactions of this type are avoided by maintaining a pH above 7 through the first three groups of the anion scheme.

In the anion procedure the ions are separated into groups based upon the solubilities of the calcium, barium, cadmium, and silver salts. These groups are as follows:

Group I includes ions whose calcium salts are insoluble in slightly basic solution.

Group II includes ions whose calcium salts are soluble but whose barium salts are insoluble in slightly basic solution.

Group III is composed of anions whose calcium and barium salts are soluble but whose cadmium salts are insoluble in slightly basic solution.

Group IV is composed of anions whose calcium, barium, and cadmium salts are soluble but whose silver salts are insoluble in a solution slightly acid with nitric acid.

Group V contains anions whose calcium, barium, cadmium, and silver salts are soluble in water and acids.

In precipitating the insoluble anion groups, the acetates of calcium, barium, cadmium, and silver are used. Solutions of these acetates are slightly basic due to hydrolysis, which aids in maintaining the proper pH for anion analysis.

In cation analysis, the separation of the cations is fairly clean because of the large difference in solubility products of the soluble and insoluble salts. This is not true for the separation of some of the anions in anion analysis. A few anions form difficulty soluble salts with more than one group reagent. For example, the sulfate ion may precipitate in Groups I and II as $CaSO_4$ and $BaSO_4$; the borate ion may precipitate incompletely in Groups I and III as $Ca(BO_2)_2$ and $Cd(BO_2)_2$. However, within the concentration limits used in this scheme, sufficient separation for satisfactory identification of all the anions is obtained.

Since the separation into insoluble groups depends upon the solutions being slightly basic, it is necessary that the sample to be analyzed be tested for acidity and adjusted to the proper pH before analysis. Also, the presence of cations other than sodium, potassium, or ammonium may interfere with anion analysis. These cations are removed by adding an excess of sodium carbonate solution. The cations are precipitated as insoluble carbonates, basic carbonates, or hydroxides, leaving the anions in solution as the sodium salts. This prepared solution will, therefore, contain an excess of carbonate ions after the cation precipitation and removal. This excess is both an advantage and a disadvantage. It is advantageous in that the carbonate ion maintains an alkalinity sufficient to prevent unwanted redox reactions between anions, but the carbonate also causes a precipitation in Group I (of $CaCO_3$), even though the members of Group I may have been absent in the original substance being analyzed.

GROUP I ANIONS

The anions of Group I are distinguished from the other groups in that their calcium salts are insoluble in neutral or slightly basic solution. The group precipitating agent is calcium acetate solution. The acetate ion has the advantage over other salts of calcium in that it does not interfere with any succeeding separations. Cations other than sodium, potassium, or ammonium must be removed by sodium carbonate treatment. The excess carbonate will always produce a precipitate in Group I, necessitating the analysis of this group even though other anions of the group are absent. However, this analysis will rid the solution of the large excess of carbonate ions.

17·1 Theoretical Discussion. There is very little theory involved in the analysis of Group I anions. If only sodium, potassium, or ammonium cations are present, the sodium carbonate treatment should be omitted. However, the pH of the original solution should be adjusted with dilute KOH and dilute HAc until the resulting solution is barely alkaline, as indicated by litmus paper.

It is obvious that the test for the carbonate ion must be made on the original solid, since the unknown sample is usually subjected to the sodium carbonate treatment. It is also possible and even advantageous to test for the fluoride ion on the original solid. The test given in this scheme is specific for the fluoride ion, and it may be even more sensitive when made upon the original substance.

17·2 Analysis of Group I Anions. The anions of Group I are divided into two subgroups by the action of dilute acetic acid. Calcium fluoride

ANALYSIS OF GROUP I ANIONS

Procedure 1. Detection of Carbonate Ion. In a test tube, dilute 10 drops of $3 F$ HCl with an equal quantity of water and add 0.1 g (a level microspatulaful) of $KClO_3$. (1) To this acid solution add a level microspatulaful of the original sample. (2) If original unknown is a solution, use 10 drops for this test. Vigorous effervescence indicates presence of CARBONATE ION.

Procedure 2. Removal of Heavy-metal Ions. To a level microspatulaful of the sample (2 ml if it is a solution), add 2 ml of water and heat in water bath for 2 min. Now add 2 ml of $1.5 F$ Na_2CO_3 solution and heat in water bath for 10 min. Replace any water which may be lost in evaporation and centrifuge. **Centrifugate** contains anions in the form of soluble sodium salts and is analyzed according to Procedure 3. Discard precipitate, which is composed of carbonates and hydroxides of heavy-metal **ions.**

ANALYSIS OF GROUP I ANIONS (*Continued*)

Procedure 3. Precipitation of Group I Anions. To centrifugate (3) from Procedure 2, add 2 F Ca(Ac)$_2$, drop by drop, until precipitation is complete. (4) Centrifuge. **Centrifugate** contains anions of Groups II–V and is reserved for Procedure 7. **Residue** may be composed of insoluble calcium salts of carbonate, sulfite, arsenite, arsenate, phosphate, oxalate, or fluoride ions. (5) Wash residue three times with water and discard washings. (6) Analyze residue as directed in Procedure 4.

Procedure 4. Separation of Group I Anions into Subgroups. To residue from Procedure 3 add 15 drops of 3 F HAc (7), stir *thoroughly*, and centrifuge.

Centrifugate may contain sulfite, arsenite, arsenate, or phosphate ions. Analyze as directed in Procedure 5 under Group 1A.

Residue which does not dissolve in HAc may be CaC$_2$O$_4$ or CaF$_2$ or both. Analyze as directed in Procedure 6 under Group IB.

Procedure 5. Identification of Group IA Anions. Centrifugate from Procedure 4 may contain sulfite, arsenite, arsenate, and phosphate ions. Divide into four portions and test as follows:

First portion.	Second portion.	Third portion.	Fourth portion.
Add 2 drops of concentrated HCl and 5 drops of Ba(Ac)$_2$. Centrifuge and discard any precipitate which may have formed. To clear centrifugate add 5 drops of H$_2$O$_2$. Formation of white precipitate confirms presence of SULFITE. (8)	Add 2 drops of 3 F HCl and 2 drops of water. Heat to boiling and saturate with H$_2$S. Immediate formation of yellow precipitate confirms presence of ARSENITE. (9)	Add 2 drops of 3 F HCl and heat in water bath for 2 min. (10) Add a few crystals of KI. If solution turns brown, presence of ARSENATE is indicated. (11) Add 10 drops of CCl$_4$ and shake vigorously for 1 min. Pink color in the CCl$_4$ layer further indicates presence of ARSENATE.	Add 5 drops of concentrated HNO$_3$ and 0.2 g (a heaping microspatulaful) of solid tartaric acid. (12) Stir solution thoroughly and add 5 drops of ammonium molybdate solution. Warm (13) in water bath for 1 min. Formation of yellow precipitate confirms presence of PHOSPHATE. (14)

Procedure 6. Identification of Group IB Anions. Residue from Procedure 4 may be CaC$_2$O$_4$ or CaF$_2$ or both of these substances. Wash twice with water and discard washings. (15) Divide into two portions and test as follows:

First portion.	Second portion.
Add 10 drops of 1.5 F H$_2$SO$_4$. Heat with stirring in water bath for 1 min. Add 2 drops of 0.01 F KMnO$_4$ solution. Disappearance of pink color indicates presence of OXALATE. (16)	Transfer to surface of a clean, clear watch glass. Heat watch glass over water bath until residue is dry. (17) Add 1 drop of concentrated H$_2$SO$_4$ upon dry residue on the watch glass and continue to heat over water bath for 5 min. Allow to stand for 20 min, then wash the glass thoroughly. Etching of the glass confirms presence of FLUORIDE. (18)

Notes on the Analysis of Group I Anions

1. The addition of $KClO_3$ will oxidize the sulfite, sulfide, and thiosulfate ions, in an acid solution, to the sulfate ion or free sulfur. These ions would otherwise produce gases in acid solution which might be mistaken for carbon dioxide in the test for the carbonate.

2. The presence of cations other than sodium, potassium, and ammonium would produce interference in anion analysis. The heavy-metal cations are removed by the sodium carbonate treatment described in Procedure 2. This treatment adds the carbonate ion to the solution to be analyzed for anions; therefore, it is necessary to test for the presence of the carbonate ion upon the original sample.

3. The sodium carbonate treatment in Procedure 2 may be omitted if it is known that only sodium, potassium, or ammonium salts are present. If procedure is omitted, dissolve 0.1 g of the original sample in 2 ml of water and analyze according to Procedure 3.

4. If the prepared solution is made according to Procedure 2, there will be a large excess of carbonate ions present which will precipitate at this point as white, gelatinous calcium carbonate. Heating tends to convert the gelatinous precipitate to a more workable consistency.

5. The presence of an appreciable concentration of SO_4^- ions may cause the precipitation of $CaSO_4$ with Group I anions. This precipitate is insoluble in strong acids.

6. If the original prepared solution, or dissolved sample, is yellow in color, the presence of the CrO_4^- ion is indicated. Contamination of the Group I precipitate with this ion will interfere with the analysis of the anions of this group. If the yellow color is present, the residue must be washed until the color is removed.

7. If the prepared solution is made according to Procedure 2, it will be necessary to add more than 15 drops of acetic acid. In this event, add acetic acid as long as the precipitate appears to dissolve.

8. Hydrogen peroxide oxidizes the sulfite ion to the sulfate. In the acid solution, the sulfate ion is precipitated as $BaSO_4$.

9. If a yellow precipitate does not form immediately, the arsenite ion is absent. The arsenate ion will give a yellow precipitate of arsenic pentasulfide after a period of 60 sec or more.

10. The sulfite ion, if present, must be destroyed by heating in an acid solution; otherwise, this ion will react with free iodine liberated in the arsenate test.

11. The iodine may be extracted from the brown-colored water solution by shaking with CCl_4, because of the greater solubility of iodine in the latter solvent. A solution of iodine in CCl_4 produces a pink color.

12. The excess tartaric acid, in strongly acid solution, forms a complex with arsenic; otherwise, the arsenate ion would precipitate with ammonium molybdate in the confirmatory test for the phosphate.

13. Do not boil, because it is possible that the soluble complex between tartaric acid and arsenic may be broken down with heat.

14. In the absence of the phosphate ion, a white precipitate quite often results, due to the decomposition of the ammonium molybdate reagent. Disregard such a precipitate.

15. Thorough washing of the residue is necessary to remove traces of reducing ions, such as sulfite and arsenite, which interfere with the test for the oxalate ion.

16. The pink-colored MnO_4^- ion is reduced by oxalic acid (produced by calcium oxalate in acid solution) to the manganous ion which is colorless in this dilution.

17. The presence of water interferes with the etching test for the fluoride ion by forming insoluble silicic acid with volatile silicon tetrafluoride.

18. Concentrated H_2SO_4 reacts with CaF_2 to form hydrogen fluoride, and the latter etches glass by producing gaseous SiF_4.   This etching test is specific for the fluoride ion and may be repeated upon the original solid sample.

---

and calcium oxalate are insoluble in $3\ F$ HAc, whereas the other members of the group dissolve.   The soluble subgroup should be analyzed immediately after solution is effected.   This subgroup contains the sulfite and arsenite ions which may be oxidized to sulfate and arsenate, by atmospheric oxygen, upon standing.

17·3   Pertinent Chemical Reactions Involved in the Separation and Identification of Group I Anions.   The following equations are given in the order in which the reactions are encountered in the scheme of analysis.

Precipitation of Group I *Anions.*   The anions of Group I are precipitated from slightly alkaline solution by calcium acetate solution.

$$CO_3^= + Ca^{++} \rightleftharpoons CaCO_3$$
$$C_2O_4^= + Ca^{++} \rightleftharpoons CaC_2O_4$$
$$2F^- + Ca^{++} \rightleftharpoons CaF_2$$
$$SO_3^= + Ca^{++} \rightleftharpoons CaSO_3$$
$$2AsO_2^- + Ca^{++} \rightleftharpoons Ca(AsO_2)_2$$
$$2AsO_4^{3-} + 3Ca^{++} \rightleftharpoons Ca_3(AsO_4)_2$$
$$2PO_4^{3-} + 3Ca^{++} \rightleftharpoons Ca_3(PO_4)_2$$

Identification of Carbonate Ion.   Dilute HCl decomposes carbonates with an effervescence due to the evolution of carbon dioxide.

$$CaCO_3 + 2H_3O^+ \rightleftharpoons Ca^{++} + 3H_2O + CO_2$$

This test identifies the carbonate ion by the liberation of a gas.   Other anions which produce gases in acid solution, such as the sulfite, thiosulfate, and sulfide, are oxidized by the addition of $KClO_3$.   In their oxidized form such anions produce no gases to interfere with the carbonate test.   Examples of the oxidation of these interfering anions are as follows:

$$3H_2SO_3 + ClO_3^- + 6H_2O \rightleftharpoons 3SO_4^= + Cl^- + 6H_3O^+$$
$$3H_2S + ClO_3^- \rightleftharpoons Cl^- + 3H_2O + 3S$$

Action of Dilute Acetic Acid upon Group I *Anion Precipitate.*   All the insoluble calcium salts of Group I anions dissolve in dilute acetic acid except calcium fluoride and calcium oxalate.

$$CaCO_3 + 2HAc \rightleftharpoons Ca^{++} + H_2O + CO_2 + 2Ac^-$$
$$CaSO_3 + 2HAc \rightleftharpoons Ca^{++} + H_2SO_3 + 2Ac^-$$
$$Ca(AsO_2)_2 + 2HAc + 2H_2O \rightleftharpoons Ca^{++} + 2H_3AsO_3 + 2Ac^-$$
$$Ca_3(AsO_4)_2 + 4HAc \rightleftharpoons 3Ca^{++} + 2H_2AsO_4^- + 4Ac^-$$
$$Ca_3(PO_4)_2 + 4HAc \rightleftharpoons 3Ca^{++} + 2H_2PO_4^- + 4Ac^-$$

Identification of Sulfite Ion. The sulfite ion is oxidized by hydrogen peroxide to the sulfate. The latter is precipitated as $BaSO_4$, insoluble in strong acids.

$$H_2SO_3 + H_2O_2 + H_2O \rightleftharpoons SO_4^= + 2H_3O^+$$
$$SO_4^= + Ba^{++} \rightleftharpoons BaSO_4$$

Test for Arsenite Ion. Hydrogen sulfide produces an immediate precipitate of yellow As_2S_3 when passed into a solution of arsenite ions.

$$2H_3AsO_3 + 3H_2S \rightleftharpoons As_2S_3 + 6H_2O$$

Under the same conditions, the arsenate ion gives a yellow precipitate of arsenic sulfide which precipitates slowly.

$$2H_2AsO_4^- + 5H_2S + 2H_3O^+ \rightleftharpoons As_2S_5 + 10H_2O$$

Detection of Arsenate Ion. The arsenate ion is reduced by the iodide ion, in an acid solution, with the liberation of iodine.

$$H_2AsO_4^- + 3H_3O^+ + 2I^- \rightleftharpoons H_3AsO_3 + I_2 + 4H_2O$$

Identification of Phosphate Ion. The phosphate ion reacts with ammonium molybdate in a nitric acid solution to form a yellow, voluminous precipitate of ammonium phosphomolybdate.

$$H_2PO_4^- + 12MoO_4^= + 22H_3O^+ + 3NH_4^+$$
$$\rightleftharpoons (NH_4)_3PO_4 \cdot 12MoO_3 + 34H_2O$$

Confirmation of Presence of Oxalate Ion. Sulfuric acid added to a precipitate of CaC_2O_4 produces soluble oxalic acid. Oxalic acid, in the presence of a high concentration of hydronium ions, reduces permanganate ions to manganous ions. The color of the solution changes from purple to colorless.

$$CaC_2O_4 + 2H_3O^+ \rightleftharpoons Ca^{++} + H_2C_2O_4 + 2H_2O$$
$$5H_2C_2O_4 + 2MnO_4^- + 6H_3O^+ \rightleftharpoons 2Mn^{++} + 10CO_2 + 14H_2O$$

Identification of Fluoride Ion. Concentrated sulfuric acid liberates volatile hydrogen fluoride from a precipitate of calcium fluoride.

$$CaF_2 + 2H_3O^+ \rightleftharpoons Ca^{++} + 2H_2O + 2HF$$

Hydrogen fluoride attacks silica, or any silicate, evolving silicon tetrafluoride.

$$SiO_2 + 4HF \rightleftharpoons SiF_4 + 2H_2O$$

CHAPTER 18

GROUP II ANIONS

This group contains only the chromate and sulfate ions. These ions are precipitated by the group reagent, barium acetate, as $BaCrO_4$ and $BaSO_4$ in a slightly basic solution.

The analysis of this group involves no difficulties. The presence of the chromate is indicated by a yellow color. If the centrifugate from Group I anions is colorless the test for the chromate ion may be omitted. However, the presence of a yellow color in this centrifugate does not confirm the presence of the chromate ion, since the ferrocyanide and ferricyanide ions of Group III anions may also impart a yellow color to the solution.

18·1 Analysis of Group II Anions. Barium sulfate is separated from barium chromate by its insolubility in $3\ F$ HCl. The chromate ion is confirmed by reprecipitating $BaCrO_4$ from the centrifugate of the acid solution.

ANALYSIS OF GROUP II ANIONS

Procedure 7. Precipitation of Group II Anions. Centrifugate from Procedure 3 may contain any or all of the anions of Groups II–V. Add $1\ F\ Ba(Ac)_2$, dropwise, until precipitation is complete. Centrifuge. Centrifugate contains Groups III–V anions and is reserved for Procedure 9. Precipitate may be composed of $BaSO_4$ and $BaCrO_4$. (1) Analyze according to Procedure 8.

Procedure 8. Separation and Identification of Group II Anions. Wash precipitate with 10 drops of water and discard washings. Treat precipitate with 5 drops of $3\ F$ HCl, stir, and centrifuge.

Residue may be $BaSO_4$. Add 10 drops of $3\ F$ HCl. (2) White residue confirms presence of SULFATE.	**Centrifugate** may contain chromate ion. Add 10 drops of $2.5\ F$ sodium acetate. (3) Yellow precipitate confirms presence of CHROMATE.

NOTES ON THE ANALYSIS OF GROUP II ANIONS

1. If the precipitate is white the absence of the chromate ion is confirmed.

2. A white precipitate from Procedure 7 indicates the presence of $BaSO_4$. Additional HCl is added to dissolve Group I anions which may have been incompletely removed in Procedure 5.

3. Sodium acetate buffers the hydronium-ion concentration of the solution suffi-

231

ciently to permit the precipitation of $BaCrO_4$. Additional confirmation of the chromate ion may be obtained by utilizing the identification test for the chromium ion as given in the cation scheme.

18·2   Pertinent Chemical Reactions Involved in the Separation and Identification of Group II Anions.   The equations for these reactions are simple and few in number.

Precipitation of Group II *Anions.*   The anions of Group II are precipitated from slightly basic solution by the addition of barium acetate solution.

$$SO_4^= + Ba^{++} \rightleftharpoons BaSO_4$$
$$CrO_4^= + Ba^{++} \rightleftharpoons BaCrO_4$$

Identification of Sulfate Ion.   A white precipitate, produced by the addition of barium ions and insoluble in strong acids, confirms the presence of the sulfate ion.

$$SO_4^= + Ba^{++} \rightleftharpoons BaSO_4$$

Detection of Chromate Ion.   A yellow group precipitate for Group II anions indicates the presence of the chromate ion.   The yellow precipitate is barium chromate, $BaCrO_4$, which is soluble in dilute HCl.

$$BaCrO_4 + H_3O^+ \rightleftharpoons HCrO_4^- + Ba^{++} + H_2O$$

The addition of sodium acetate solution to the acid chromate solution lowers the hydronium-ion concentration sufficiently to permit the reprecipitation of barium chromate.

$$Ba^{++} + HCrO_4^- + Ac^- \rightleftharpoons HAc + BaCrO_4$$

The presence of the chromate ion may be confirmed by the addition of H_2O_2 to the dilute acid solution.   This reaction produces a blue-colored compound, CrO_5, which is so unstable that it fades rapidly.   This is the same test used to confirm the presence of chromium in the cation scheme (Sec. 14·3).

$$HCrO_4^- + 2H_2O_2 + H_3O^+ \rightleftharpoons CrO_5 + 4H_2O$$

CHAPTER 19

GROUP III ANIONS

Group III anions are those ions whose calcium and barium salts are soluble but whose cadmium salts are insoluble in neutral or slightly basic solutions. The precipitation of the sulfide, ferrocyanide, and ferricyanide ions by cadmium ions is fairly complete. Traces of $Cd(BO_2)_2$ or $Cd(OH)_2$ may precipitate with these ions, but these slight precipitates should not interfere with the analysis of the group.

19·1 Theoretical Discussion. Although the sulfide and ferricyanide ions precipitate as insoluble cadmium salts, the two ions cannot exist together in solution. The ferricyanide will oxidize the sulfide ion to free sulfur, being reduced to the ferrocyanide in the course of the reaction. Consequently, the presence of either the sulfide or the ferricyanide ion confirms the absence of the other ion.

The test for the sulfide depends upon the formation of a metallic sulfide. The sulfide is converted to H_2S, which may be detected by its action on lead acetate paper to produce black lead sulfide.

The tests for the ferrocyanide and ferricyanide ions depend upon the blue precipitates formed with the ferric and ferrous ions. These precipitates are called prussian blue and Turnbull's blue and have been assigned the formulas $Fe_4[Fe(CN)_6]_3$ and $Fe_3[Fe(CN)_6]_2$, but the compositions of these precipitates have not been proved.

19·2 Analysis of Group III Anions. No separation is involved in the analysis of this group. The tests for the three anions are made on separate portions of the group precipitate since they offer no interference with each other.

ANALYSIS OF GROUP III ANIONS

Procedure 9. Precipitation of Group III Anions. To centrifugate from Group II anions (Procedure 7), add 1 F $Cd(Ac)_2$, dropwise, until precipitation is complete. (1) Centrifuge. Centrifugate contains anions of Groups IV–V and is reserved for Procedure 11. Precipitate may contain CdS, $Cd_2Fe(CN)_6$, and $Cd_3[Fe(CN)_6]_2$ and is analyzed as described in Procedure 10. (2)

Procedure 10. Identification of Group III Anions. Wash precipitate twice with hot water, discarding washings. (3) Divide precipitate into three portions and test as follows:

ANALYSIS OF GROUP III ANIONS (*Continued*)

First portion is placed in a small test tube to which 3 drops of 3 F HCl is added. Cover mouth of the test tube with a strip of filter paper moistened with 0.5 F Pb(Ac)$_2$. Brown or black coloration of test paper, caused by formation of PbS, indicates presence of SULFIDE.	**Second portion** is placed in a depression of a spot plate. Add 1 drop of 3 F HCl (4) and 1 drop of 1 F FeCl$_3$. Dark blue precipitate (5) confirms presence of FERROCYANIDE.	**Third portion** is placed in a depression of a spot plate, and dissolved with 1 drop of 3 F HCl. Add 3 drops of water and a small crystal of ferrous sulfate to the solution. Formation of dark blue precipitate (6) confirms presence of FERRICYANIDE.

NOTES ON THE ANALYSIS OF GROUP III ANIONS

1. Since this solution is slightly alkaline, some precipitation of cadmium hydroxide usually takes place. The presence of Group III is confirmed only when a definite precipitate, usually colored, is obtained.

2. The color of the precipitate may indicate its composition. Of the cadmium salts in this precipitate, the sulfide is bright yellow, the ferrocyanide is pale yellow (almost white), and the ferricyanide is orange.

3. The precipitate is washed thoroughly to remove any contamination of the thiocyanate ion from Group IV anions. This ion will interfere with the test for the ferrocyanide since both ions react with the ferric ion, which is the identification reagent.

4. Dilute HCl should be added until the precipitate is dissolved and the solution is barely acid. If the solution is made too acid, the identifying blue precipitate may not be obtained, because of its solubility in HCl.

5. The dark blue precipitate has been assigned the formula of Fe$_4$[Fe(CN)$_6$]$_3$ and is sometimes called prussian blue. If a green solution is obtained upon the addition of ferric chloride solution, the presence of the ferricyanide ion is indicated.

6. This dark blue precipitate has been assigned the formula of Fe$_3$[Fe(CN)$_6$]$_2$ and is called Turnbull's blue.

19·3 Pertinent Chemical Reactions Involved in the Separation and Identification of Group III Anions. The equations are given in the order in which the chemical reactions for these anions are encountered in the scheme of analysis.

Precipitation of Group III Anions. The three anions of this group are precipitated as the insoluble cadmium salts.

$$S^= + Cd^{++} \rightleftharpoons CdS$$
$$\text{yellow}$$
$$Fe(CN)_6{}^{4-} + 2Cd^{++} \rightleftharpoons Cd_2Fe(CN)_6$$
$$\text{cream, almost white}$$
$$2Fe(CN)_6{}^{3-} + 3Cd^{++} \rightleftharpoons Cd_3[Fe(CN)_6]_2$$
$$\text{orange}$$

Detection of Sulfide Ion. Cadmium sulfide dissolves in dilute hydrochloric acid.

$$CdS + 2H_3O^+ \rightleftharpoons Cd^{++} + H_2S + 2H_2O$$

The hydrogen sulfide liberated in this reaction causes a blackening of filter paper moistened with lead acetate solution, due to the formation of PbS.

$$Pb(Ac)_2 + H_2S \rightleftharpoons PbS + 2HAc$$

The formula for lead acetate is written in the molecular form, since it is only slightly ionized.

Identification of Ferrocyanide Ion. Cadmium ferrocyanide dissolves in dilute hydrochloric acid.

$$Cd_2Fe(CN)_6 + 2H_3O^+ \rightleftharpoons H_2Fe(CN)_6^= + 2Cd^{++} + 2H_2O$$

The ferrocyanide ion produced by this reaction reacts with ferric ions to form a dark blue precipitate, sometimes called prussian blue.

$$3H_2Fe(CN)_6^= + 4Fe^{3+} + 6H_2O \rightleftharpoons Fe_4[Fe(CN)_6]_3 + 6H_3O^+$$

Confirmatory Test for Ferricyanide Ion. Cadmium ferricyanide dissolves in dilute hydrochloric acid.

$$Cd_3[Fe(CN)_6]_2 + 2H_3O^+ \rightleftharpoons 2H\ Fe(CN)_6^= + 3Cd^{++} + 2H_2O$$

The ferricyanide ion forms a dark blue precipitate, known as Turnbull's blue, with ferrous ions.

$$2H\ Fe(CN)_6^= + 3Fe^{++} + 2H_2O \rightleftharpoons Fe_3[Fe(CN)_6]_2 + 2H_3O^+$$

There is some evidence that the precipitate known as Turnbull's blue is identical with prussian blue. It is possible that the ferricyanide oxidizes the ferrous ion to ferric ions.

$$H\ Fe(CN)_6^= + Fe^{++} + H_3O^+ \rightleftharpoons H_2\ Fe(CN)_6^= + Fe^{3+} + H_2O$$

The products of this redox reaction will react to give ferric ferrocyanide.

$$3H_2\ Fe(CN)_6^= + 4Fe^{3+} + 6H_2O \rightleftharpoons Fe_4[Fe(CN)_6]_3 + 6H_3O^+$$

It is also possible for the ferrocyanide to reduce ferric ions and to precipitate as ferrous ferricyanide. Therefore, the composition of the blue precipitate obtained in the ferrocyanide and ferricyanide tests may be identical, and the formula for the precipitate may not be either $Fe_4[Fe(CN)_6]_3$ or $Fe_3[Fe(CN)_6]_2$.

Reaction of Ferricyanide Ion with Sulfide Ion. These two ions are incompatible in solution and will react as follows:

$$2Fe(CN)_6^{3-} + S^= \rightleftharpoons 2Fe(CN)_6^{4-} + S$$

CHAPTER 20

GROUP IV ANIONS

The anions of this group are distinguished from those of the other groups by the insolubility of their silver salts in acid solutions. The group reagent is silver acetate, which is only soluble to the extent of approximately $0.07\ F$. This necessitates a larger volume of the reagent for group precipitation than is used in precipitating Groups I to III.

20·1 Theoretical Discussion. Silver thiosulfate is unstable in acid solution and undergoes a series of characteristic color changes which serve to identify this ion during the process of group precipitation.

Silver chloride has the largest solubility product of any of the precipitating anions of Group IV and is, therefore, more soluble in ammonia than the other members of the group. AgCl is separated and identified through its solubility in ammoniacal silver nitrate. The presence of $Ag(NH_3)_2^+$ ions in ammoniacal silver nitrate prevents solution of AgCNS and AgBr, which would otherwise dissolve to some extent.

Silver thiocyanate will react with a solution of ferric chloride to give the characteristic color of the complex ion, $Fe(CNS)_6^{3-}$. Solution of AgCNS is not necessary for this test, which is effected upon a portion of the group residue.

The iodide and bromide anions, in the form of the insoluble silver salts, are brought into solution by the action of zinc dust in a slightly acid solution. This is a redox reaction in which silver ions are reduced to metallic silver, and zinc is oxidized to zinc ions. The bromide and iodide ions are converted from insoluble silver salts to soluble zinc salts in the reaction.

The iodide and bromide ions are oxidized to the free elements and identified by the characteristic color of their carbon tetrachloride solutions. These tests will produce interference with each other. Separation is effected by the action of nitrous acid, which oxidizes the iodide ion but not the bromide ion. In this separation, the iodide is oxidized to free iodine, and the latter extracted by shaking with portions of carbon tetrachloride. After removal of the iodide as iodine, the bromide ion is oxidized by concentrated nitric acid to free bromine and extracted with carbon tetrachloride.

20·2 Analysis of Group IV Anions. The theory of the separation of the members of this group has been explained. In practice, this separa-

ANALYSIS OF GROUP IV ANIONS

Procedure 11. Preliminary Group Test. To 3 drops of centrifugate from Procedure 9, add 5 drops of AgAc solution and acidify with 3 F HNO_3. (1) A precipitate indicates presence of Group IV anions. (If no precipitate forms, proceed to Group V with main portion of centrifugate.)

Identification of Thiosulfate Ion. If, in preliminary group test (Procedure 11) or in group precipitation (Procedure 12), precipitate changes color from white through possible color changes of yellow, orange, and brown to a final color of black, presence of THIOSULFATES is confirmed. (2)

Procedure 12. Precipitation of Group IV Anions. If preliminary test indicates presence of Group IV anions, then to entire centrifugate from Group III (Procedure 9) add slowly, with stirring, saturated AgAc solution until precipitation is complete. (3) Acidify with acetic acid. Stir thoroughly, then centrifuge. **Centrifugate** contains anions of Group V and is reserved for Procedure 14. **Precipitate** (4) may contain Ag_2S, AgCl, AgCNS, AgI, and AgBr. Analyze according to Procedure 13.

Procedure 13. Separation and Identification of Group IV Anions. Wash precipitate from Procedure 12 thoroughly with water containing a few drops of 3 F HNO_3, until removed washings no longer give a precipitate with dilute HCl. (5) Discard washings. Wash once again with distilled water to remove HNO_3 and discard washings. Treat washed precipitate with 10 drops of *ammoniacal* $AgNO_3$. Stir thoroughly and centrifuge.

Centrifugate may contain chloride ion. Add 3 F HNO_3 until solution is decidedly acid. Formation of white precipitate (6) indicates presence of CHLORIDE.	**Residue** may contain Ag_2S, AgCNS, AgI, and AgBr. Divide into two unequal portions, one-third and two-thirds of the residue.		
	Small portion of residue is transferred to a spot plate. Add 1 drop of 3 F HCl and 1 drop 1 F $FeCl_3$. Formation of red coloration confirms presence of THIO-CYANATE ION.	**Large portion** is placed in a test tube. Add 10 drops of water, acidify withe excess 3 F HAc, and add 1 g of zinc dust (a heaping microspatulaful). Stir thoroughly for 5 min and centrifuge. (7)	
		Residue is Ag and excess Zn. Discard.	**Centrifugate** (8) may contain I⁻ and Br⁻ anions. Add 10 drops of CCl_4 and a *few* small crystals of $NaNO_2$. (9) Dilute to 2 ml and shake vigorously. Violet color in CCl_4 layer indicates presence of IODIDE. [*If iodides are present* (10) remove water layer with a micropipette and discard colored CCl_4 layer. Add a fresh portion of CCl_4 and shake again, and again discard CCl_4 layer. Repeat operation until CCl_4 remains colorless. Transfer water layer to a casserole, add 5 drops of 1.5 F H_2SO_4, and evaporate mixture to one-half its original volume. After cooling, pour solution back into a test tube and proceed with bromide test.]

ANALYSIS OF GROUP IV ANIONS (*Continued*)

		Test for bromide ion as follows: To 10 drops of the aqueous solution to be tested, add 10 drops of concentrated HNO_3 and 10 drops of CCl_4. Place in boiling-water bath for *not more* than 20 sec. Remove and agitate test tube vigorously. Yellow or orange color in CCl_4 layer indicates the presence of BROMIDE.

tion is not as clean as might be desired. The detailed analysis is given in Procedures 11 to 13.

NOTES ON THE ANALYSIS OF GROUP IV ANIONS

1. In the preliminary test, the solution must be acid—test with litmus paper.

2. Silver acetate, the group reagent, precipitates $Ag_2S_2O_3$ which is a white precipitate when first formed. It rapidly undergoes hydrolysis, with possible intermediate color changes, to black Ag_2S.

3. Silver acetate is not very soluble, and the complete precipitation of the Group IV anions may require ten times as much of the reagent as compared with the quantities of the reagents used in precipitating the anions of Groups I to III.

4. The composition of the precipitate may be indicated by its color. A black precipitate of Ag_2S results from the hydrolysis of $Ag_2S_2O_3$. A white precipitate is either AgCl or AgCNS. AgBr is cream-colored, and AgI is yellow.

5. The presence of excess silver ions in the precipitate will decrease the solubility of silver chloride in ammoniacal silver nitrate.

6. In the presence of excess $Ag(NH_3)_2{}^+$ ions, AgI and AgBr are insoluble and AgCNS is only slightly soluble in ammonia water. However, AgCl is readily soluble in ammoniacal silver nitrate. If the chloride is present, the test should give a good precipitate. Since all reagents contain traces of chloride and it is also possible that a small amount of the AgCNS may dissolve in ammoniacal $AgNO_3$, the appearance of a cloudiness for this test should be disregarded.

7. Zinc reduces Ag^+ in AgBr and AgI, depositing Ag and bringing Br^- and I^- into solution. The thiocyanate ion is destroyed in the solution.

8. The centrifugate should be acid from the previous treatment.

9. The nitrite ion, in an acid solution, oxidizes the iodide ion to free iodine.

10. If the iodide ion is absent, continue to the bromide test.

20·3 Pertinent Chemical Reactions Involved in the Separation and Identification of Group IV Anions. The equations for these reactions are given in the same sequence as they are encountered in the scheme of analysis.

Precipitation of Group IV Anions. The ions of this group are precipitated by silver acetate in a solution, acid with acetic acid.

$$S_2O_3{}^= + 2Ag^+ \rightleftharpoons Ag_2S_2O_3$$
$$Cl^- + Ag^+ \rightleftharpoons AgCl$$
$$CNS^- + Ag^+ \rightleftharpoons AgCNS$$
$$I^- + Ag^+ \rightleftharpoons AgI$$
$$Br^- + Ag^+ \rightleftharpoons AgBr$$

Identification of Thiosulfate Ion. The group precipitating agent, the silver ion in an acid solution, produces a white precipitate with the thiosulfate ion.

$$2Ag^+ + S_2O_3^= \rightleftharpoons Ag_2S_2O_3$$

Silver thiosulfate is unstable and breaks down into silver sulfide at room temperature. The precipitate may undergo color changes from white through yellow, orange, brown to black.

$$Ag_2S_2O_3 + 2H_2O \rightleftharpoons Ag_2S + H_3O^+ + HSO_4^-$$

Solvent Action of Ammoniacal Silver Nitrate upon Group IV Anion Precipitates. In a solution of ammonia, Ag_2S and AgI are insoluble, $AgBr$ is slightly soluble, $AgCNS$ fairly soluble, and $AgCl$ quite soluble. If silver ions are added to the ammonia water (Miller's reagent), the solubilities of the above precipitates are decreased because of the common-ion effect of the complex ion, $Ag(NH_3)_2^+$. The solubilities are so decreased that only $AgCl$ dissolves appreciably, thus permitting a separation of the chloride ion from the other anions of Group IV.

$$AgCl + 2NH_3 \rightleftharpoons Ag(NH_3)_2^+ + Cl^-$$

Confirmatory Test for Chloride Ion. The silver complex with ammonia is readily broken down in acid solution. If chloride ions are present, a white precipitate of $AgCl$ results. This precipitate is insoluble in nitric acid.

$$Ag(NH_3)_2^+ + Cl^- + 2H_3O^+ \rightleftharpoons AgCl + 2NH_4^+ + 2H_2O$$

Identification of Thiocyanate Ion. If a portion of the Group IV anion precipitate, containing $AgCNS$, is treated with hydrochloric acid and ferric chloride solution, a red coloration is produced. In this test $AgCNS$ dissolves to some extent in HCl, depending upon the concentration of the chloride ion.

$$AgCNS + Cl^- \rightleftharpoons AgCl + CNS^-$$

The thiocyanate ion produces a colored complex ion with the ferric ion.

$$Fe^{3+} + 6CNS^- \rightleftharpoons Fe(CNS)_6^{3-}$$

Action of Zinc upon Residue of Group IV Analysis. This residue contains Ag_2S, $AgCNS$, AgI, and $AgBr$. If an acid solution containing this residue is treated with zinc dust, metallic silver precipitates from solution. Zinc, being higher in the potential series, replaces silver ions in its compounds. In this redox reaction the anions are brought into solution, although the thiocyanate is destroyed in the process.

With Ag_2S, produced by the hydrolysis of the thiosulfate ion, zinc releases hydrogen sulfide.

$$Ag_2S + Zn + 2H_3O^+ \rightleftharpoons Zn^{++} + 2Ag + H_2S + 2H_2O$$

Zinc, in acid solution, decomposes the thiocyanate ion to form hydrogen cyanide and hydrogen sulfide.

$$3Zn + 2AgCNS + 6H_3O^+ \rightleftharpoons 2Ag + 3Zn^{++} + 2H_2S + 2HCN + 6H_2O$$

With AgBr and AgI, zinc precipitates Ag, converting the anions into soluble salts.

$$2AgBr + Zn \rightleftharpoons 2Ag + 2Br^- + Zn^{++}$$
$$2AgI + Zn \rightleftharpoons 2Ag + 2I^- + Zn^{++}$$

Identification of Iodide Ion. The centrifugate from the treatment of the residue with zinc in an acid solution contains the iodide and bromide ions. Nitrous acid oxidizes the iodide ion to iodine with no action upon the bromide. The addition of sodium nitrite to the acid solution produces nitrous acid.

$$NO_2^- + H_3O^+ \rightleftharpoons HNO_2 + H_2O$$
$$2HNO_2 + 2H_3O^+ + 2I^- \rightleftharpoons 2NO + I_2 + 4H_2O$$

Free iodine imparts a brown color to the water solution. When shaken with CCl_4, the iodine is concentrated in the CCl_4 layer in which it is more soluble. Iodine in carbon tetrachloride solution is violet in color.

Identification of Bromide Ion. Since the final identification for the bromide ion depends upon the brown color of a solution of bromine in CCl_4, it is necessary to remove all iodine from the solution. The violet color of iodine will mask the brown color of bromine. Two or three extractions with CCl_4 are sufficient for this removal.

Concentrated HNO_3 oxidizes the bromide ion to bromine. The latter is identified by extraction with CCl_4, to which it imparts a yellow or orange color.

$$6Br^- + 2NO_3^- + 8H_3O^+ \rightleftharpoons 3Br_2 + 2NO + 12H_2O$$

CHAPTER 21

GROUP V ANIONS

This group includes those anions, the nitrite, nitrate, chlorate, and borate ions, which are not precipitated in the first four groups of the anion scheme. This group might be designated as the *water-soluble* group, since most of the common salts of these anions are soluble in water. This statement is not entirely true in regard to the borate ion, the salts of which are not readily soluble in water, and which may be incompletely precipitated as the metaborate in any or all of the first four groups of anions. However, the borate ion is sufficiently soluble to pass through the anion scheme and be identified as a member of Group V anions.

21·1 Theoretical Discussion. Since there is no satisfactory inorganic test for the borate ion, it is necessary to resort to the use of an organic reagent. Many hydroxyanthraquinones (a family of organic dyes), in sulfuric acid solution, change color in the presence of boric acid. The particular dye used for the borate test in this scheme is carminic acid dissolved in sulfuric acid.

The chlorate and nitrite ions are incompatible in the acid centrifugate from Group IV anions, as indicated by the following reaction:

$$ClO_3^- + 3NO_2^- \rightleftharpoons Cl^- + 3NO_3^-$$

Therefore, if either the nitrite or chlorate ion is present it precludes the presence of the other. The action of nitrous acid upon a chlorate is used to identify the chlorate ion. In this reaction, the chlorate is reduced to the chloride ion and precipitated as $AgCl$.

The nitrite ion is identified in the presence of other members of this group by its specific oxidizing action upon urea, in which nitrogen and carbon dioxide are evolved.

Two tests for the nitrate ion are given. The oxidation of α-naphthylamine to a colored product is the more reliable of the two tests, although the course of this reaction is not definitely known. The brown-ring test for the nitrate ion is satisfactory only in the absence of the nitrite ion, which gives the same test. The presence of other anions such as the chromate, bromide, iodide, ferrocyanide, ferricyanide, thiocyanate, and chlorate may cause interference in making this test. However, all interfering anions, except the nitrite and chlorate ions, are precipitated and largely removed in the analysis of the first four groups of anions. The nitrite ion is destroyed by its reaction with ammonium sulfate and sulfuric acid. The slight interference of the chlorate ion is due to the formation of a yellow color and easily distinguishable from the brown-ring test.

21·2 Analysis of Group V Anions. No separation is necessary for the analysis of this group. The confirmatory tests for the four anions are made upon separate portions of the solution containing these ions.

ANALYSIS OF GROUP V ANIONS

Procedure 14. Identification of Group V Anions. Centrifugate from Procedure 12 may contain ClO_3^-, BO_2^-, NO_2^-, and NO_3^- ions. Divide into four equal portions and test as follows:

First portion.	Second portion.	Third portion.	Fourth portion.
Add 5 drops of concentrated HNO_3 and 2 drops of 0.5 F $AgNO_3$ and allow mixture to stand for 2 min. Centrifuge and discard any precipitate which may have formed. To clear centrifugate add a few small crystals of $NaNO_2$ and stir. Formation of white precipitate confirms presence of CHLORATE ION. (1)	Place in a casserole and add 5 drops of concentrated H_2SO_4. Evaporate to almost dryness. (2) Let casserole cool. Add 3 drops of carminic acid and warm *slightly*. Change of red color to bluish-violet confirms presence of BORATE ION.	To this portion contained in a test tube, add an equal volume of urea in HCl solution. Vigorous evolution of a gas indicates presence of NITRITE ION.	Make two tests for nitrate ion as follows: *Test One.* To 1 drop of this portion in a spot-plate depression add 2 drops of concentrated H_2SO_4 and 1 drop of α-naphthylamine. Allow test to stand for 3 min. Appearance of a purple ring around the drop of reagent indicates presence of NITRATE ION. (3) *Test Two.* (4) Place a small crystal of ferrous sulfate in a depression of a spot plate. Add 1 drop of the solution to be tested and 1 drop of concentrated H_2SO_4. Formation of a brown ring around the crystal indicates presence of NITRATE ION. (5)

NOTES ON THE ANALYSIS OF GROUP V ANIONS

1. The appearance of a slight cloudiness for this test should be disregarded.

2. The chlorate and nitrate ions interfere with the test for the borate ion. These interfering anions are destroyed by evaporating the solution with concentrated sulfuric acid.

3. The α-napthylamine is oxidized by the nitrate ion, in sulfuric acid solution, to a compound of fugitive color.

4. Since the nitrite and nitrate ions react similarly in this test, it is necessary to remove the nitrite ion, *if it is present*, before proceeding with the brown-ring test for the nitrate ion. This removal is accomplished as follows: To this portion add 3 drops

of 1.5 F H_2SO_4 and 3 drops of 1 F $(NH_4)_2SO_4$ solution. Place in a casserole and slowly evaporate until a paste results. The solution must not be evaporated to dryness, otherwise the nitrate ion will be lost in the form of volatile nitric acid. After cooling, redissolve the paste with 10 drops of water and test for the nitrate ion according to the procedure for Test Two.

5. The presence of chromate, iodide, bromide, ferrocyanide, ferricyanide, thiocyanate, chlorate, and nitrite anions interferes with the brown-ring test for the nitrate ion. However, all these anions except the nitrite and chlorate are precipitated in the anion scheme.

21·3 Pertinent Chemical Reactions Involved in the Identification of Anions of Group V. The equations for the chemical reactions produced in the analysis of Group V anions are given in the order in which they are encountered within the analytical scheme.

Identification of Chlorate Ion. The chlorate ion is reduced by nitrous acid to the chloride ion; the latter is then precipitated as AgCl.

$$ClO_3^- + 3HNO_2 + 3H_2O \rightleftharpoons Cl^- + 3NO_3^- + 3H_3O^+$$
$$Cl^- + Ag^+ \rightleftharpoons AgCl$$

Identification of Borate Ion. Most borates are difficulty soluble in water. The metaborate ion may precipitate incompletely in all the first four groups of the anion scheme. However, none of these precipitations is complete, and the borate ion is found in Group V in sufficient concentration for its detection. For the purpose of identification, it is more convenient to consider the borate ion as a member of the water-soluble anion group.

Certain hydroxyanthraquinones (alizarin dyes), dissolved in concentrated sulfuric acid, give characteristic color changes with boric acid. The particular dye used in this scheme is a sulfuric acid solution of carminic acid, which changes from red to bluish-violet in the presence of boric acid. The chemistry of this test is beyond the scope of elementary qualitative analysis. Oxidizing agents interfere with this test; therefore, the other anions of this group must be removed or destroyed. This is accomplished by heating with concentrated sulfuric acid.

The chlorate ion is converted into perchloric acid which volatilizes at this temperature.

$$3HClO_3 \rightleftharpoons HClO_4 + 2ClO_2 + H_2O$$

(The equation for this reaction is written in a molecular form, because under the conditions of the reaction there is little ionization.)

When heated with concentrated sulfuric acid, the nitrate ion is in the form of nitric acid, which boils off at 86°C with some decomposition into NO_2, H_2O, and O_2.

$$4HNO_3 \rightleftharpoons 2H_2O + 4NO_2 + O_2$$

When heated in the presence of concentrated sulfuric acid, the nitrite ion, in the form of nitrous acid, is decomposed into H_2O, NO_2, and NO, all of which are volatile.

$$2HNO_2 \rightleftharpoons H_2O + NO_2 + NO$$

Detection of Nitrite Ion. The nitrite ion in dilute hydrochloric acid solution reacts with urea to evolve nitrogen and carbon dioxide as redox products.

$$CO(NH_2)_2 + 7H_2O \rightleftharpoons CO_2 + N_2 + 6H_3O^+ + 6e$$
$$6e + 2NO_2^- + 8H_3O^+ \rightleftharpoons N_2 + 12H_2O$$
$$\overline{CO(NH_2)_2 + 2NO_2^- + 2H_3O^+ \rightleftharpoons CO_2 + 2N_2 + 5H_2O}$$

Destruction of Nitrite Ion. In the brown-ring test, the nitrate ion cannot be identified in the presence of the nitrite ion, since the two ions give the same test. Therefore, the nitrite ion must be removed. In an acid solution, the nitrite ion reacts with ammonium salts to produce nitrogen gas. Ammonium sulfate is used for this purpose.

$$NO_2^- + NH_4^+ \rightleftharpoons N_2 + 2H_2O$$

Identification of Nitrate Ion. In the absence of the nitrite ion, the presence of the nitrate ion is confirmed by the reduction of nitric acid by ferrous ions in a high concentration of sulfuric acid. Nitric oxide, from the reduction of nitric acid, combines with excess ferrous ions to produce the unstable brown complex, $Fe(H_2O)_5NO^{++}$.

$$3Fe(H_2O)_6^{++} + NO_3^- + 4H_3O^+ \rightleftharpoons 3Fe(H_2O)_6^{3+} + NO + 6H_2O$$
$$Fe(H_2O)_6^{++} + NO \rightleftharpoons Fe(H_2O)_5NO^{++} + H_2O$$

CHAPTER 22

COMPLETE ANALYSIS

PRELIMINARY EXAMINATION OF A SAMPLE TO BE ANALYZED

Samples submitted to students for analysis may be classified into the following general types:

1. A solution
2. A nonmetallic solid (a single compound or a mixture of compounds)
3. A metal, a mixture of metals, or an alloy
4. Any mixture of the above three types

Before beginning the systematic analysis of a sample, valuable information may be indicated by the physical properties of the sample. This is particularly true as to color. Crystal structure may also be indicative, but a student in elementary qualitative analysis has not had sufficient experience in crystallography to make much use of this physical aspect. Chemical handbooks, with their information as to crystalline structure and color of the most common compounds, are of assistance in the physical examination of salts.

Solubility tests with water and various acids as solvents add to the useful information about a sample before systematic analysis. Again, a handbook may be of service through the use of solubility tables and catalogued facts on the solubility of individual compounds.

22·1 General Procedure for the Examination and Analysis of an Unknown Sample. The following outline for the examination of the three general types of samples may be of aid to the student in a systematic examination of his unknown samples:

I. The Unknown Is a Solution
    A. Physical Examination
        1. Color of the Solution
            (Examination as to color is limited, since color is dependent upon concentration, and certain colors may neutralize each other to produce colorless solutions.)
            Cupric ion is blue or bluish-green.
            Nickelous ion is green or bluish-green. This color is less intense than that of the cupric ion and decidedly more green.
            Manganous ion is pink, almost colorless in a dilute solution.
            Cobaltous ion is pink, a deeper pink than that of the man-

ganous ion. The pink color is that of the hydrated ion. If treated with concentrated HCl, the hydrated ion changes color to an intense blue. This color change has been explained as a dehydration process, which results in the formation of the complex $CoCl_4^=$ ion.

Ferric ion is yellow to brown, depending upon concentration.

Chromic ion is either deep blue or greenish-black. The difference between the green and blue salt is the difference in the number of coordinated water molecules and anions in the complex.

Chromate is yellow, and the *dichromate* is orange-red.

Ferricyanide is yellow, lighter yellow than the chromate but darker than the ferrocyanide.

Ferrocyanide is pale yellow.

2. Color of Flame Tests

Many ions impart characteristic colors to a nonluminous bunsen flame. Some of these colors are too feeble to serve as indicative tests. The common ions which produce a decided color to a nonluminous flame are:

Volatile Compound	Color of Flame
Sodium	*Yellow* (The intensity of the color serves to distinguish between a contamination and the presence of an added amount.)
Potassium	*Violet* to the naked eye, *lavender* when viewed through a cobalt glass
Calcium	*Red* (usually referred to as brick-red)
Strontium	*Crimson*
Barium	*Yellow-green*
Boric acid	*Yellow-green*
Arsenic	*Pale blue*
Copper	*Emerald green*

B. Chemical Examination

1. Reaction with Litmus Paper

A neutral reaction indicates a solution of a salt whose ions are equally aprotic in aqueous solution. An example of such a neutral salt would be sodium chloride. An acid solution indicates that either an acid has been added to hold the substance in solution, *e.g.*, HCl with stannic chloride, or that a salt is present which ionizes to give cations that are amphiprotic. An example of such a salt would be aluminum sulfate. A basic reaction with litmus indicates the presence of an amphiprotic anion such as the hydroxide ion, carbonate ion, etc.

2. Anion Analysis
   Follow procedures beginning with Sec. 17·2.

3. Cation Analysis
   If no interfering substances are present, follow procedures beginning with Sec. 12·2. If interfering substances are present, they must be removed according to the procedure in Sec. 22·7.

II. The Unknown Is a Nonmetallic Solid or a Mixture of Such Solid Substances

  A. Physical Examination

    1. Crystal Structure
       Crystals are divided into systems according to their geometrical forms. However, crystal form is of little use to a student in qualitative analysis except where known substances are available to compare with unknown substances.

    2. Color
       The extent of hydration quite often determines the color of a substance. The following list gives many of the common colored substances, but is far from being all-inclusive.

       Black: Ag_2S, PbS, Hg_2S, HgS, Cu_2S, CuS, CuO, Sb_2S_3, NiS, CoS, MnO_2, Fe_3O_4, FeO, and FeS

       Blue: Hydrated copper and anhydrous cobaltous salts

       Brown: PbO_2, $CuCrO_4$, CdO, Bi_2O_3, Bi_2S_3, and hydrated Fe_2O_3

       Green: Hydrated ferrous salts, nickel salts, certain chromic salts, and a few copper salts

       Orange: Sb_2S_5, and some dichromates and ferricyanides

       Pink: Manganous salts and hydrated cobaltous salts

       Red: Pb_3O_4, Cu_2O, HgO, HgS, Fe_2O_3, Sb_2S_3, HgI_2, and a few other iodides, and some chromates and dichromates

       Reddish-brown: $HgCO_3$

       Yellow: PbO, HgO, CdS, As_2S_3, As_2S_5, SnS_2, and some iodides and ferrocyanides

  B. Solubility Tests

    1. Powdering the Unknown for Solubility Tests
       Since substances are more readily acted upon by reagents when in a state of fine subdivision, it is desirable to reduce the sample to a powder before determining the action of various solvents. If the unknown substance is not already in this condition, a very small trial portion should be ground *cautiously* in a mortar to determine if a larger portion may be pulverized safely. This precaution is necessary because of the possibility of explosive reactions between active oxidizing and reducing substances.

2. Types of Solubilities

a. Compounds soluble in water

Solubility in water permits the elimination of those insoluble substances indicated in solubility charts. Litmus tests may denote the amphiprotic nature of the ions produced in water solution. Flame tests may be made, under most conditions, directly upon the water solution of the sample.

b. Compounds soluble in acid

(1). Characteristics of acid-soluble compounds

The great majority of acid-soluble compounds are substances containing amphiprotic anions—those anions which are strong bases, and which tend to gain protons. For example, calcium carbonate, which is not soluble in water but is soluble in acid, is dissolved by acids because the carbonate ion is a strong base which combines with protons from the acid to form the soluble, slightly dissociated bicarbonate ion. Examples of acid-soluble compounds other than carbonates are sulfides, sulfites, phosphates, arsenates, borates, chromates, arsenites, and nitrites.

(2). Choice of acids

The three most common acids of the laboratory are HCl, HNO_3, and H_2SO_4. For purposes of solubility tests, sulfuric acid is the least desirable of the three acids. Several sulfates are insoluble and many only partly soluble in water or acid. Usually samples are dissolved in either nitric or hydrochloric acid, or a combination of the two. As a general rule, it is preferable to use a single acid if possible.

(a). Advantages and disadvantages of nitric acid as a solvent acid

Advantages: All nitrates are soluble, generally more soluble than chlorides. Nitrates are less volatile than chlorides and if the solution is evaporated to remove excess acid, there is less likelihood of losing nitrates. Nitric acid acts as a solvent, not only as an excellent source of hydronium ions, but also as an oxidizing agent. The nitrate ion in the presence of hydronium ions oxidizes to a soluble form certain substances which are unaffected by hydronium ions alone.

Disadvantages: After solution has been effected, the oxidizing action of HNO_3 is undesirable throughout the cation scheme. Nitric acid oxidizes the sulfide ion to a mixture of free sulfur and sulfate ions. The precipitated sulfur is a source of annoyance and confusion in making precipitation tests for certain cations. The sulfate ion will cause precipitation of the alkaline earth ions in Cation Groups II and III where they are unwanted and no provision is made for identifying them. Nitric acid will not dissolve water-insoluble oxidizing agents such as MnO_2, SnO_2, and PbO_2.

(b). Advantages and disadvantages of hydrochloric acid as a solvent acid

Advantages: Hydrochloric acid will dissolve water-insoluble oxidizing agents such as SnO_2 and MnO_2 which are insoluble in HNO_3. Cations dissolved in hydrochloric acid display flame tests better than when dissolved in nitric acid, because of the greater volatility of the chloride compounds. *Disadvantages:* Silver, lead, and mercurous ions form insoluble chlorides with hydrochloric acid. The chloride ion in excess acts as a complexing agent. For example, mercuric chloride will form the $HgCl_4^=$ ion with excess chloride ions, and this complex is so stable that the mercuric ion cannot be identified without destroying the complex. Hydrochloric acid fails to dissolve many water-insoluble sulfides, which are dissolved by nitric acid. Arsenic chloride and mercuric chloride volatilize from a hot hydrochloric acid solution.

c. Compounds insoluble in water and in acids

Substances which are insoluble in water or any acid combination usually fall into one of the following categories:

Type	Specific Examples
Certain inorganic fluorides	CaF_2, SrF_2
Anhydrous chromic salts	$CrCl_3$, $Cr_2(SO_4)_3$
Certain lead salts	$PbCl_2$, $PbSO_4$
Many silicates and silica	$CaSiO_3$, SiO_2
Certain silver salts	$AgCl$, $AgBr$
Ignited oxides	Al_2O_3, Cr_2O_3
Certain sulfates	$BaSO_4$, $SrSO_4$

C. Chemical Examination

    1. Anion Analysis

      If the substance is soluble in water, follow the procedures beginning with Sec. 17·2. If the substance is insoluble in water, the sodium carbonate treatment must be prolonged. The procedure for analyzing such samples is given in Sec. 22·2.

    2. Cation Analysis

      If the substance is soluble in water and no interfering substances are present, follow the analysis of cations beginning with Sec. 12·2. If interfering substances are present, they must be removed according to the procedure in Sec. 22·7. If the substance is insoluble in water, follow the procedure given in Sec. 22·3.

III. The Unknown Is a Metal, Mixture of Metals, or an Alloy

  A. Physical Examination

    The information that may be obtained from the physical examination of a metal or alloy is limited and sometimes misleading. Metals with clean surfaces are usually gray or silver in color, with a definite luster. An appreciable percentage of copper is indicated by a reddish color, or yellow, in the case of brass. The density of a metal or alloy may sometimes be suggestive of its composition. For example, a very light metal could be magnesium or aluminum, and a very heavy metal might be lead.

  B. Solubility Tests

    1. Only those metals above hydrogen in the emf series dissolve in hydrochloric acid. The speed of solution, in hydrochloric acid, should diminish for metals nearest hydrogen in this series.

    2. Nitric acid, diluted with an equal quantity of water, dissolves all metals of the cation scheme except antimony and tin. These metals are oxidized by nitric acid to insoluble white precipitates of Sb_2O_3 and SnO_2.

    3. Nitric acid dissolves aluminum and chromium slowly.

    4. Aqua regia, a mixture of hydrochloric and nitric acids, dissolves all the metals of the cation scheme except Group I cations, which are precipitated as the chlorides. It is inadvisable to use this reagent if any single acid is suitable.

  C. Chemical Examination

    The composition of alloys is usually restricted to those metals whose cations are found in the first three groups of the cation scheme, and magnesium of Group IV. The procedure for obtaining a solution of a metal or alloy is given in Sec. 22·4.

THE PREPARATION OF A SOLID SAMPLE FOR ANALYSIS

The analysis of a solid sample involves three different types of preliminary treatment to obtain a satisfactory solution for systematic analysis. These are

1. Preparation of a solution for anion analysis.

2. Preparation of a solution for cation analysis.

3. Dissolving metal, mixture of metals, or alloy for cation analysis. The details of these special treatments are given in Secs. 22·2, 22·3, and 22·4.

22·2 Preparation of Solution for Anion Analysis. *If the sample is soluble in water,* follow the procedure for analysis of the anions beginning with Sec. 17·2. If the sample is insoluble or difficulty soluble in water, the sodium carbonate treatment must be prolonged in order to convert the anions to a soluble form. This procedure is given in the next paragraph.

If the sample is insoluble in water, treat as follows: Place a level microspatulaful of the solid sample (0.1 g) in a small casserole and add 2 ml of 1.5 F sodium carbonate solution. Cover the casserole with a watch glass and boil for 15 min. As the water boils away, it should be replenished to keep the volume close to the original 2 ml. After cooling, transfer the mixture of liquid and solid to a centrifuge tube and centrifuge. Wash the residue twice with water, and add washings to the centrifugate. Save both the centrifugate and residue. The *centrifugate* is analyzed according to the anion scheme beginning with Procedure 3, Sec. 17·2. The *residue* is used for the analysis of those anions which may not have been rendered soluble by the sodium carbonate treatment. This treatment should convert a considerable portion of all insoluble salts except silicates, certain phosphates, fluorides, and sulfides, and the halides of silver into soluble sodium salts and insoluble carbonates, basic carbonates, or hydroxides. Divide the *residue* into four portions and test as follows:

Test for sulfides (if not found in the anion analysis) by placing this portion of the residue in a small test tube and covering with zinc dust. Add 1 ml of 3 F HCl and cover the mouth of the test tube with a piece of filter paper, moistened with lead acetate solution. A blackening of the lead acetate paper indicates the presence of SULFIDES. (Since zinc dust may contain a contamination of sulfides, a blank should be determined upon this reagent.)

Test for phosphates by treating a portion of the residue with 5 drops of water, 5 drops of concentrated HNO_3, and 10 drops of ammonium molybdate. Warm in a water bath for 2 min. The appearance of a yellow precipitate confirms the presence of PHOSPHATES. In the absence of the phosphate ion, a white precipitate quite often results because of decomposition of the ammonium molybdate reagent. Disregard such a precipitate.

Test for fluorides as follows: Treat this portion with 1 ml of 3 F HAc. After effervescence has ceased, centrifuge and discard the centrifugate. Transfer the residue to the surface of a clean, clear watch glass. Heat the watch glass over a water bath until the residue is dry. Add 1 drop of concentrated H_2SO_4 upon the dry residue on the watch glass, and continue to heat over the water bath for 5 min. Allow to stand for 20 min, then wash the glass thoroughly. An etching of the glass confirms the presence of FLUORIDES.

Test for silver halides as follows: Treat this portion with 1 ml of 3 F HNO_3. After effervescence has ceased, centrifuge and discard the centrifugate. To the residue, if any, add 1 ml of 3 F NH_3, and pass in hydrogen sulfide until the solution is saturated. The silver ions of the residue are converted to Ag_2S, bringing the chloride, bromide, and iodide anions into solution. Centrifuge and discard the residue. The *centrifugate* is analyzed for CHLORIDE, BROMIDE, and IODIDE ions according to the regular scheme of analysis. This analysis begins with Procedure 12, Sec. 20·2.

22·3 Preparation of Sample for Cation Analysis. *If the sample is soluble in water* and if no interfering substances are present, follow the analysis for cations beginning with Sec. 12·2. However, in case interfering anions or organic material are present, such interfering substances must be removed (see Sec. 22·7 for an explanation of this interference, and procedures for the removal of these substances).

If the sample is insoluble in water, determine the best possible solvent acid by treating small portions of the finely pulverized sample with

1. Nitric acid, dilute and concentrated
2. Hydrochloric acid, dilute and concentrated
3. Mixtures of dilute and concentrated nitric and hydrochloric acids

The solubility tests should be made in the order given. If little action is noted, heat the above mixtures, since heat may speed the rate of solution.

If the sample is soluble in acid, a microspatulaful (0.1 g) may be dissolved in at least 2 ml of the acid or combination of acids. The analysis for cations is made as usual, beginning with Sec. 12·2, provided organic matter or interfering anions are not present. If either or both are present, they must be removed as outlined in Sec. 22·7. The sample is best dissolved in acid contained in a casserole and heated under a hood. The acid should be replenished if it evaporates appreciably.

If the sample is insoluble in water and acids and if nitric acid, hydrochloric acid, or aqua regia does not completely dissolve the sample, centrifuge and save the centrifugate, which may contain some of the dissolved substance. (If the sample appears to be totally acid-insoluble, the mixture may be discarded.)

Place the residue from the acid treatment (if insoluble in acid, use a new portion of the sample) in a small casserole and add 2 ml of 1.5 F sodium carbonate solution. Cover the casserole with a watch glass and boil for 20 min. As the water boils away it should be replenished to keep the volume close to the original 2 ml. After cooling, transfer the mixture of liquid and solid to a centrifuge tube and centrifuge. Discard the centrifugate. Wash twice with water and discard washings. Add 10 drops of 3 F HNO_3 to the residue; after effervescence has ceased, add this solution to the original acid solution, if any of the original dissolved in the acid treatment. Proceed with the regular cation analysis, beginning with Sec. 12·2.

If a residue still remains, repeat the treatment with Na_2CO_3 solution on the insoluble residue, following the same procedure given above. Combine the resulting solution with the other solution to be used for cation analysis.

If a residue remains after the second sodium carbonate solution treatment (after addition of 3 F HNO_3), it will be necessary to resort to sodium carbonate fusion. If the residue is small, the fusion may best be performed as follows: Make a small loop in the end of a platinum wire by bending the wire around the small end of a pencil. Heat the platinum loop in a bunsen flame until red-hot and then quickly dip it into a portion of solid sodium carbonate. Return the loop containing a lump of sodium carbonate to the flame and heat until the sodium carbonate is converted into a small transparent mass. Repeat this procedure until sufficient sodium carbonate is on the wire to form a clear, transparent bead completely filling the loop. Heat the bead in the flame and then touch it to the insoluble residue. Return the bead and portion of the residue to the flame and heat until the residue is fused into the bead. Gently crush the bead in a mortar and dissolve it in dilute nitric acid. Add this solution to the solutions obtained from the previous acid treatment and sodium carbonate treatments. Proceed with the analysis of the cations, beginning with Sec. 12·2. (The carbonate fusion converts acid-insoluble chromic compounds into water-soluble chromates. Make confirmatory test for chromate with hydrogen peroxide as described in Procedure 9, Sec. 14·2.)

22·4 Solution of a Metal, Mixture of Metals, or Alloy for Cation Analysis. Preliminary solubility tests as outlined in Sec. 22·1 may indicate the presence or absence of certain metals. The preliminary tests should indicate the presence of antimony and tin, and perhaps, that of aluminum and chromium. If these metals are absent, the sample will dissolve in 8 F nitric acid. (Concentrated HNO_3 diluted with an equal quantity of water.)

Procedure: Treat 0.1 g of the sample (about the size of a large pinhead) with 2 ml of 8 F nitric acid. Heat in a water bath, if necessary, to hasten solution. If the sample dissolves rapidly to give a clear solution, the absence of antimony and tin is indicated, and the possible absence of aluminum and chromium. The latter two metals usually dissolve slowly in nitric acid. If the sample dissolves without residue, evaporate to dryness in a casserole under a hood. Add 10 drops of 3 F nitric acid and 10 drops of water to the residue. After the residue from the evaporation has dissolved, proceed with cation analysis beginning with Sec. 12·2. Analyze only for metals of the first three groups of cations, and magnesium of Group IV.

If a white residue remains after the treatment of the sample with 8 F nitric acid, centrifuge, and save both centrifugate and residue. Evaporate the *centrifugate* to dryness in a casserole under a hood and redissolve the residue in 10 drops of 3 F nitric acid and 10 drops of water. Analyze for metals of the first three groups of cations, and magnesium of Group IV, but omit the tests for antimony and tin. The white *residue* from the nitric acid treatment is washed twice with water to remove excess nitric acid. Add 10 drops of concentrated HCl and heat to boiling in a water bath. (Freshly precipitated Sb_2O_5 and SnO_2 dissolve readily in concentrated HCl, but if allowed to stand for a long period or if digested for some time in nitric acid, they may become insoluble in any acid combination.) After solution is effected, analyze for Group II cations, beginning with Procedure 3, Sec. 13·2. Note particularly the tests for antimony and tin.

INTERFERENCE IN SYSTEMATIC CATION ANALYSIS

22·5 Interfering Substances. There are two general classes of substances whose presence interferes with the systematic analysis of cations.

Organic Matter. Certain organic compounds, such as sugars, glycerin, lactates, citrates, tartrates, etc., contain hydroxy groups which tend to tie up certain cations as stable complex anions. Iron, aluminum, and chromium form such complexes readily, and the majority of the heavy-metal cations may be complexed to some extent. If these organic compounds are present, their complexing action is greatest in a basic solution. When the solution for Group III cation precipitation is made basic, the cations of this group may be tied up so tightly as complex ions by organic substances that they fail to precipitate with the group precipitating agent.

Anions Which Form Insoluble Compounds with Certain Cations. Phosphates, fluorides, and oxalates produce no interference in the analysis of cations in an acid solution, but when the solution for Group III precipitation is made basic, the presence of these anions causes the precipitation of magnesium, calcium, strontium, and barium ions. Consequently, Group IV cations precipitate with Group III cations, where they are unwanted and where no provision is made for testing for them.

22·6   Tests for the Presence of Interfering Substances: *Test for the Presence of Organic Matter.*   Place 0.1 g (a level microspatulaful) of the unknown sample in a small pyrex test tube.   Heat the test tube, gently at first, until the tube becomes red.   Charring accompanied by fumes with an odor of incomplete combustion indicate the presence of organic matter.   Blackening alone does not necessarily indicate organic matter since certain salts, such as those of nickel, cobalt, and copper, are decomposed at a high temperature to produce black oxides.

Test for the Presence of Interfering Anions.   From the foregoing discussion it is obvious that interfering substances must be tested for and removed before cation analysis is completed.   This indicates that time will be saved by making the anion analysis first, to determine if any interfering anions are present.   Follow the regular anion procedure to determine the presence or absence of interfering anions.

22·7   Removal of Interfering Substances: *Removal of Organic Matter.* To 0.1 g (a level microspatulaful) of the sample in a small casserole, add 1 ml of concentrated H_2SO_4 and 1 ml of concentrated HNO_3.   Heat under a hood until dense white fumes of sulfur trioxide appear.   Cool, and examine the liquid.   If it is straw-colored, the organic matter has been destroyed.   If the liquid is dark, add 1 ml of concentrated HNO_3 and repeat the heating until white fumes appear.   After the organic matter has been destroyed, evaporate almost to dryness.   Add 2 ml of water and 5 drops of 3 F HNO_3.   Transfer to a centrifuge tube and centrifuge. The *centrifugate* contains all the cations except lead, barium, and strontium.   Analyze according to the cation procedure commencing with Sec. 12·2.   The *residue* contains lead, barium, and strontium ions as the insoluble sulfates.   The residue may also contain SnO_2 and Sb_2O_5 and small amounts of bismuth, chromium, and iron sulfates.   To analyze for these cations which may be in the residue, the latter is subjected to the sodium carbonate treatment as outlined in Sec. 22·3.

Removal of Interfering Anions.   The drastic oxidation of the sample with concentrated H_2SO_4 and concentrated HNO_3 for the purpose of destroying organic matter will also remove the fluoride and oxalate anions.   This treatment will not remove the phosphate anions.   The interfering anions (oxalate, fluoride, and phosphate) cause no interference in cation analysis in acid solution; therefore, these anions are more conveniently removed after the analyses of Cation Groups I and II, and before beginning the analysis of Cation Group III. (These procedures are given in the next two sections.)

Removal of Fluoride and Oxalate Ions. To the centrifugate from Procedure 3, Sec. 13·2 of the cation scheme, contained in a casserole, add 1 ml of concentrated HCl and 5 drops of concentrated HNO_3. Evaporate slowly for 15 min to almost dryness. Dissolve the residue in 2 ml of water, add a few drops of $3 F$ HCl if necessary to effect solution, and continue to the analysis of Group III cations beginning with Procedure 7, Sec. 14·2.

Removal of Phosphate Ion. The phosphate ion may be removed as insoluble $FePO_4$ from the centrifugate from Procedure 3 of the cation scheme of analysis. Since the phosphate anion is precipitated with the ferric ion, it is necessary to test for the presence of the latter ion in the unknown before this precipitation.

Procedure: To 2 drops of the centrifugate from Procedure 3 add 1 drop of $3 F$ HNO_3. Warm the solution to oxidize any ferrous ions which may be present to the ferric state. Cool, and add 5 drops of water and 1 drop of $3 F$ NH_4CNS. A deep red color confirms the presence of FERRIC ions in the original solution.

To the remainder of the centrifugate from Procedure 3 (from which H_2S has been expelled), add $3 F$ NH_3 until the solution is ammoniacal and 5 drops in excess. Neutralize the ammoniacal solution with $3 F$ HAc and then add 5 drops of the acid in excess. These additions produce a highly buffered acetate–acetic acid solution in which the phosphates of aluminum, chromium, and iron will precipitate. Since these ions may not be in sufficient concentration to remove the phosphate ion completely, it is necessary to add $1 F$ ferric chloride, dropwise, until the solution attains a deep reddish-brown color. Dilute with water to a volume of 2 ml and heat in a boiling-water bath for 3 min. Centrifuge and retain both the centrifugate and the precipitate.

The *centrifugate* may contain cobalt, nickel, zinc, and manganese ions of Group III and also the cations of Groups IV and V. Analyze this solution for these cations beginning with Procedure 7, Sec. 14·2. (Omit the tests for ferric, aluminum, and chromium ions.)

The *precipitate* may contain ferric, aluminum, and chromic phosphates, and basic ferric acetate. Add 10 drops of water, 10 drops of $3 F$ KOH, and 0.2 g (a heaping microspatulaful) of sodium peroxide. Stir thoroughly, heat in a boiling-water bath for 3 min, then centrifuge. Discard the residue. The *centrifugate* may contain the aluminate and chromate ions. Analyze for these two ions according to Procedure 9, Sec. 14·2.

APPENDIX

SPECIAL LABORATORY DIRECTIONS

A·1 Analysis of Group I Cations: Known I and Unknown I Solutions.
Read Sec. 12·1 before attempting any laboratory work.

Analysis of Known I Solution. Two analyses using the procedures for
Group I cations are to be made. The first is the analysis of a solution
containing the known cations, and the second is the analysis of a solution
of unknown cations. The student is required to submit to the instructor
a completed report form indicating the results obtained in each of these
analyses. Blank report forms will be issued by the instructor. The
insistence upon the analysis of a known solution for each group of cations, during the progress of the laboratory course, is for the purpose of
familiarizing the student with the procedures for each cation group, and
with the identifying tests for those cations which make up each group.

Laboratory Procedure: On the side shelf is a series of solutions labeled
Test Solutions, which contain all the cations and anions that are to be
analyzed in the laboratory procedures. Using these solutions, place 3
drops of lead nitrate, 3 drops of mercurous nitrate, and 3 drops of silver
nitrate into a small test tube. Dilute with distilled water to 1 ml. This
solution is to be analyzed beginning with Procedure 1, Sec. 12·2.

Analysis of Unknown I Solution. After the report of the known solution has been submitted to the instructor, an unknown solution containing any possible combination of Group I cations will be issued to the
student. This solution is to be analyzed, as was the known solution,
according to the procedures in Sec. 12·2. The positive results obtained
in this analysis are to be submitted on the report form furnished by the
instructor. After grading, this report will be returned to the student.

**A·2 Analysis of Group II Cations: Known II and Unknown II Solu-
tions.** Read Secs. 13·1 and 22·1 before attempting any laboratory work.

Analysis of Known II Solution. Place 3 drops of each of the following test solutions into a small test tube: mercuric nitrate, copper nitrate,
cadmium nitrate, bismuth nitrate, lead nitrate, antimony chloride, stannic chloride, and arsenic chloride. Dilute this solution with an equal
volume of water. The formation of a precipitate in this mixture is probable, but this will have no effect upon the analysis. Stir the mixture and
remove 10 drops, *with some of the precipitate,* to use for analysis, accord-

ing to Procedure 3, Sec. 13·2.   This procedure simply divides the Group II cations into two subgroups by the action of 3 F KOH.   The analyses of the two subgroups are to be found in Procedures 5 and 6.   Fill out a report form for this analysis.

Analysis of Unknown II *Solution.*   This solution may contain any or all of the cations of Groups I and II.   Therefore, the analysis of this unknown commences with Procedure 1, Sec. 12·2, and continues through Procedure 6, Sec. 13·2.   Do not dilute the unknown solution before analysis.   Report the cations present.

A·3   Analysis of Group III Cations: Known III and Unknown III Solutions.   Before attempting any laboratory work, read Secs. 14·1 and 22·1.

Analysis of Known III *Solution.*   Place 3 drops of each of the following test solutions into a test tube: chromium nitrate, aluminum nitrate, zinc nitrate, manganese nitrate, ferric nitrate, cobalt nitrate, and nickel nitrate.   Dilute this solution with an equal volume of water.   Stir the mixture and remove 10 drops for analysis, starting with Procedure 7 in Sec. 14·2.   After completing Procedures 7 and 8, continue through Procedures 9 and 10.   Fill out the report form for this analysis.

Analysis of Unknown III *Solution.*   This solution may contain any or all of the cations of Groups I, II, and III; consequently, the analysis will start with Procedure 1, Sec. 12·2.   Do not dilute the unknown solution. Using 10 drops of the solution, follow the respective procedures for Groups I, II, and III.   Report the cations present.

A·4   Analysis of Groups IV and V Cations: Known IV and Unknown IV Solutions.   Before attempting any laboratory work, read Secs. 15·1, 16·1, and 22·1.

Analysis of the Known Solution Containing Cations of Groups IV *and* V. Since Groups IV and V of the cation scheme are comparatively short and simple, the two groups are analyzed together for the known solution.

Place 3 drops of each of the following test solutions into a small test tube: magnesium nitrate, barium nitrate, strontium nitrate, calcium nitrate, sodium nitrate, potassium nitrate, and ammonium nitrate. Test for the NH_4^+ ion according to Procedure 14, Sec. 16·2.   Using the entire solution without dilution, start with Procedure 11, Sec. 15·2, and continue the analysis through Procedure 14, Sec. 16·2.   Fill out a report form for the analysis of Cation Groups IV and V.

Analysis of Unknown IV *Solution.*   This solution may contain any or all of the cations of Groups I to V; therefore, after testing for the ammonium ion according to Procedure 14, the analysis begins with Procedure 1, Sec. 12·2, and continues through all the cation groups.

A·5   Analysis of Groups I and II Anions: Unknown V Solid.   Before attempting any laboratory work, read Secs. 17·1 and 22·1.

Analysis of Unknown V *Solid.*   The salts used in making unknowns V and VI are those of sodium, potassium, or ammonium; therefore, Procedure 2, Sec. 17·2, may be omitted in the analyses of these two unknowns. (The omission of Procedure 2 applies only to unknowns V and VI. This procedure must be included in the analyses of unknowns VII, VIII, and IX.)

This solid unknown contains any or all of the anions of Groups I and II. The analyses of knowns for the anion groups is not necessary. The student should have received sufficient training in the cation analyses to follow these procedures intelligently.

Procedure: Transfer a level microspatulaful of the solid unknown to a small test tube. Add 2 ml of water and heat in a water bath for 2 min. Clear the solution by centrifuging, if necessary; draw off the clear liquid, dilute to 4 ml, shake well, and use 2 ml of this solution for the analysis of the anions. Add 1 drop of 3 *F* KOH, and begin with Procedure 3, Sec. 17·2. (Do not forget Procedure 1, which is the test for the CARBONATE upon the original solid.) Report the anions present.

A·6 Analysis of Groups III to V Anions: Unknown VI Solid. Before attempting any laboratory work, read Secs. 19·1, 20·1, 21·1, and 22·1.

Analysis of Unknown VI *Solid.* This solid contains any of the anions found in Groups I through V. The salts used in making this unknown are sodium, potassium, or ammonium; therefore, Procedure 2, Sec. 17·2, may be omitted. Prepare the solid for analysis as in unknown V. Report the anions present.

A·7 Analysis of Unknown VII Solid. Review Sec. 22·1 before attempting any laboratory work.

This unknown requires complete anion and cation analyses; it is water-soluble and contains no substances which interfere with cation analysis. Since this solid may contain any of the heavy-metal cations, they must be removed before beginning the anion analysis. This removal is accomplished by Procedure 2, Sec. 17·2.

Preparation of Unknown VII *Solid for Analysis.* Transfer a level microspatulaful of the solid to a small test tube, add 2 ml of water, and heat in a water bath for 2 min. Dilute the solution to 4 ml, shake well, and use 10 drops for cation analysis, beginning with Procedure 1, Sec. 12·2. Use 2 ml of the same solution for anion analysis beginning with Procedure 2, Sec. 17·2. (Test for the presence of CARBONATES upon the original solid as directed in Procedure 1, Sec. 17·2.) Report the cations and anions present.

A·8 Analyses of Unknown VIII and IX Solids. Review Sec. 22·1 and read Secs. 22·2 and 22·3 before attempting these analyses.

General Directions: These unknowns require complete anion and cation analyses, and are progressively more difficult to analyze.

Unknown VIII contains at least one (perhaps more) component which is not soluble in water.   This unknown is, however, sufficiently soluble in an acid or combinations of acids for cation analysis.

Unknown IX contains one or more components insoluble or difficulty soluble in water and acid.   Some of the insoluble cations may be brought into solution by repeated evaporation with sodium carbonate solution and treatment of the residue with an acid or combination of acids. Other insoluble cations must be brought into solution by sodium carbonate fusion and subsequent treatment with an acid.

The presence of organic substances containing complexing groups or certain anions, such as phosphate, oxalate, and fluoride, will interfere with regular cation analysis.   Consequently, it is customary to perform the anion analysis before the cation analysis.

Two general outlines are given in Secs. 22·2 and 22·3 for obtaining solutions for anion and cation analyses.   These outlines do not cover all possibilities for insoluble substances, because many such solids require specific and special treatments.   All the unknowns issued in this laboratory course should respond to these two treatments sufficiently for satisfactory confirmatory cation and anion tests, even though the solution of the solid may be somewhat incomplete.

A·9   Analysis of Unknown X Solid.   Review Sec. 22·1, and read Sec. 22·4 before attempting any laboratory work.

General Directions: Unknown X is a metal, a mixture of metals, or an alloy.   The analysis, as outlined in Sec. 22·4, is comparatively simple. *Caution*—do not use too large a sample for analysis.

Notebook Record of Analytical Results

A·10 General Type of Report Form. This form is to be used by the student in recording the results obtained in the analysis of either a known solution or an unknown substance. (It is suggested that the instructor mimeograph a supply of these forms for student use.)

Substance	Reagent	Result	Conclusion
Unknown I solution	3 F HCl	White ppt	Group I present
Precipitate 1*	Hot water	Partial solution	Presence of Pb^{++} indicated
Solution 2	1 F K_2CrO_4	Yellow ppt	Pb^{++} present
Residue 2	3 F NH_3	Ppt blackens; partly soluble	Hg_2^{++} present; Ag^+ indicated
Solution 4	3 F HNO_3	White ppt	Ag^+ present
Residue 4	Aqua regia	Solution	Hg_2^{++} indicated
Solution 6	$SnCl_2$ solution	Gray ppt	Hg_2^{++} present

NAME_____John Doe_____ IONS PRESENT_____Pb^{++}, Ag^+, and Hg_2^{++}_____

* Number refers to particular line, or step, from which solution or precipitate is obtained.

Assignment Schedule

A·11. Suggested Program of Class and Laboratory Assignments for a One-semester Course. The following assignments are suggested for an 8-hr course (two class hours, and two laboratory periods of 3 hr each per week) in qualitative analysis.

Period	Class	Laboratory
1	Chap. 10. Balancing of Oxidation-Reduction Equations	Check in equipment. Read Chap. 11. Construct apparatus, Sec. 11·2
2	Chap. 1. Forces between Atoms, Secs. 1·1 through 1·5	Analyses of known I and unknown I solutions, Sec. A·1
3	Chap. 1. Forces between Atoms, Secs. 1·6 through 1·9	Analysis of known II solution, Sec. A·2
4	Chap. 1. Forces between Atoms, Secs. 1·10, 1·11, and Exercises	Commence analysis of unknown II solution, Sec. A·2
5	Chap. 2. Solutions, Secs. 2·1 through 2·6	Complete analysis of unknown II solution, Sec. A·2
6	Chap. 2. Solutions, Sec. 2·7, Exercises	Analysis of known III solution, Sec. A·3
7	Chap. 3. Chemical Equilibrium	Commence analysis of unknown III solution, Sec. A·3
8	Quiz covering Chaps 1, 2, 3, and 10	Complete analysis of unknown III solution, Sec. A·3
9	Chap. 4. Ionization of Weak Electrolytes, Secs. 4·1 to 4·6	Analysis of known IV solution, Sec. A·4
10	Chap. 4. Ionization of Weak Electrolytes, Secs. 4·7 to 4·9	Commence analysis of unknown IV solution, Sec. A·4
11	Chap. 4. Weak Electrolytes, Sec. 4·10 and Exercises	Complete analysis of unknown IV solution, Sec. A·4
12	Chap. 5. The Solubility Product Principle, Secs. 5·1 to 5·5	Quiz on laboratory assignments covering Chaps. 11 through 16
13	Chap. 5. The Solubility Product Principle, Secs. 5·6 to 5·10	Analyze unknown V solid, Sec. A·5
14	Chap. 5. The Solubility Product Principle, Secs. 5·11 to 5·13	Commence analysis of unknown VI solid, Sec. A·6

Assignment Schedule *(Continued)*

Period	Class	Laboratory
15	Chap. 5. The Solubility Product Principle, Exercises	Complete analysis of unknown VI solid, Sec. A·6
16	Quiz covering Chaps. 4 and 5	Commence analysis of unknown VII solid, Sec. A·7
17	Chap. 6. Hydrolysis, Secs. 6·1 to 6·4	Continue analysis of unknown VII solid, Sec. A·7
18	Chap. 6. Hydrolysis. Secs. 6·5 and 6·6	Complete analysis of unknown VII solid, Sec. A·7
19	Chap. 6. Hydrolysis, Exercises	Commence analysis of unknown VIII solid, Sec. A·8
20	Chap. 7. Complex Ions, Secs. 7·1 to 7·3	Continue analysis of unknown VIII solid, Sec. A·8
21	Chap. 7. Complex Ions, Secs. 7·4 to 7·6	Complete analysis of unknown VIII solid, Sec. A·8
22	Chap. 7. Complex Ions, Secs. 7.7 and 7·8	Quiz on laboratory assignments covering Chaps. 17 through 22
23	Chap. 7. Complex Ions, Exercises	Commence analysis of unknown IX solid, Sec. A·8
24	Quiz covering Chaps. 6 and 7	Continue analysis of unknown IX solid, Sec. A·8
25	Chap. 8. Colloids, Secs. 8·1 through 8·5	Continue analysis of unknown IX solid, Sec. A·8
26	Chap. 8. Colloids, Secs. 8·6 through 8·8	Complete analysis of unknown IX solid, Sec. A·8
27	Chap. 9. Oxidation and Reduction Theory, Secs. 9·1 to 9·4	Commence analysis of unknown X solid, Sec. A·9
28	Chap. 9. Oxidation and Reduction Theory, Secs. 9·5 to 9·7	Continue analysis of unknown X solid, Sec. A·9
29	Chap. 9. Oxidation and Reduction Theory, Exercises	Complete analysis of unknown X solid, Sec. A·9
30	Quiz covering Chaps. 8 and 9	Check-out period

TABLE A·1 LIST OF DESK APPARATUS

1 Bath rack, aluminum	1 Pipette, graduated, 1 ml
2 Beakers, 50 ml	1 Ring support, iron
2 Beakers, 250 ml	4 Rods, glass, 125 × 3 mm
1 Bottle, dropping, 250 ml (container for distilled H_2O)	1 Spatula, micro (Monel metal)
1 Brush, centrifuge tube	1 Sponge
3 Bulbs for dropper pipettes	1 Stopper, rubber, No. 1, 1-hole
1 Burner with rubber tubing	1 Stopper, rubber, No. 4, 1-hole
1 Casserole, 30 ml	1 Test plate
1 Clamp, test-tube, small	10 Test tubes, 100 × 13 mm, pyrex
1 Clamp, utility	4 Test tubes, tapered, 100 × 13 mm
2 Cobalt glasses	1 Test tube, 200 × 25 mm, pyrex (Aitch-Tu-Ess generator)
5 Corks, No. 2	1 Test-tube stand, wood
1 Cylinder, graduated, 10 ml	2 Towels
1 File, triangular	1 Tube, connecting (drying)
1 box Filter paper, 55 mm	1 Tube, glass, 750 × 6 mm
1 Funnel, 55-mm diameter	1 Tube, glass 750 × 7 mm (for making dropper pipettes)
1 vial Litmus paper, blue	1 Tube, rubber, 30 cm in length (8 mm)
1 vial Litmus paper, red	2 Watch glasses, 75 mm
4 boxes Matches	1 Wing top
2 Medicine droppers	1 Wire gauze, 100 × 100 mm
1 Pencil, wax	1 Wire, platinum (in test tube)

also

1 Centrifuge (designed for 13 × 100-mm test tubes) for each five students

TABLE A·2 REAGENTS

Acids and Bases

Acetic acid, 17 F	Glacial acetic acid
Acetic acid, 3 F	180 ml of glacial acetic acid in a liter of solution
Ammonia, 15 F	Concentrated ammonia
Ammonia, 3 F	200 ml of concentrated NH_3 in a liter of solution
Hydrochloric acid, 12 F	Concentrated hydrochloric acid
Hydrochloric acid, 3 F	250 ml of concentrated HCl in a liter of solution
Nitric acid, 15 F	Concentrated nitric acid
Nitric acid, 3 F	190 ml of concentrated HNO_3 in a liter of solution
Potassium hydroxide, 3 F	190 g of KOH in a liter of solution
Sulfuric acid, 18 F	Concentrated sulfuric acid
Sulfuric acid, 1.5 F	160 ml of concentrated H_2SO_4 in a liter of solution

Reagent Solutions

Aluminon: 1 g of the ammonium salt of aurintricarboxylic acid dissolved in 1 liter of water

Ammoniacal silver nitrate (Miller's reagent): 1.7 g of $AgNO_3$, 25 g of KNO_3, and 17 ml of concentrated NH_3 dissolved in water and diluted to 1 liter

Ammonium acetate, saturated: 460 g of $NH_4C_2H_3O_2$ dissolved in water and diluted to 1 liter

Ammonium chloride, saturated: 350 g of NH_4Cl dissolved in water and diluted to 1 liter

Ammonium molybdate: 200 g of ammonium molybdate and 160 ml of concentrated ammonia dissolved in water and diluted to 1 liter

TABLE A·2   REAGENTS (Continued)

Ammonium oxalate, 0.25 F: 35.5 g of $(NH_4)_2C_2O_4 \cdot H_2O$ dissolved in water and diluted to 1 liter

Ammonium phosphate, 0.5 F: 66 g of $(NH_4)_2HPO_4$ dissolved in water and diluted to 1 liter

Ammonium sulfate, 1 F: 132 g of $(NH_4)_2SO_4$ dissolved in water and diluted to 1 liter

Ammonium thiocyanate, alcoholic solution: A saturated solution of NH_4CNS in 95 per cent ethyl alcohol.

Ammonium thiocyanate, 3 F: 228 g of NH_4CNS dissolved in water and diluted to 1 liter

Barium acetate, 1 F: 273.5 g of $Ba(C_2H_3O_2)_2 \cdot H_2O$ dissolved in water and diluted to 1 liter

Cadmium acetate, 1 F: 266.5 g of $Cd(C_2H_3O_2)_2 \cdot 2H_2O$ dissolved in water and diluted to 1 liter

Calcium acetate, 2 F: 352.4 g of $Ca(C_2H_3O_2)_2H_2O$ dissolved in water and diluted to 1 liter

Carbon tetrachloride

Carminic acid: 1 g of carminic acid dissolved in 1 liter of concentrated sulfuric acid

Dimethylglyoxime: 12 g of the reagent dissolved in 1 liter of 95 per cent ethyl alcohol

Ferric chloride, 1 F: 270 g of $FeCl_3 \cdot 6H_2O$ dissolved in water and diluted to 1 liter

Hydrogen peroxide: A 3 per cent solution

Lead acetate, 0.5 F: 190 g of $Pb(C_2H_3O_2)_2 \cdot 3H_2O$ dissolved in water and diluted to 1 liter

Mercuric chloride, saturated: 70 g of $HgCl_2$ added to 1 liter of water

α-Naphthylamine: 3 g of the reagent dissolved in 1 liter of water; filtered if not clear

p-Nitrobenzeneazoresorcinol: 5 g of the dye dissolved in 1 liter of 0.25 F sodium hydroxide solution

Potassium chromate, 1 F: 194 g of K_2CrO_4 dissolved in water and diluted to 1 liter

Potassium cyanide, 1 F: 66 g of KCN dissolved in water and diluted to 1 liter

Potassium permanganate, 0.1 F: 1.6 g of $KMnO_4$ dissolved in water and diluted to 1 liter

Rhodamine B: 0.1 g of the reagent dissolved in 1 liter of water.

Silver acetate, saturated: 10 g of $AgC_2H_3O_2$ added to 1 liter of water

Silver nitrate, 0.5 F: 85 g of $AgNO_3$ dissolved in water and diluted to 1 liter

Sodium acetate, 2.5 F: 340 g of $NaC_2H_3O_2 \cdot 3H_2O$ dissolved in water and diluted to 1 liter

Sodium carbonate, 1.5 F: 159 g of Na_2CO_3 dissolved in water and diluted to 1 liter

Sodium hypochlorite: A 5 per cent solution (commercial solutions such as Zonite and Clorox are satisfactory)

Stannous chloride: 56 g of $SnCl_2 \cdot 2H_2O$ dissolved in 100 ml of concentrated HCl, allowed to stand until clear, and then diluted to 1 liter, with addition of a few pieces of metallic tin to the solution

Urea: 200 g of urea dissolved in 1 liter of 3 F HCl

Solid Reagents

Aitch-Tu-Ess (commercial material for generating H_2S in laboratory)	Sodium fluoride
Ferrous sulfate	Sodium nitrite
Magnesium ribbon	Sodium peroxide
Potassium chlorate	Tartaric acid
Potassium iodide	Tin (metal)
Sodium bismuthate	Zinc dust

TABLE A·3 TEST SOLUTIONS

(Solutions made according to the following directions contain 10 mg of the cation or anion per milliliter)

Compound	Formula	Ion	Grams per liter of solution
Aluminum nitrate	$Al(NO_3)_3 \cdot 9H_2O$	Aluminum	139.0
Ammonium nitrate	NH_4NO_3	Ammonium	44.5
Ammonium oxalate	$(NH_4)_2C_2O_4 \cdot H_2O$	Oxalate	16.2
Antimony chloride	$SbCl_3$ in 6 F HCl	Antimony	18.8
Arsenic chloride	As_2O_3 in 6 F HCl	Arsenic	13.2
Barium nitrate	$Ba(NO_3)_2$	Barium	19.0
Bismuth nitrate	$Bi(NO_3)_3 \cdot 5H_2O$ in 3 F HNO_3	Bismuth	23.3
Cadmium nitrate	$Cd(NO_3)_2 \cdot 4H_2O$	Cadmium	27.8
Calcium nitrate	$Ca(NO_3)_2 \cdot 4H_2O$	Calcium	59.0
Chromium nitrate	$Cr(NO_3)_3 \cdot 4H_2O$	Chromium	77.0
Cobalt nitrate	$Co(NO_3)_2 \cdot 6H_2O$	Cobalt	50.0
Copper nitrate	$Cu(NO_3)_2 \cdot 3H_2O$	Copper	38.0
Ferric nitrate	$Fe(NO_3)_3 \cdot 9H_2O$	Ferric	72.8
Lead nitrate	$Pb(NO_3)_2$	Lead	16.0
Magnesium nitrate	$Mg(NO_3)_2 \cdot 6H_2O$	Magnesium	106.0
Manganese nitrate	$Mn(NO_3)_2 \cdot 6H_2O$	Manganese	52.4
Mercuric nitrate	$Hg(NO_3)_2 \cdot \frac{1}{2}H_2O$	Mercuric	16.7
Mercurous nitrate	$Hg_2(NO_3)_2 \cdot H_2O$ in 1 F HNO_3	Mercurous	14.0
Nickel nitrate	$Ni(NO_3)_2 \cdot 6H_2O$	Nickel	50.0
Potassium bromide	KBr	Bromide	14.9
Potassium chlorate	$KClO_3$	Chlorate	14.7
Potassium chromate	K_2CrO_4	Chromate	16.7
Potassium ferricyanide	$K_3Fe(CN)_6$	Ferricyanide	15.5
Potassium ferrocyanide	$K_4Fe(CN)_6$	Ferrocyanide	19.8
Potassium iodide	KI	Iodide	13.1
Potassium nitrate*	KNO_3	Potassium	25.9
Potassium thiocyanate	KCNS	Thiocyanate	16.7
Silver nitrate	$AgNO_3$	Silver	15.7
Sodium arsenate	$Na_2HAsO_4 \cdot 7H_2O$	Arsenate	22.5
Sodium arsenite	$NaAsO_2$	Arsenite	12.0
Sodium borate	$Na_2B_4O_7 \cdot 10H_2O$	Borate	22.3
Sodium carbonate	$Na_2CO_3 \cdot 10H_2O$	Carbonate	22.0
Sodium chloride	NaCl	Chloride	16.5
Sodium fluoride	NaF	Fluoride	22.0
Sodium nitrate	$NaNO_3$	Sodium	37.0
Sodium nitrite	$NaNO_2$	Nitrite	15.0
Sodium phosphate	$Na_2HPO_4 \cdot 12H_2O$	Phosphate	37.7
Sodium sulfate	$Na_2SO_4 \cdot 10H_2O$	Sulfate	33.3
Sodium sulfide	$Na_2S \cdot 9H_2O$	Sulfide	75.2
Sodium sulfite	$Na_2SO_3 \cdot 7H_2O$	Sulfite	31.5
Sodium thiosulfate	$Na_2S_2O_3 \cdot 5H_2O$	Thiosulfate	22.1
Stannic chloride	$SnCl_4 \cdot 5H_2O$ in 6 F HCl	Stannic	29.4
Strontium nitrate	$Sr(NO_3)_2 \cdot 4H_2O$	Strontium	32.4
Zinc nitrate	$Zn(NO_3)_2 \cdot 6H_2O$	Zinc	45.5

* Potassium nitrate may be used as a source of nitrate ions.

TABLE A·4 DISTRIBUTION OF ELECTRONS IN THE ATOMS OF THE ELEMENTS

		K	L		M			N				O				P			Q
		1s	2s	2p	3s	3p	3d	4s	4p	4d	4f	5s	5p	5d	5f	6s	6p	6d	7s
H	1	1																	
He	2	2																	
Li	3	2	1																
Be	4	2	2																
B	5	2	2	1															
C	6	2	2	2															
N	7	2	2	3															
O	8	2	2	4															
F	9	2	2	5															
Ne	10	2	2	6															
Na	11	2	2	6	1														
Mg	12	2	2	6	2														
Al	13	2	2	6	2	1													
Si	14	2	2	6	2	2													
P	15	2	2	6	2	3													
S	16	2	2	6	2	4													
Cl	17	2	2	6	2	5													
A	18	2	2	6	2	6													
K	19	2	2	6	2	6		1											
Ca	20	2	2	6	2	6		2											
Sc	21	2	2	6	2	6	1	2											
Ti	22	2	2	6	2	6	2	2											
V	23	2	2	6	2	6	3	2											
Cr	24	2	2	6	2	6	5	1											
Mn	25	2	2	6	2	6	5	2											
Fe	26	2	2	6	2	6	6	2											
Co	27	2	2	6	2	6	7	2											
Ni	28	2	2	6	2	6	8	2											
Cu	29	2	2	6	2	6	10	1											
Zn	30	2	2	6	2	6	10	2											
Ga	31	2	2	6	2	6	10	2	1										
Ge	32	2	2	6	2	6	10	2	2										
As	33	2	2	6	2	6	10	2	3										
Se	34	2	2	6	2	6	10	2	4										
Br	35	2	2	6	2	6	10	2	5										
Kr	36	2	2	6	2	6	10	2	6										
Rb	37	2	2	6	2	6	10	2	6			1							
Sr	38	2	2	6	2	6	10	2	6			2							
Y	39	2	2	6	2	6	10	2	6	1		2							
Zr	40	2	2	6	2	6	10	2	6	2		2							
Nb	41	2	2	6	2	6	10	2	6	4		1							
Mo	42	2	2	6	2	6	10	2	6	5		1							
Tc	43	2	2	6	2	6	10	2	6	6		1							
Ru	44	2	2	6	2	6	10	2	6	7		1							
Rh	45	2	2	6	2	6	10	2	6	8		1							
Pd	46	2	2	6	2	6	10	2	6	10									
Ag	47	2	2	6	2	6	10	2	6	10		1							
Cd	48	2	2	6	2	6	10	2	6	10		2							
In	49	2	2	6	2	6	10	2	6	10		2	1						
Sn	50	2	2	6	2	6	10	2	6	10		2	2						
Sb	51	2	2	6	2	6	10	2	6	10		2	3						
Te	52	2	2	6	2	6	10	2	6	10		2	4						
I	53	2	2	6	2	6	10	2	6	10		2	5						

TABLE A·4   DISTRIBUTION OF ELECTRONS IN THE ATOMS OF THE ELEMENTS
(*Continued*)

		K	L		M			N				O				P			Q
		1s	2s	2p	3s	3p	3d	4s	4p	4d	4f	5s	5p	5d	5f	6s	6p	6d	7s
Xe	54	2	2	6	2	6	10	2	6	10		2	6						
Cs	55	2	2	6	2	6	10	2	6	10		2	6			1			
Ba	56	2	2	6	2	6	10	2	6	10		2	6			2			
La	57	2	2	6	2	6	10	2	6	10		2	6	1		2			
Ce	58	2	2	6	2	6	10	2	6	10	1	2	6	1		2			
Pr	59	2	2	6	2	6	10	2	6	10	2	2	6	1		2			
Nd	60	2	2	6	2	6	10	2	6	10	3	2	6	1		2			
Pm	61	2	2	6	2	6	10	2	6	10	4	2	6	1		2			
Sm	62	2	2	6	2	6	10	2	6	10	5	2	6	1		2			
Eu	63	2	2	6	2	6	10	2	6	10	6	2	6	1		2			
Gd	64	2	2	6	2	6	10	2	6	10	7	2	6	1		2			
Tb	65	2	2	6	2	6	10	2	6	10	8	2	6	1		2			
Dy	66	2	2	6	2	6	10	2	6	10	9	2	6	1		2			
Ho	67	2	2	6	2	6	10	2	6	10	10	2	6	1		2			
Er	68	2	2	6	2	6	10	2	6	10	11	2	6	1		2			
Tm	69	2	2	6	2	6	10	2	6	10	12	2	6	1		2			
Yb	70	2	2	6	2	6	10	2	6	10	13	2	6	1		2			
Lu	71	2	2	6	2	6	10	2	6	10	14	2	6	1		2			
Hf	72	2	2	6	2	6	10	2	6	10	14	2	6	2		2			
Ta	73	2	2	6	2	6	10	2	6	10	14	2	6	3		2			
W	74	2	2	6	2	6	10	2	6	10	14	2	6	4		2			
Re	75	2	2	6	2	6	10	2	6	10	14	2	6	5		2			
Os	76	2	2	6	2	6	10	2	6	10	14	2	6	6		2			
Ir	77	2	2	6	2	6	10	2	6	10	14	2	6	7		2			
Pt	78	2	2	6	2	6	10	2	6	10	14	2	6	9		1			
Au	79	2	2	6	2	6	10	2	6	10	14	2	6	10		1			
Hg	80	2	2	6	2	6	10	2	6	10	14	2	6	10		2			
Tl	81	2	2	6	2	6	10	2	6	10	14	2	6	10		2	1		
Pb	82	2	2	6	2	6	10	2	6	10	14	2	6	10		2	2		
Bi	83	2	2	6	2	6	10	2	6	10	14	2	6	10		2	3		
Po	84	2	2	6	2	6	10	2	6	10	14	2	6	10		2	4		
At	85	2	2	6	2	6	10	2	6	10	14	2	6	10		2	5		
Rn	86	2	2	6	2	6	10	2	6	10	14	2	6	10		2	6		
Fr	87	2	2	6	2	6	10	2	6	10	14	2	6	10		2	6		1
Ra	88	2	2	6	2	6	10	2	6	10	14	2	6	10		2	6		2
Ac	89	2	2	6	2	6	10	2	6	10	14	2	6	10		2	6	1	2
Th	90	2	2	6	2	6	10	2	6	10	14	2	6	10	1	2	6	1	2
Pa	91	2	2	6	2	6	10	2	6	10	14	2	6	10	2	2	6	1	2
U	92	2	2	6	2	6	10	2	6	10	14	2	6	10	3	2	6	1	2
Np	93	2	2	6	2	6	10	2	6	10	14	2	6	10	4	2	6	1	2
Pu	94	2	2	6	2	6	10	2	6	10	14	2	6	10	5	2	6	1	2
Am	95	2	2	6	2	6	10	2	6	10	14	2	6	10	6	2	6	1	2
Cm	96	2	2	6	2	6	10	2	6	10	14	2	6	10	7	2	6	1	2
Bk	97	2	2	6	2	6	10	2	6	10	14	2	6	10	8	2	6	1	2
Cf	98	2	2	6	2	6	10	2	6	10	14	2	6	10	9	2	6	1	2

TABLE A·5   IONIZATION CONSTANTS OF WEAK BASES AT ROOM TEMPERATURE

Base	Formula	Ionization constant
Ammonia	NH_3	1.8×10^{-5}
Aniline	$C_6H_5NH_2$	3.8×10^{-10}
Dimethylamine	$(CH_3)_2NH_2$	5.12×10^{-4}
Ethanolamine	$C_2H_5ONH_2$	2.77×10^{-5}
Ethylamine	$C_2H_5NH_2$	5.6×10^{-4}
Hydrazine	$(NH_2)_2$	3×10^{-6}
Methylamine	CH_3NH_2	4.38×10^{-4}
Pyridine	C_5H_5N	1.4×10^{-9}
Trimethylamine	$(CH_3)_3N$	5.27×10^{-5}

TABLE A·6   IONIZATION CONSTANTS OF WEAK ACIDS AT ROOM TEMPERATURE

Acid	Formula	Ionization constant		
		K_1	K_2	K_3
Acetic	$HC_2H_3O_2$	1.75×10^{-5}		
Arsenic	H_3AsO_4	5×10^{-3}	8.3×10^{-8}	6×10^{-10}
Arsenious	H_3AsO_3	6×10^{-10}		
Benzoic	$HC_7H_5O_2$	6.3×10^{-5}		
Boric	H_3BO_3	5.8×10^{-10}		
Carbonic	H_2CO_3	4.3×10^{-7}	5.6×10^{-11}	
Chloroacetic	$HC_2H_2O_2Cl$	1.4×10^{-3}		
Chromic	H_2CrO_4	2×10^{-1}	3.2×10^{-7}	
Citric	$H_3C_6H_5O_7$	8.7×10^{-4}	1.8×10^{-5}	4×10^{-6}
Cyanic	$HCNO$	2×10^{-4}		
Dichloroacetic	$HC_2HO_2Cl_2$	5×10^{-2}		
Formic	$HCHO_2$	1.77×10^{-4}		
Hydrazoic	HN_3	2.6×10^{-5}		
Hydrocyanic	HCN	7.2×10^{-10}		
Hydrofluoric	HF	7.2×10^{-4}		
Hydrogen sulfide	H_2S	5.7×10^{-8}	1.2×10^{-15}	
Hypochlorous	$HOCl$	3.5×10^{-8}		
Iodic	HIO_3	1.67×10^{-1}		
Lactic	$HC_3H_5O_3$	1.39×10^{-4}		
Nitrous	HNO_2	4×10^{-4}		
Oxalic	$H_2C_2O_4$	6.5×10^{-2}	6.1×10^{-5}	
Phenol	HC_6H_5O	1.3×10^{-10}		
Phosphoric	H_3PO_4	7.5×10^{-3}	6.2×10^{-8}	4.8×10^{-13}
Phosphorous	H_3PO_3	1.6×10^{-2}	7×10^{-7}	
Phthalic	$H_2C_8H_4O_4$	1.3×10^{-3}	3.9×10^{-6}	
Propionic	$HC_3H_5O_2$	1.34×10^{-3}		
Succinic	$H_2C_4H_4O_4$	6.4×10^{-5}	2.7×10^{-6}	
Sulfuric	H_2SO_4		1.2×10^{-2}	
Sulfurous	H_2SO_3	1.72×10^{-2}	6.24×10^{-8}	
Tartaric	$H_2C_4H_4O_6$	9.6×10^{-4}	2.9×10^{-5}	

TABLE A·7 ACID CONSTANTS OF HYDRATED IONS AND HYDROXIDES

Equilibrium	Acid constant
$Al(H_2O)_6{}^{3+} + H_2O = Al(OH)(H_2O)_5{}^{++} + H_3O^+$	1.4×10^{-5}
$Al(OH)_3(H_2O)_3 + H_2O = Al(OH)_4(H_2O)_2{}^- + H_3O^+$	4×10^{-13}
$Cr(H_2O)_6{}^{3+} + H_2O = Cr(OH)(H_2O)_5{}^{++} + H_3O^+$	1.5×10^{-4}
$Cr(OH)_3(H_2O)_3 + H_2O = Cr(OH)_4(H_2O)_2{}^- + H_3O^+$	9×10^{-17}
$Fe(H_2O)_6{}^{3+} + H_2O = Fe(OH)(H_2O)_5{}^{++} + H_3O^+$	6.0×10^{-3}
$Pb(OH)_2(H_2O)_2 + H_2O = Pb(OH)_3(H_2O)^- + H_3O^+$	2.1×10^{-16}
$Sn(OH)_2(H_2O)_2 + H_2O = Sn(OH)_3(H_2O)^- + H_3O^+$	3.8×10^{-15}
$Zn(H_2O)_6{}^{++} + H_2O = Zn(OH)(H_2O)_5{}^+ + H_3O^+$	2.45×10^{-10}
$Zn(OH)_2(H_2O)_4 + 2H_2O = Zn(OH)_4(H_2O)_2{}^- + 2H_3O^+$	1×10^{-29}

TABLE A·8 DISSOCIATION CONSTANTS OF COMPLEX IONS

Dissociation equilibrium	Dissociation constant
$Al(OH)_4{}^- = Al(OH)_3(s) + OH^-$	2.5×10^{-2}
$Cd(NH_3)_4{}^{++} = Cd^{++} + 4NH_3$	2.5×10^{-7}
$Cd(CN)_4{}^- = Cd^{++} + 4CN^-$	1.4×10^{-17}
$CdI_4{}^- = Cd^{++} + 4I^-$	5×10^{-7}
$Co(NH_3)_6{}^{++} = Co^{++} + 6NH_3$	1.25×10^{-5}
$Co(NH_3)_6{}^{3+} = Co^{3+} + 6NH_3$	2.2×10^{-34}
$Cr(OH)_4{}^- = Cr(OH)_3(s) + OH^-$	1×10^{-2}
$Cu(NH_3)_4{}^{++} = Cu^{++} + 4NH_3$	4.6×10^{-14}
$Cu(CN)_3{}^- = Cu^+ + 3CN^-$	5×10^{-28}
$Fe(CNS)_6{}^- = Fe^{3+} + 6CNS^-$	8×10^{-10}
$Fe(CNS)^{++} = Fe^{3+} + CNS^-$	3.3×10^{-2}
$Pb(OH)_3{}^- = Pb(OH)_2(s) + OH^-$	50
$HgBr_4{}^- = Hg^{++} + 4Br^-$	2.2×10^{-22}
$HgCl_4{}^- = Hg^{++} + 4Cl^-$	1.1×10^{-16}
$HgI_4{}^- = Hg^{++} + 4I^-$	5×10^{-31}
$Hg(CN)_4{}^- = Hg^{++} + 4CN^-$	4×10^{-42}
$Hg(CNS)_4{}^- = Hg^{++} + 4CNS^-$	1×10^{-22}
$Ni(CN)_4{}^- = Ni^{++} + 4CN^-$	1×10^{-22}
$Ni(NH_3)_4{}^{++} = Ni^{++} + 4NH_3$	4.8×10^{-8}
$Ag(NH_3)_2{}^+ = Ag^+ + 2NH_3$	6.8×10^{-8}
$Ag(CN)_2{}^- = Ag^+ + 2CN^-$	1.8×10^{-19}
$Ag(S_2O_3)_2{}^{3-} = Ag^+ + 2S_2O_3{}^-$	6×10^{-14}
$Sn(OH)_3{}^- = Sn(OH)_2(s) + OH^-$	2×10^3
$Sn(OH)_6{}^- = Sn(OH)_4(s) + 2OH^-$	5×10^3
$Zn(NH_3)_4{}^{++} = Zn^{++} + 4NH_3$	2.6×10^{-10}
$Zn(CN)_4{}^- = Zn^{++} + 4CN^-$	2×10^{-17}
$Zn(OH)_4{}^- = Zn(OH)_2(s) + 2OH^-$	10

TABLE A·9   SOLUBILITY PRODUCT CONSTANTS AT ROOM TEMPERATURE

Substance	Formula	Solubility product
Aluminum hydroxide	$Al(OH)_3$	1.9×10^{-33}
Barium carbonate	$BaCO_3$	8.1×10^{-9}
Barium chromate	$BaCrO_4$	2.4×10^{-10}
Barium fluoride	BaF_2	1.7×10^{-6}
Barium iodate	$Ba(IO_3)_2 \cdot 2H_2O$	6.5×10^{-10}
Barium oxalate	$BaC_2O_4 \cdot 2H_2O$	1.5×10^{-7}
Barium sulfate	$BaSO_4$	1.1×10^{-10}
Bismuthyl chloride	$BiOCl$	2×10^{-9}
Bismuth sulfide	Bi_2S_3	1.6×10^{-72}
Cadmium carbonate	$CdCO_3$	2.5×10^{-14}
Cadmium oxalate	$CdC_2O_4 \cdot 3H_2O$	1.5×10^{-8}
Cadmium sulfide	CdS	3.6×10^{-29}
Calcium carbonate	$CaCO_3$	8.7×10^{-9}
Calcium fluoride	CaF_2	4.0×10^{-11}
Calcium iodate	$Ca(IO_3)_2 \cdot 6H_2O$	6.5×10^{-7}
Calcium oxalate	$CaC_2O_4 \cdot H_2O$	2.3×10^{-9}
Calcium sulfate	$CaSO_4$	6.1×10^{-5}
Chromium hydroxide	$Cr(OH)_3$	1×10^{-30}
Cobalt sulfide	CoS	7×10^{-23}
Cupric hydroxide	$Cu(OH)_2$	5.6×10^{-20}
Cupric oxalate	CuC_2O_4	2.9×10^{-8}
Cupric iodate	$Cu(IO_3)_2$	1.4×10^{-7}
Cupric sulfide	CuS	8.5×10^{-45}
Cuprous bromide	$CuBr$	4.1×10^{-8}
Cuprous chloride	$CuCl$	1.8×10^{-7}
Cuprous iodide	CuI	5.0×10^{-12}
Cuprous sulfide	Cu_2S	2×10^{-47}
Ferric hydroxide	$Fe(OH)_3$	6×10^{-38}
Ferrous hydroxide	$Fe(OH)_2$	2×10^{-14}
Ferrous oxalate	FeC_2O_4	2.1×10^{-7}
Ferrous sulfide	FeS	3.7×10^{-19}
Lead carbonate	$PbCO_3$	4.0×10^{-14}
Lead chloride	$PbCl_2$	1.0×10^{-4}
Lead chromate	$PbCrO_4$	2×10^{-14}
Lead fluoride	PbF_2	3.7×10^{-8}
Lead hydroxide	$Pb(OH)_2$	2.5×10^{-16}
Lead iodate	$Pb(IO_3)_2$	2.6×10^{-13}
Lead iodide	PbI_2	1.4×10^{-8}
Lead oxalate	PbC_2O_4	2.8×10^{-11}
Lead sulfate	$PbSO_4$	1.1×10^{-8}
Lead sulfide	PbS	3.4×10^{-28}
Magnesium ammonium phosphate	$MgNH_4PO_4$	2.5×10^{-13}
Magnesium carbonate	$MgCO_3$	1×10^{-5}
Magnesium fluoride	MgF_2	6.4×10^{-9}
Magnesium hydroxide	$Mg(OH)_2$	1.2×10^{-11}
Magnesium oxalate	MgC_2O_4	8.6×10^{-5}

TABLE A·9 SOLUBILITY PRODUCT CONSTANTS AT ROOM TEMPERATURE (*Continued*)

Substance	Formula	Solubility product
Manganous carbonate	$MnCO_3$	8.8×10^{-11}
Manganous hydroxide	$Mn(OH)_2$	4.5×10^{-14}
Manganese sulfide	MnS	1.4×10^{-15}
Mercuric sulfide	HgS	3×10^{-53}
Mercurous bromide	Hg_2Br_2	4×10^{-23}
Mercurous chloride	Hg_2Cl_2	2×10^{-18}
Mercurous iodide	Hg_2I_2	4×10^{-29}
Nickel hydroxide	$Ni(OH)_2$	2×10^{-14}
Nickel sulfide	NiS	1.4×10^{-24}
Silver acetate	$AgC_2H_3O_2$	1.8×10^{-3}
Silver bromate	$AgBrO_3$	6×10^{-5}
Silver bromide	$AgBr$	7.7×10^{-13}
Silver carbonate	Ag_2CO_3	6.2×10^{-12}
Silver chloride	$AgCl$	1.56×10^{-10}
Silver chromate	Ag_2CrO_4	9×10^{-12}
Silver cyanide	$AgCN$	2.2×10^{-12}
Silver iodate	$AgIO_3$	1×10^{-8}
Silver iodide	AgI	1.5×10^{-16}
Silver phosphate	Ag_3PO_4	1.8×10^{-18}
Silver sulfide	Ag_2S	1.6×10^{-49}
Silver thiocyanate	$AgCNS$	1.2×10^{-12}
Strontium carbonate	$SrCO_3$	1.6×10^{-9}
Strontium fluoride	SrF_2	2.8×10^{-9}
Strontium oxalate	SrC_2O_4	5.8×10^{-8}
Strontium sulfate	$SrSO_4$	2.9×10^{-7}
Zinc hydroxide	$Zn(OH)_2$	4.5×10^{-17}
Zinc oxalate	ZnC_2O_4	1.5×10^{-9}
Zinc sulfide	ZnS	1.2×10^{-23}

LOGARITHMS

No.	0	1	2	3	4	5	6	7	8	9	1	2	3	4	5	6	7	8	9
10	0000	0043	0086	0128	0170	0212	0253	0294	0334	0374	4	8	12	17	21	25	29	33	37
11	0414	0453	0492	0531	0569	0607	0645	0682	0719	0755	4	8	11	15	19	23	26	30	34
12	0792	0828	0864	0899	0934	0969	1004	1038	1072	1106	3	7	10	14	17	21	24	28	31
13	1139	1173	1206	1239	1271	1303	1335	1367	1399	1430	3	6	10	13	16	19	23	26	29
14	1461	1492	1523	1553	1584	1614	1644	1673	1703	1732	3	6	9	12	15	18	21	24	27
15	1761	1790	1818	1847	1875	1903	1931	1959	1987	2014	3	6	8	11	14	17	20	22	25
16	2041	2068	2095	2122	2148	2175	2201	2227	2253	2279	3	5	8	11	13	16	18	21	24
17	2304	2330	2355	2380	2405	2430	2455	2480	2504	2529	2	5	7	10	12	15	17	20	22
18	2553	2577	2601	2625	2648	2672	2695	2718	2742	2765	2	5	7	9	12	14	16	19	21
19	2788	2810	2833	2856	2878	2900	2923	2945	2967	2989	2	4	7	9	11	13	16	18	20
20	3010	3032	3054	3075	3096	3118	3139	3160	3181	3201	2	4	6	8	11	13	15	17	19
21	3222	3243	3263	3284	3304	3324	3345	3365	3385	3404	2	4	6	8	10	12	14	16	18
22	3424	3444	3464	3483	3502	3522	3541	3560	3579	3598	2	4	6	8	10	12	14	15	17
23	3617	3636	3655	3674	3692	3711	3729	3747	3766	3784	2	4	6	7	9	11	13	15	17
24	3802	3820	3838	3856	3874	3892	3909	3927	3945	3962	2	4	5	7	9	11	12	14	16
25	3979	3997	4014	4031	4048	4065	4082	4099	4116	4133	2	3	5	7	9	10	12	14	15
26	4150	4166	4183	4200	4216	4232	4249	4265	4281	4298	2	3	5	7	8	10	11	13	15
27	4314	4330	4346	4362	4378	4393	4409	4425	4440	4456	2	3	5	6	8	9	11	13	14
28	4472	4487	4502	4518	4533	4548	4564	4579	4594	4609	2	3	5	6	8	9	11	12	14
29	4624	4639	4654	4669	4683	4698	4713	4728	4742	4757	1	3	4	6	7	9	10	12	13
30	4771	4786	4800	4814	4829	4843	4857	4871	4886	4900	1	3	4	6	7	9	10	11	13
31	4914	4928	4942	4955	4969	4983	4997	5011	5024	5038	1	3	4	6	7	8	10	11	12
32	5051	5065	5079	5092	5105	5119	5132	5145	5159	5172	1	3	4	5	7	8	9	11	12
33	5185	5198	5211	5224	5237	5250	5263	5276	5289	5302	1	3	4	5	6	8	9	10	12
34	5315	5328	5340	5353	5366	5378	5391	5403	5416	5428	1	3	4	5	6	8	9	10	11
35	5441	5453	5465	5478	5490	5502	5514	5527	5539	5551	1	2	4	5	6	7	9	10	11
36	5563	5575	5587	5599	5611	5623	5635	5647	5658	5670	1	2	4	5	6	7	8	10	11
37	5682	5694	5705	5717	5729	5740	5752	5763	5775	5786	1	2	3	5	6	7	8	9	10
38	5798	5809	5821	5832	5843	5855	5866	5877	5888	5899	1	2	3	5	6	7	8	9	10
39	5911	5922	5933	5944	5955	5966	5977	5988	5999	6010	1	2	3	4	5	7	8	9	10
40	6021	6031	6042	6053	6064	6075	6085	6096	6107	6117	1	2	3	4	5	6	8	9	10
41	6128	6138	6149	6160	6170	6180	6191	6201	6212	6222	1	2	3	4	5	6	7	8	9
42	6232	6243	6253	6263	6274	6284	6294	6304	6314	6325	1	2	3	4	5	6	7	8	9
43	6335	6345	6355	6365	6375	6386	6395	6405	6415	6425	1	2	3	4	5	6	7	8	9
44	6435	6444	6454	6464	6474	6484	6493	6503	6513	6522	1	2	3	4	5	6	7	8	9
45	6532	6542	6551	6561	6571	6580	6590	6599	6609	6618	1	2	3	4	5	6	7	8	9
46	6628	6637	6646	6656	6665	6675	6684	6693	6702	6712	1	2	3	4	5	6	7	7	8
47	6721	6730	6739	6749	6758	6767	6776	6785	6794	6803	1	2	3	4	5	5	6	7	8
48	6812	6821	6830	6839	6848	6857	6866	6875	6884	6893	1	2	3	4	4	5	6	7	8
49	6902	6911	6920	6928	6937	6946	6955	6964	6972	6981	1	2	3	4	4	5	6	7	8
50	6990	6998	7007	7016	7024	7033	7042	7050	7059	7067	1	2	3	3	4	5	6	7	8
51	7076	7084	7093	7101	7110	7118	7126	7135	7143	7152	1	2	3	3	4	5	6	7	8
52	7160	7168	7177	7185	7193	7202	7210	7218	7226	7235	1	2	2	3	4	5	6	7	7
53	7243	7251	7259	7267	7275	7284	7292	7300	7308	7316	1	2	2	3	4	5	6	6	7
54	7324	7332	7340	7348	7356	7364	7372	7380	7388	7396	1	2	2	3	4	5	6	6	7

LOGARITHMS　(*Continued*)

No.	0	1	2	3	4	5	6	7	8	9	1 2 3	4 5 6	7 8 9
55	7404	7412	7419	7427	7435	7443	7451	7459	7466	7474	1 2 2	3 4 5	5 6 7
56	7482	7490	7497	7505	7513	7520	7528	7536	7543	7551	1 2 2	3 4 5	5 6 7
57	7559	7566	7574	7582	7589	7597	7604	7612	7619	7627	1 2 2	3 4 5	5 6 7
58	7634	7642	7649	7657	7664	7672	7679	7686	7694	7701	1 1 2	3 4 4	5 6 7
59	7709	7716	7723	7731	7738	7745	7752	7760	7767	7774	1 1 2	3 4 4	5 6 7
60	7782	7789	7796	7803	7810	7818	7825	7832	7839	7846	1 1 2	3 4 4	5 6 6
61	7853	7860	7868	7875	7882	7889	7896	7903	7910	7917	1 1 2	3 4 4	5 6 6
62	7924	7931	7938	7945	7952	7959	7966	7973	7980	7987	1 1 2	3 3 4	5 6 6
63	7992	8000	8007	8014	8021	8028	8035	8041	8048	8055	1 1 2	3 3 4	5 5 6
64	8062	8069	8075	8082	8089	8096	8102	8109	8116	8122	1 1 2	3 3 4	5 5 6
65	8129	8136	8142	8149	8156	8162	8169	8176	8182	8189	1 1 2	3 3 4	5 5 6
66	8195	8202	8209	8215	8222	8228	8235	8241	8248	8254	1 1 2	3 3 4	5 5 6
67	8261	8267	8274	8280	8287	8293	8299	8306	8312	8319	1 1 2	3 3 4	5 5 6
68	8325	8331	8338	8344	8351	8357	8363	8370	8376	8382	1 1 2	3 3 4	4 5 6
69	8388	8395	8401	8407	8414	8420	8426	8432	8439	8445	1 1 2	2 3 4	4 5 6
70	8451	8457	8463	8470	8476	8482	8488	8494	8500	8506	1 1 2	2 3 4	4 5 6
71	8513	8519	8525	8531	8537	8543	8549	8555	8561	8567	1 1 2	2 3 4	4 5 5
72	8573	8579	8585	8591	8597	8603	8609	8615	8621	8627	1 1 2	2 3 4	4 5 5
73	8633	8639	8645	8651	8657	8663	8669	8675	8681	8686	1 1 2	2 3 4	4 5 5
74	8692	8698	8704	8710	8716	8722	8727	8733	8739	8745	1 1 2	2 3 4	4 5 5
75	8751	8756	8762	8768	8774	8779	8785	8791	8797	8802	1 1 2	2 3 3	4 5 5
76	8808	8814	8820	8825	8831	8837	8842	8848	8854	8859	1 1 2	2 3 3	4 5 5
77	8865	8871	8876	8882	8887	8893	8899	8904	8910	8915	1 1 2	2 3 3	4 4 5
78	8921	8927	8932	8938	8943	8949	8954	8960	8965	8971	1 1 2	2 3 3	4 4 5
79	8976	8982	8987	8993	8998	9004	9009	9015	9020	9025	1 1 2	2 3 3	4 4 4
80	9031	9036	9042	9047	9053	9058	9063	9069	9074	9079	1 1 2	2 3 3	4 4 5
81	9085	9090	9096	9101	9106	9112	9117	9122	9128	9133	1 1 2	2 3 3	4 4 5
82	9138	9143	9149	9154	9159	9165	9170	9175	9180	9186	1 1 2	2 3 3	4 4 5
83	9191	9196	9201	9206	9212	9217	9222	9227	9232	9238	1 1 2	2 3 3	4 4 5
84	9243	9248	9253	9258	9263	9269	9274	9279	9284	9289	1 1 2	2 3 3	4 4 5
85	9294	9299	9304	9309	9315	9320	9325	9330	9335	9340	1 1 2	2 3 3	4 4 5
86	9345	9350	9355	9360	9365	9370	9375	9380	9385	9390	1 1 2	2 3 3	4 4 5
87	9395	9400	9405	9410	9415	9420	9425	9430	9435	9440	0 1 1	2 2 3	3 4 4
88	9445	9450	9455	9460	9465	9469	9474	9479	9484	9489	0 1 1	2 2 3	3 4 4
89	9494	9499	9504	9509	9513	9518	9523	9528	9533	9538	0 1 1	2 2 3	3 4 4
90	9542	9547	9552	9557	9562	9566	9571	9576	9581	9586	0 1 1	2 2 3	3 4 4
91	9590	9595	9600	9605	9609	9614	9619	9624	9628	9633	0 1 1	2 2 3	3 4 4
92	9638	9643	9647	9652	9657	9661	9666	9671	9675	9680	0 1 1	2 2 3	3 4 4
93	9685	9689	9594	9699	9703	9708	9713	9717	9722	9727	0 1 1	2 2 3	3 4 4
94	9731	9736	9741	9745	9750	9754	9759	9763	9768	9773	0 1 1	2 2 3	3 4 4
95	9777	9782	9786	9791	9795	9800	9805	9809	9814	9818	0 1 1	2 2 3	3 4 4
96	9823	9827	9832	9836	9841	9845	9850	9854	9859	9863	0 1 1	2 2 3	3 4 4
97	9868	9872	9877	9881	9886	9890	9894	9899	9903	9908	0 1 1	2 2 3	3 4 4
98	9912	9917	9921	9926	9930	9934	9939	9943	9948	9952	0 1 1	2 2 3	3 4 4
99	9956	9961	9965	9969	9974	9978	9983	9987	9991	9996	0 1 1	2 2 3	3 3 4

INDEX

Acetate buffer, 72–73
Acetate ion, hydrolysis, 105
Acetic acid, ionization constant, 63
  ionization equilibrium, 61
  ionization reaction, 37, 43
Acid buffers, 70–71
Acidity, reserve, in buffer solutions, 73
Acids, Brønsted's definition, 44–45, 60, 63, 104–105
  common-ion effect, 66, 70–71
  conjugate, 44
  definition, 44
  diprotic, 75–76
  equivalent weight, 29
  ionization, of strong, 35, 60
    of weak, 35, 60–63
  ionization constants, 61, 269
  monoprotic, 60–63
  polyprotic, 75–76
Activity, coefficient, 43, 67
Activity relation to electrode potential, 158
Adsorption, selective, 146–147
  by sols, 145–148
Aitch-Tu-Ess to produce hydrogen sulfide, 180
Alkaline earth group (see Cations, Group IV)
Alloys, analysis, 250, 253–254
  solution, 253–254
Aluminate ion, 131, 206, 207, 210
Aluminon reagent, preparation, 264
  test for aluminum, 136, 207, 212
Aluminum hydroxide, amphoteric properties, 130–131, 205, 210
  complex, 121–122, 127, 131
Aluminum ion, acid constant, 127
  analysis for, 206–207
  hydrated, 121–122, 209, 210
  hydrolysis, 113, 127
  reactions, 209, 210, 212
  test for, 136, 207

Ammonia, base, 64
  complex ions, 119–120, 127–128, 200
  equilibrium with water, 64, 220, 223
  ionization, 64
  ionization constant for, 64
  precipitating agent, 204–206, 209
  reaction with silver halides, 188
  solubility, 223
  structure, 21
Ammoniates, 128
Ammonium acetate, hydrolysis, 114–115
Ammonium chloride, effect on ammonia, 205, 207, 209
  hydrolysis, 111–112
Ammonium cyanide, hydrolysis, 116
Ammonium ion, acid, 44, 111
  confirmation, 221
  hydrolysis, 111–112
  removal, 218, 220
  structure, 21
Ammonium molybdate, decomposition, 228, 252
  reagent for phosphate, 227, 230, 251
  reaction, 230
  preparation of reagent, 264
Ammonium oxalate, precipitating reagent, 216, 219
Ammonium phosphate, precipitating reagent, 216, 218
Amphoteric (amphiprotic) hydroxides, 130–132
  action, with acids, 131
    with bases, 131
  dissociation constants, 131–132
  equilibrium with water, 132
  as hydrated ions, 131–132
Amphoterism, application to analysis, 199, 210
  calculations pertaining to, 137–138
  problems, 139–140
Analysis, alloys and metals, 250, 253–254

Analysis, anion, discussion, 224–226
  cation, discussion, 183–184
  complete, 245
  definition of qualitative and quantitative, 3, 4
  interference in, 254–255
  macro, 179
  preliminary examination before, 245
  preparation of sample for, 251–254
  report form, 261
  semimicro, 179–182
  of unknowns, 182
Anions, analysis, preparation of solution for, 251–252
  removal of heavy metals before, 226
  classification, 5, 225
  discussion, 224–226
  Group I, analysis, 226–227
    discussion, 226
    notes, 228–229
    reactions, 229–230
  Group II, analysis, 231
    notes, 231–232
    reactions, 232
  Group III, analysis, 233–234
    discussion, 233
    notes, 234
    reactions, 234–235
  Group IV, analysis, 237–238
    discussion, 236
    notes, 238
    reactions, 238–240
  Group V, analysis, 242
    discussion, 241–242
    notes, 242–243
    reactions, 243–244
  homoatomic, 130
Antimony ion, complexes, 198
  hydrolysis, 187, 198
  reactions, 198, 199
  tests for, 196, 202, 203
Antimony oxychloride, 187, 198
  solution in acids, 187, 198
Antimony sulfide, precipitation, 193, 196, 199, 202
  reaction with KOH, 193, 199
  solubility in acids, 196, 202
Apparatus list, 264
Aprotic ions, 105
Aqua regia, 194, 199
Aquo-complex ions, 121–122
Arrhenius theory, 39

Arsenate ion, analysis, anion, 227
  reactions, 198, 202
    with calcium acetate, 229
    with hydrogen sulfide, 198, 230
    with iodide, 230
Arsenic ion, analysis for, 196
  reactions, 198, 202
  separation from antimony and tin, 196
  sulfide complexes, 202
  tests for, 196, 202
Arsenic sulfide, action with KOH, 193, 199
  precipitation, 193, 198
  solution, 193, 196, 199
Arsenious acid, 198
Arsenious sulfide, reactions, 199, 202
  sol, 148–149
  solution, 199, 202
Arsenite ion, analysis, anion, 227
  reactions, 199, 202, 229, 230
  thioarsenites, 199
Assignment schedule, 262
Association of molecules, 28
Atom, nucleus, 6
  radius, 6
Atomic mass, 6
Atomic number, 6
Atomic orbitals, 10, 12–16, 21, 123–127
Atomic structure, 6–14
Atomic weight defined, 7
Atomic weights (inside front cover)
Atoms, composition, 6–7
  electron arrangement, 7–14, 267–268
  isotopes, 6–7
Attraction of ions, 15
Auxiliary valence, 119

Balancing of equations, ionic, 41, 168
  oxidation-reduction, 168–175
    ion-electron method, 171–172
    valence-change method, 172–173
Barium acetate as precipitating reagent, 231, 232
Barium chromate, precipitation, 216, 218
  solubility in acids, 216–218
Barium ion, analysis, 216
  flame test, 216–218
  reactions, 217, 218
Barium phosphate, precipitation, 216, 218
  solubility, 216, 218

Barium sulfate, precipitation, 231, 232
solubility, 96, 232
function of particle size, 96
Bases, Brønsted's definition, 44–45, 63, 104–105
conjugate, 44–45
equilibria involving weak, 64
equivalent conductance, of strong, 37
of weak, 37
ionization, 64
ionization constant, 64, 269
strong, 35
weak, 35, 64
Basic buffers, 74
Bath, hot water, 181
Beryllium chloride, covalency, 19
Beryllium ion, hydration, 123, 128
Bicarbonate ion, hydrolysis, 109–110
Bismuth chloride, hydrolysis, 187
Bismuth complex ions, 129, 130, 200
Bismuth hydroxide, precipitation, 195, 200
reaction with stannite ion, 200
Bismuth ion, hydrolysis, 187
reactions, 198, 200
separation from copper and cadmium, 195, 200
test for, 195, 200
Bismuth oxychloride, 187
Bismuth sulfide, precipitation, 193, 198
solubility, 199
Bismuthate test for manganese, 208, 213
Boiling point, 38
elevation, 38
by electrolytes, 38, 42
by nonelectrolytes, 38
of solutions, 38
Bond, chemical, 7, 14
coordinate, 21, 120, 123–127
covalent, 9, 10, 14–17, 19
electrostatic, 15, 16, 19
hydrogen, 21–22, 28, 31–34
ion-dipole, 121–122
ionic, 15, 16
polar, 22
Borate ion, analysis, 242
partial precipitation in anion analysis, 225, 233, 241
test for, 242, 243
Boric acid, 243
Boron trichloride, covalency, 19
Bottles, reagent, 180

Bromide ion, confirmation, 238
reactions, 238, 240
Brønsted definitions, 44, 60, 63, 104–105
and amphoterism, 131
and hydrolysis, 105
Brown-ring test for nitrates, 242, 244
interfering ions, 243
Brownian movement, 145
Buffer solutions, 72–74
acid, 70–73
applications, 60
basic, 74
calculations pertaining to, 72–74
definition, 72

Cadmium acetate as precipitating reagent, 225, 233
Cadmium ion, analysis, 195
complex ions, 128, 129, 135, 200, 201
ammonia, 128, 135
cyanide, 129
halide, 129
equilibria involving, 135
reactions, 198, 200, 201
Cadmium sulfide, colloidal dispersion, 144
precipitation, 193, 198, 201
solution, 194
Calcium acetate as precipitating reagent, 225, 226
Calcium carbonate, 226, 228, 229
Calcium ion, analysis, 216
flame test, 216–218
precipitation, 216
reactions, 218, 219
Calcium oxalate, 216, 219
Calcium phosphate, precipitation, 216, 218
solubility, 216, 218
Calculations involving, buffer solutions, 72–74, 79–80
common-ion effect, 70–71, 79–80
complex ion dissociation, 137–139
electrode potentials, 160–166
equilibrium constants, 61–63, 78–80
formal solubility, 28–29, 45–46
hydrolysis, 109–115
hydronium ion concentration, 61–63, 66, 78–80
ionization constant, 61–63, 78–80
molar solubility, 28

Calculations involving, pH of solutions, 67–68, 80
polyprotic acids, 76–78, 80–81
solubility product, 86–89, 91–92, 98–100
weak acids, 61–63, 78–81
weak bases, 64, 79
Carbonate fusion, 253
Carbonate ion, equilibrium involving, 109
hydrolysis, 109–110
identification, 226, 229
reactions, 229
Catalysts, adsorption, 49
contact, 49
definition, 49
effect of, on an equilibrium, 58
on reaction velocity, 49–50
negative, 49
Cations, analysis, preparation of solution for, 252–253
classification, 5, 183, 184
discussion, 183–184
Group I, analysis, 186
discussion, 185–186
notes, 187
reactions, 188–189
Group II, analysis, 193–196
discussion, 190–192
notes, 193–197
reactions, 197–203
Group III, analysis, 205–208
discussion, 204–205
notes, 206–209
reactions, 209–214
Group IV, analysis, 216
discussion, 215
notes, 217–218
reactions, 218–219
Group V, analysis, 221
discussion, 220
notes, 221–222
reactions, 222–223
Centrifuge use, 181
Chelate complexes, structure, 133
types, 133–134
Chemical bonds (see Bond)
Chemical equilibrium, 54–56, 153
Chlorate ion, confirmation, 242
oxidizing action, 229, 241, 243
reactions, 229, 241, 243
Chloride ion, complexes, 128–129
confirmation, 237, 239

Chloride ion, reactions, 238, 239
structure, 9
Chromate ion, confirmation, 213, 231, 232
oxidizing action, 217, 218
reactions, 212, 218, 232
Chromic hydroxide, 205
Chromic ion, complexes, 128, 131
confirmation, 207, 212–213
oxidation to chromate, 206–207
reactions, 209–212
Chromite ion, 174
Coagulation of colloids, 148–149
Cobalt ion, complexes, 119, 120, 128, 129, 209, 214
confirmation, 208, 214
reactions, 209, 210, 212–214
structure, 120
Colligative properties of solutions, 37–39
electrolytes, 37–39, 42
nonelectrolytes, 37–39
Collisions, effective, 49
Colloids, adsorption by, 145–148
analytical applications, 149–150
charges on, 146–150
coagulation, 148–149
hydrophilic and hydrophobic, 142–143
methods of preparing, 143–144
particle size, 141
prevention of formation, 149
types, 142
Common-ion effect, applied to solubility, 90–92
in buffer solutions, 72–75
calculations for weak acids and bases, 70–71, 78–81
problems, 71, 72–74, 79, 82
in selective precipitations, 205, 206
Complex ions, ammonia, 119–120, 127–128, 200
anions, 128–134
binding forces, 121–127
calculations involving, 137–139
cations, 128–134
coordinate bonds, 120, 123–127
cyanides, 129, 201
dissociation constants, 134–136, 270
electrovalence, 120–122
halides, 128–129, 187, 202, 203
hydrated, 118, 121–122, 126–128
acid constants of, 127, 270

Complex ions, hydroxides, 130–132, 199, 200, 202
  ion-dipole bonds, 121–122
  organic, 132–134, 136–137
  sulfide, 130, 199, 202
  thiocyanate, 129, 213, 239
  types, 127
Concentration, and conductance, 35–37
  effect of, on emf of cells, 161–163
    on speed of reaction, 50, 57
  effective, 43, 67, 158
  hydronium-ion (see Hydronium-ion concentration)
  units of, 28–29
    formal, 28
    molal, 29
    molar, 28
    normal, 29
    per cent, 29
Concentration cells, 162–163
Conductance, and concentration, 35–37
  of electrolytes, 35, 37, 41, 42
  equivalent, 35–37, 41
  of weak electrolytes, 35, 37
Conjugate acids and bases, 44–45, 64
Constants, equilibrium, 55, 61
  hydrolysis, 106
  instability, 135–136, 138–139
  ionization, of acids, 61, 269
    of bases, 64, 269
  proportionality, 51
  solubility product, 84–86, 271–272
Coordinate bond, 21, 120, 123–127
Coordinate valence, 120, 123–127
Coordination, number, 119
  sphere, 119–120
  theory, 119–121, 123–127
Copper ion, ammonia complex, 128, 201
  analysis, 195
  cyanide complex, 128, 129, 135, 195, 201
  flame test, 246
  reactions, 198, 200, 201
  tests for, 195, 200
Coulomb's law, 122
Covalence (see Valence)
Covalent bond, 9, 10, 14–17, 19
Covalent chlorides, 20
Crystallization, mechanism, 97, 144
  rate, 85, 93
Cupric sulfide, precipitation, 193, 198
  solubility, 194, 199

Cuprocyanide ion, 135, 201
Cuprous ion, complexes, 129, 130, 135, 201
Cyanide ion, hydrolysis, 116
Cyanogen, 201

Dative bond (coordinate bond), 21, 120, 123–127
Debye-Hückel theory, 42–43, 93–94
Degree, of hydrolysis, 109, 110, 111, 116
  of ionization, acids and bases, 44–45, 60–66
    common-ion effect, 70–71
    dilution and, 36–37
    salts, 39
    theories, 39–45
    weak electrolytes, 37, 43, 60
Depression of freezing point, 37–38
Dialysis, 145
Dimethylglyoxime, 133
Dipole and dipole moments, 23, 32
Diprotic acids, 76
Dispersions, classes, 141
  types, 142
Dissociation, apparent degree, 43
  of complex ions, 134–136, 270
  of salts, 42
  of strong acids and bases, 35, 39
  theories, 39–45
  of weak acids, 35, 37, 60
  of weak bases, 35, 64
Dissociation constants, of complex ions, 134–136, 270
  of weak acids, 61
  of weak bases, 64
Dissolving of electrovalent substances, 39–40, 83
Double salts, 119
Drag effect, 42–43, 93–94
Drop, volume of, 179
Dynamic equilibrium, 48

Effective collisions, 49
Effective concentration, 43, 67, 158
Electric moment, 32
Electrical double layer, 147
Electrochemical conventions, 157–161
  examples, 161
Electrode, hydrogen, 156–157
  reactions, 159–160

Electrode, reference, 156–157, 161
  single, 156–157
  types, 157–158
Electrode potential, and activity, 158
  applications, 160–161
  and emf, 154–156
  and equilibrium constant, 163–164
  expression for, 158
  oxidation, 158
  sign, 160
  standard, 156–157
    table, 160–161
Electrolytes, classification, 35, 42
  colligative properties, 37–39, 42
  conductance, 35–37, 41, 42
  definition, 3
  electronic structure, 9
  ionization, 15, 18, 83
  solid, 15, 39, 83
  strong, 35, 39, 42–43
  weak, 35, 42–43, 60
Electrolytic solution pressure, 155
Electromotive force (emf), of cells, 160–161
  and concentration, 161–163
  and free-energy change, 154
  and temperature, 156
Electromotive series, 159–160
Electron, 7
Electron affinity, 17–19
Electron spin, 11–13
Electronegativity of the elements, 23–24
Electronic charge, 7
Electronic structure, ammonia complexes, 120
  ammonium ion, 21
  carbon tetrachloride, 10
  chloride ion, 9
  chlorine molecule, 22
  hydrogen chloride, 23–24
  inert gases, 8
  iodine chloride, 23
  phosphorus atom, 13–14
  sodium chloride, 22
  sodium ion, 9, 22
  sulfur atom, 13–14
  water, 24–25
Electrons, arrangement in atoms, 7–14, 267–268
  differentiating, 7–8
  energy levels, 7, 10, 11
  extranuclear, 7

Electrons, mass, 7
  pairing of, 12–14
  sharing, 9, 10, 14–17, 19
  stable configuration, 7
  transfer, 9
  valence, 8
Electrophoresis, 145
Electrovalency (see Valence)
Elements, atomic weights (inside front cover)
  electronegativity, 24
  periodic table (inside back cover)
  transition, 8, 123–127
  types, 7
Energy of solvation, 19–20, 84
Energy levels of atoms, 7, 10, 11
Equations, balancing (see Balancing of equations)
  hydrolysis, 106, 107, 109, 111, 113, 114
  oxidation-reduction, 168–175
  pertinent to analysis, of anions, Group I, 229–230
    Group II, 232
    Group III, 234–235
    Group IV, 238–240
    Group V, 243–244
  of cations, Group I, 188–189
    Group II, 197–203
    Group III, 209–214
    Group IV, 218–219
    Group V, 222–223
  quadratic, 63
  writing, 168–175
Equilibrium, acetic acid, 61
  ammonia, 48, 64
  amphoteric substances, 130–132
  chemical, 54–56,
    free energy and, 153
  derivation of general expression for, 55–56, 84–86
  dynamic, 48
  effect on, of catalysts, 49–50
    of concentration, 50, 57
    of pressure, 56–57
    of temperature, 50, 65
  general mathematical equation for, 55–56, 84–86
  heterogeneous, 58, 83
  homogeneous, 58, 83
  oxidation-reduction, 163–164
  and reaction velocity, 48–49
  in saturated solutions, 84–86

Equilibrium, water and its ions, 64–65
Equilibrium constants, complex ions, 131, 134–135
  from electrode potentials, 163–164
  hydrolysis, 106
  instability, 134–135
  ion product of water, 64–65, 104
  ionization, 61
    weak acids, 61–63
    weak bases, 64
  solubility product, 84–86
Equivalent conductance, compounds, 37
  definition, 35
  ions, 36
  solutions, 35–37, 41
  table, 37
Equivalent weights, 29
Evaporation, procedure for, 181
Exclusion principle of Pauli, 11, 124

Ferric acetate, basic, 256
Ferric chloride method for removal of phosphate, 256
Ferric hydroxide, precipitation, 206, 209, 211
  solubility, 205
Ferric ion, cyanide complex, 129
  hydrated, 127, 209, 211
  hydrolysis, 127
  reactions, 209–211, 213
  structure, 125
  tests for, 208, 213
  thiocyanate complexes, 129, 213
Ferricyanide ion, analysis, 234
  oxidizing action, 233, 235
  reactions, 234, 235
  structure, 124–126
Ferrocyanide ion, identification, 234
  reactions, 234, 235
Ferrous ion, in identification of nitrate ion, 242, 244
Flame tests, colors, 246
  technique for making, 217
Fluoride ion, complex ions, 124, 129, 208, 213
  reactions, 213, 229, 230
  test for, 227, 228, 252
Formal solutions, 28
Formality, 28
Formula weights, 28

Free energy, and chemical equilibrium, 153
  and emf, 154
  and maximum work, 152
Freezing point, 37
  depression of, 37–38, 42
Fusion of samples, 253

Galvanic cells, 144–145
Gram-equivalent weight, 29
Gram-formula weight, 28
Gram-molecular weight, 28

Half-cells, 156–157
Halide complex ions, 128–129, 187, 202, 203
Heating solutions, semimicro technique, 181
Helium atom, electronic structure, 8, 17
Heterogeneous equilibrium, 58, 83
Homoatomic anions, 130
Homogeneous equilibrium, 58, 83
Hydrated ions, 113–114, 118, 121–122, 126–128
Hydrates, 121–122, 126–127
Hydrochloric acid, properties, 39, 249
Hydrogen bond, 21–22, 28, 33–34
Hydrogen electrode, 156–157
Hydrogen peroxide, as oxidizing agent, 174, 207, 211–212
  test for chromate, 207, 213
Hydrogen sulfide, effect of hydronium ions, 99, 102
  generator, 180
  ionization constants, 76
    primary, 76
    secondary, 76
  as precipitation reagent, 97–100
Hydrolysis, of ammonium acetate, 114–115
  of ammonium chloride, 111–112
  anions that are proton acceptors, 105, 107–111
  of antimony chloride, 198
  aprotic, 105–107
  of bismuth chloride, 187
  Brønsted definitions, 105, 106
  cations that are proton donors, 105, 111–114
  constant, 106

Hydrolysis, degree of, 109–111, 116
  of hydrated metal ions, 113–114
  of salts of polyprotic acids, 109–111
  of sodium acetate, 107–109
Hydronium-ion concentration, 66
  of buffer solutions, 72–74
    acid, 72–73
    basic, 74
    effect on acid-base indicators, 68–70
    evaluation, 62–63
  of hydrolyzed salt solutions, 108–115
  relation of, to hydroxide ion concentration, 66
    to pH, 66–67
  in water, 64–65
Hydrophilic sol, 142–143
Hydrophobic sol, 142–143
Hydroxide ion, of basic buffers, 74
  complexes, 130–132, 199, 200, 202
  effect on sulfide concentration, 98
  evaluation, 64
  relation to pOH and pH, 65–68
  in water, 65
Hydroxides, amphoteric, 130–132
  precipitation, 128, 200, 209–212
  solubility, 128, 210–213

Indicators, acid-base, 68–70
  constant, 69–70
  pH range, 68–69
  table, 69
Inert gases (noble gases), 8, 9
Instability constants, calculation, 135–136
  calculation of concentration from, 138–139
Interionic-attraction theory, 42–43, 93–94
Iodide ion, analysis, 237
  complexes, 129, 130
  reactions, 238, 239
  reduction of arsenate by, 230
Iodine complex with iodide, 130
Ion-electron method, 171–172
Ionic atmosphere, 42–43
Ionic bond, 15, 16
Ionic compounds, dissolution, 5, 39
  electronic structure, 9, 15–16
Ionization, of acetic acid, 37, 60–63
  of ammonia, 64

Ionization, apparent degree, 43
  Arrhenius theory, 39
  calculation, 62, 79
  complete, theory of, 39–45
  Debye-Hückel theory, 39
  "drag effect," 42–43, 93–94
  of hydrogen sulfide, 76–77, 97–98
  modern theory, 39–45
  of phosphoric acid, 75
  in solids, 15, 39, 83
  of water, 64–65, 104
  of weak acids, 60–63
  of weak bases, 64
Ionization constant, application, 60
  derivation, 61
  determination, 61–63
  of monoprotic weak acids, 60–63
  of polyprotic weak acids, 75–76
  relation to hydrolysis constant, 106
  of weak bases, 64
Ionization energy, 16–19
Ions, adsorption, 146–148
  attraction, 15
  flocculating power of certain, 148–149
  hydration, 113–114, 118, 121–122, 126–128
  hydrolysis, 105
  negative, 40
  positive, 40
  velocity, 36
  (See also specific ions)
Isotopes, 6–7

Kinetic theory and Brownian movement, 145
Known solutions, preparation, 182, 257–258

Laboratory directions, apparatus, 179–180
  manipulations, 180–182
  records, 182, 261
  special, 257–260
Lake, formation of, 136, 150
Lattice energy, 18–20, 84
Laws, chemical-equilibrium, 54–56
  Le Chatelier, 56, 57
  mass-action, 50–54
Lead chloride, precipitation, 188
  solubility, 185, 187

Lead chromate, precipitation, 188, 200
 solubility, 188
Lead ion, analysis, 186, 195
 complexes, 129–131
 reactions, 188, 198–200
Lead sulfate, precipitation, 199
 solubility, 200
Le Chatelier principle, 56, 57
Logarithms, in pH conversions, 67
 table, 273–274

Macro analysis, 179
Magnesium ammonium phosphate, pre-cipitation, 216, 218
 solubility, 217, 218
Magnesium hydroxide, in lake formation, 216, 219
 precipitation, 216, 219
Magnesium ion, confirmation, 216, 219
 precipitation, 216
 reactions, 218, 219
Magnetic moment, explanation, 124–125
 orbital contribution, 124
 relationship to unpaired electrons, 124–126
 spin contribution, 124
Magnetic susceptibility, 124
Manganese dioxide, hydrated, 213
Manganous ion, in alkaline solutions, 211
 oxidation to permanganate, 208, 213
 reactions, 209–211, 213
 test for, 208, 213
Manganous sulfide, precipitation, 206, 209
 solubility, 210
Manipulations, laboratory, 180–182
Mass-action law, 50–54
 applications, 54
 derivation, 51–54
 mathematical expression for, 51
Mass number, 6
Mercuric ion, analysis, 195
 complexes, 129, 130
 reactions, 197, 199
Mercuric sulfide, precipitation, 193, 197
 solubility, 192, 194
Mercurous chloride, precipitation, 188
 solubility, 185, 187, 189
Mercurous ion, reactions, 188, 189
 separation from silver ions, 186, 188
 test for, 186, 189

Metals, analysis, 253
 reactions with acids, 250
Molal depression constant, 39
Molal elevation constant, 38
Molal solution, 29
Molality, 29
Molar solution, 28
Molarity, 28
Molecular weight, 28
Molecules, association, 28
 nonpolar and polar, 22, 31–34
 polarity (see Polarity of molecules)
 structure, 16, 17, 19, 33–34
 carbon tetrachloride, 10
 chlorine, 22
 iodine chloride, 23
 water, 24
Molybdate test for phosphates, 227, 230, 251

Negative ions, 40
Nernst equation, 161
Neutron, 6
Nickel dimethylglyoxime, 133, 134, 214
Nickel hydroxide, precipitation, 212
 solubility, 213
Nickel ion, complexes, 128, 129, 133, 209
 reactions, 209, 210, 212–214
 test for, 208, 214
Nickel sulfide, precipitation, 206, 209
 solubility, 206, 207, 210
Nitrate ion, as oxidizing agent, 244
 reactions, 244
 tests for, 242, 244
Nitric acid, properties, 248–249
Nitrite ion, as oxidizing agent, 244
 reactions, 241, 243, 244
 as reducing agent, 241, 243
 tests for, 242, 244
Noble gases, structure, 8, 9
Nonelectrolytes, 35
Nonpolar molecules, 22
Normal solutions, 29
Normality, 29
Notebook, directions for keeping records, 182, 261
Nuclear theory of atoms, 7
Nucleus, 6

Octet rule, 9, 10, 13
Orbit, electron, 12

Orbit, electron, capacity, 12
Orbitals, atomic, 10, 12–16, 21, 123–127
Organic reagents, use in qualitative analysis, 136–137
Osmosis, 38
Osmotic pressure, 38, 155
Oxalate ion, detection, 227, 230
    oxidation, 227, 230
    reactions, 229, 230
Oxidation and reduction, in acid solution, 170–173
    in alkaline solution, 171, 173–174
    cells, 154–156
    definitions, 168
    equations, 169–175
    equilibrium constants, 163–164
    oxidation number, 169
    potentials, 158–161
        table of standard, 159–160
    theory, 152
Oxides, color, 247
Oxidizing agent, 168

Paramagnetic behavior, definition, 124
    examples, 124–125
Particle size, and solubility, 96–97
    solubility product, 97
Pauli's exclusion principle, 11–12, 124
Per cent solutions, 29
Perchromate, 213, 232
Periodic table (inside back cover)
Permanganate ion as oxidizing agent, 171–173, 227
pH, method of indicating hydronium-ion concentration, 66–67
    of salt solutions, 109, 110, 114, 116
    of water, 68
Phosphate ion, detection, 227, 230, 251
    interference in analysis of cations, 254–255
    as precipitating agent, 215, 218
    reactions, 218, 229, 230
    removal, 256
Phosphoric acid, ionization reactions, 75
Phosphorus atom orbitals, 13–14
Physical examination of an unknown, 245–248
pK, 68
Platinum wire, cleaning, 217
    use in making flame tests, 217
pOH, 68

Polarity of molecules, 22, 24, 25, 31
    relation to solubility, 25, 32, 83–84
Polyprotic acids, 75
Potassium ion, detection, 221, 222
    reactions, 223
Potentials, electrode, 154–156
    single, 156–157
    standard, 156–157
    determination, 160–161
    equilibrium constants, 163–164
    oxidation-reduction, table, 159–160
    sign and magnitude, 158–160
Precipitate, adsorption of ions by, 145–148
    digestion, 97
    formation, 96–97
    transferring, 182
    washing, 181–182
Precipitation, completeness, 86–88
    conditions for, 97, 144, 150
    fractional, 94–96, 99–100
    with hydrogen sulfide, 97–100
    limit of visibility, 141
    technique, 97, 180–181
Preliminary examination of sample to be analyzed, 245
Preparation of sample for analysis, anion, 251–252
    cation, 252–253
Principle of Le Chatelier, 56, 57
Problems, amphoteric substances, 139–140
    buffered solutions, 72–74, 82
    complex ions, 135, 137–140
    dilution, 45
    hydrolysis, 108–117
    ionization, 62–63
    mathematical operations, 62–63, 76–78, 100–101, 138
    pH, 67, 80
    redox, 164–167
    solubility product, 87–92, 99–103
Proton, acceptor, 44
    donor, 44
    mass and charge, 6
Prussian blue, 233, 235

Quadratic equations, solution, 63
Qualitative analysis defined, 3, 4
Quantitative analysis defined, 4
Quantum numbers, azimuthal, 11

Quantum numbers, magnetic, 11
  principal, 7, 11
  spin, 11

Reaction velocity, effect on, of catalysts, 49–50
  of concentration, 50, 57
  of temperature, 50
  measure, 49
Reactions, heterogeneous, 58, 83
  homogeneous, 58, 83
  oxidation-reduction, 168–175
  rate, 48–49
  reversible, 48
Reagent bottles, 180
Reagents, acids and bases, 264
  silver acetate, 225, 236, 238
  solid, 265
  solutions, 264–265
  test, 266
Record of laboratory operations, 182, 261
Reducing agent, 168
Removal, of interfering ions, 255
  anions, 255–256
  cations, 226, 251
  of organic matter, 255
Reversible reactions, 48
Rhodamine B test for antimony, 136

Salt bridge, 155
Salt effect, 42–43, 92–94
Salts, characteristics, 20
  classification, 105
  colored, 245–247
  double, 119
  hydrolysis, 105
  ionization, 42
  solubility, 30–31, 83–84
  true, 20
Samples, acid-soluble, 248, 260
  fusion, 253
  knowns, 182, 257–258
  preliminary examination, 245–250
  preparation for analysis, 251–254
  solution, 248–249
  test for solubility, 248
  unknowns, 182, 257–260
Semimicro analysis, technique, 179–182
Semipermeable membrane, 38

Shells, electron, 7, 10, 11
Silver acetate as reagent, 225, 236, 238
Silver chloride, adsorption by, 147–148
  precipitation, 188
  sol, 147–148
  solubility, 185, 186, 188
Silver chromate, precipitation, 91
  solubility, 92
Silver halides, action with ammonia, 188
  complex ions, 128–130
  effect of common ion, 90–91
  reduction with zinc, 237, 240
Silver ion, ammonia complex, 128, 182
  cyanide complex, 129
  equilibria involving, 135, 138
  halide complex, 128, 129, 187
  reactions, 188
  tests for, 186, 188
Silver thiocyanate, precipitation, 237, 238
  solubility, 238, 239
Silver thiosulfate, hydrolysis, 237, 239
  precipitation, 237, 238
Single-electrode potential, 156–157
Sodium carbonate, fusion with, 253
Sodium ion, analysis, 221
  flame test, 221
  reactions, 222
Sol, 142
Solid reagents, 265
Solids, preliminary treatment, for anions, 251–252
  for cations, 252–253
  X-ray pattern, 39
Sols, adsorption by, 145–148
  coagulation, 148–149
  preparation, 143–144
  properties, 144–145
Solubility, 30, 83, 92–93
  factors affecting, 30, 83
    nature of solute, 31–34
    nature of solvent, 31–34, 83
    particle size, 96–97
    temperature, 30–31
  of liquids, 33–34
  of solids, 30, 83, 93
Solubility product, 4, 86
  application, 58, 83, 86
  derivation, 84–86
  determination, 88
  effect of temperature, 90
  expressions for, 86

Solubility product, table, 271–272
  validity, 92–93
Solute, 27
Solution pressure, electrolytic, 155
Solution process, 31, 39–40, 83
Solutions, buffer, 72–75
  colligative properties, 37–39, 42
  concentration, 27
  definition, 27
  electrical properties, 34–37, 41
  equilibrium in, 58, 60, 83
  formal, 28
  heating, 181
  molal, 29
  molar, 28
  normal, 29
  properties, 34–39
  rate, 85, 93
  saturated, 84
    equilibrium in, 84–86
  supersaturated, 144
  test, 266
  types, 27
  unknown, 182
Solvation, definition, 4
  energy, 19–20, 84
Solvent, 27
  acids as, 248–249
  aqua regia, 194, 199
  water, 32–34
Standard-electrode potential, 156–158
Stannic ion, reactions, 198, 199, 202, 203
  sulfide complex, 199, 202
Stannous ion, reactions, 194, 197, 198, 200, 203
  test for, 196, 203
Steam bath, 181
Stirring rods, 179
Strong electrolytes, 35, 39, 42–43
Strontium ion, analysis, 216
  flame test, 217, 219
  reactions, 218, 219
Strontium sulfate, precipitation, 216, 219
  solubility, 219
Structure, atoms, 6–14
  complex ions, 119, 120, 122, 124–127
  crystals, 15–16, 19, 39, 85
  ionic compounds, 15, 19, 39, 41
  molecules, 16, 17, 19, 33–34
Sulfate ion, confirmation, 231
  reactions, 232
Sulfide, complex ions, 130, 199, 202

Sulfide ion, concentration, in acid solution, 98
  in basic solution, 98
  in hydrogen sulfide, 97
  equilibria involving, 97–101, 111
  hydrolysis, 111
  reactions, 234
  test for, 235, 251
Sulfides, color, 193, 194
  precipitation, 97–100, 190–193
  solubility, in acids, 100–102
  in bases, 192
  solubility product constants, 190–192
Sulfite ion, reactions, 229, 230
  as reducing agent, 230
  test for, 227
Sulfur atom, orbitals, 13–14
Supersaturation, 144

Techniques, semimicro, 179–182
Test solutions, 266
Test tubes, 180–181
Thiocyanate complex ions, 129, 213, 239
Thiocyanate ion, reactions, 129, 238–240
  test for, 237, 239
Thiosulfate complex ions, 129–130
Thiosulfate ion, reactions, 130, 238, 239
  test for, 237, 239
Tin, analysis, 196
  reactions, 194, 197, 198, 200, 202, 203
  test for, 196, 203
Transition elements, 8, 123–127
Tri-iodide ion, 130
Turnbull's blue, 233, 235
Tyndall effect, 145

Ultramicroscope, 145
Units, concentration, 27–29
Unknowns, notebook records, 182, 261
  preliminary examination, 245–250
  report blanks, 261
  systematic analysis, 182
Uranyl zinc acetate, 220, 222

Valence, auxiliary, 119
  bonds, types, 14–21
  complex ions, 119–121

Valence, coordinate, 120, 123–127
  covalence, 9, 10, 15–17
    coordinate, 21, 121
  and electrical charge, 9, 40, 168–169
  electrons, 8
  electrovalence, 15
  ion-dipole, 121–122
  shells, 7, 10, 11
  of transition elements, 123–127
Valence-change method, 172–173
Van't Hoff's law, 57
Vapor-pressure lowering, 37
Velocity, reaction, 48–49
Visibility of precipitates, 141

Washing of precipitates, 150
Water, aggregates, 21
  amphiprotic nature, 64, 66
  dissolving of salt by, 39–40
  ion product, 65, 104
  ionization, 64, 104
  in oxidation-reduction equations, 170–171
  polarity, 24–25
  reaction with ions, 44, 105
  role as solvent, 32–34

Water, vapor pressure, 37
Water bath, 181
Weak acids, ionization, 37, 43, 60
  table of ionization constants, 269
Weak bases, ionization, 64
  table of ionization constants, 269
Weak electrolytes, 35, 42–43, 60, 64
Werner's complexes, 119
Werner's theory, 119–121

Zeta potential, 147
Zinc, reduction of silver halides with, 237, 240
Zinc hydroxide, reaction, with acids, 131
  with ammonia, 128, 209
  with bases, 131, 210
Zinc ion, ammonia complex, 128, 209, 213
  equilibria involving, 131–132
  hydroxide complex, 131, 132, 210–211
  reactions, 209–211, 213
  test for, 207, 213
Zinc sulfide, precipitation, 206, 209
  solubility, 210, 213
Zinc uranyl acetate, 220, 221